CURRENT TOPICS IN

DEVELOPMENTAL BIOLOGY

VOLUME 14

IMMUNOLOGICAL APPROACHES TO EMBRYONIC DEVELOPMENT AND DIFFERENTIATION PART II

CONTRIBUTORS

KEITH BURRIDGE

PETER D'EUSTACHIO

ALBERT DORFMAN

VICTOR H. ENGELHARD

MARTIN FRIEDLANDER

KEIGI FUJIWARA

GÜNTHER GERISCH

IRVING GOLDSCHNEIDER

BRAYDON C. GUILD

ELIZABETH D. HAY

LOIS JORDAN

THOMAS G. KOSTYK

DORON LANCET

E. LENNOX

JOSE A. LOPEZ DE CASTRO

JULIE MICOU-EASTWOOD

C. MILSTEIN

PAUL S. MOSS

HARRY T. ORR

SUZANNE OSTRAND-ROSENBERG

PETER PARHAM

HIDDE L. PLOEGH

JORDAN S. POBER

THOMAS D. POLLARD

FRANK H. RUDDLE

NANCY B. SCHWARTZ

RICHARD C. STROHMAN

JACK L. STROMINGER

ARON E. SZULMAN

BARBARA M. VERTEL

KLAUS VON DER MARK

R. J. WINCHESTER

CURRENT TOPICS IN DEVELOPMENTAL BIOLOGY

EDITED BY

A. A. MOSCONA

DEPARTMENTS OF BIOLOGY AND PATHOLOGY
THE UNIVERSITY OF CHICAGO
CHICAGO, ILLINOIS

ALBERTO MONROY

STAZIONE ZOOLOGICA
NAPLES, ITALY

VOLUME 14

Immunological Approaches to Embryonic Development and Differentiation Part II

VOLUME EDITOR

MARTIN FRIEDLANDER

THE ROCKEFELLER UNIVERSITY
NEW YORK, NEW YORK

STATE UNIVERSITY OF NEW YORK
DOWNSTATE MEDICAL CENTER
BROOKLYN, NEW YORK

1980

ACADEMIC PRESS

A Subsidiary of Harcourt Brace Jovanovich, Publishers

New York   London   Toronto   Sydney   San Francisco

ACADEMIC PRESS, INC.
111 Fifth Avenue, New York, New York 10003

United Kingdom Edition published by
ACADEMIC PRESS, INC. (LONDON) LTD.
24/28 Oval Road, London NW1 7DX

LIBRARY OF CONGRESS CATALOG CARD NUMBER: 66-28604

ISBN 0-12-153114-7

PRINTED IN THE UNITED STATES OF AMERICA

80 81 82 83   9 8 7 6 5 4 3 2 1

CONTENTS

CHAPTER 4. Complete Primary Structure of Human Histocompatibility
Antigen HLA-B7: Evolutionary and Functional Implications
JACK L. STROMINGER, VICTOR H. ENGELHARD,
BRAYDON C. GUILD, THOMAS G. KOSTYK, DORON
LANCET, JOSE A. LOPEZ DE CASTRO, HARRY T. ORR,
PETER PARHAM, HIDDE L. PLOEGH, AND JORDAN
S. POBER

CHAPTER 5. Aspects of Surface Membrane Differentiation during
Maturation of Human Hematopoietic and Tumor Cells:
The Ia System
R. J. WINCHESTER

CHAPTER 10. The Application of Labeled Lectins and Antibodies to SDS
Gels and Their Use in Studying Glycoproteins and Cell
Surface Antigens during Development
KEITH BURRIDGE AND LOIS JORDAN

CHAPTER 11. Univalent Antibody Fragments as Tools for the Analysis of
Cell Interactions in *Dictyostelium*
GÜNTHER GERISCH

CHAPTER 12. Techniques for Localizing Contractile Proteins with
Fluorescent Antibodies
KEIGI FUJIWARA AND THOMAS D. POLLARD

LIST OF CONTRIBUTORS

Numbers in parentheses indicate the pages on which the authors' contributions begin.

KEITH BURRIDGE, *Cold Spring Harbor Laboratory, Cold Spring Harbor, New York 11724* (227)

PETER D'EUSTACHIO, *Department of Biology, Yale University, New Haven, Connecticut 06520* (59)

ALBERT DORFMAN, *Departments of Pediatrics and Biochemistry, Joseph P. Kennedy, Jr., Mental Retardation Research Center, Pritzker School of Medicine, University of Chicago, Chicago, Illinois 60637* (169)

VICTOR H. ENGELHARD,* *Biological Laboratories, Harvard University, Cambridge, Massachusetts 02138* (97)

MARTIN FRIEDLANDER, *The Rockefeller University, New York, New York 10021* (321)

KEIGI FUJIWARA, *Department of Anatomy, Harvard Medical School, Boston, Massachusetts 02115* (271)

GÜNTHER GERISCH, *Max-Planck-Institut für Biochemie, D-8033 Martinsried bei München, Federal Republic of Germany* (243)

IRVING GOLDSCHNEIDER, *Department of Pathology, University of Connecticut Health Center, Farmington, Connecticut 06032* (33)

BRAYDON C. GUILD, *Biological Laboratories, Harvard University, Cambridge, Massachusetts 02138* (97)

ELIZABETH D. HAY, *Harvard Medical School, Department of Anatomy, Boston, Massachusetts 02115* (359)

LOIS JORDAN, *Cold Spring Harbor Laboratory, Cold Spring Harbor, New York 11724* (227)

THOMAS G. KOSTYK, *Biological Laboratories, Harvard University, Cambridge, Massachusetts 02138* (97)

DORON LANCET, *Biological Laboratories, Harvard University, Cambridge, Massachusetts 02138* (97)

* Present address: Department of Microbiology, University of Virginia, School of Medicine, Charlottesville, Virginia 22901.

E. LENNOX, *MRC Laboratory of Molecular Biology, University Medical School, Hills Road, Cambridge CB2 2QH, England* (1)

JOSE A. LOPEZ DE CASTRO, *Biological Laboratories, Harvard University, Cambridge, Massachusetts 02138* (97)

JULIE MICOU-EASTWOOD, *Department of Zoology, University of California, Berkeley, California 94720* (297)

C. MILSTEIN, *MRC Laboratory of Molecular Biology, University Medical School, Hills Road, Cambridge CB2 2QH, England* (1)

PAUL S. MOSS, *Department of Zoology, University of California, Berkeley, California 94720* (297)

HARRY T. ORR, *Biological Laboratories, Harvard University, Cambridge, Massachusetts 02138* (97)

SUZANNE OSTRAND-ROSENBERG, *Department of Biological Sciences, University of Maryland Baltimore County, Catonsville, Maryland 21228* (147)

PETER PARHAM, *Biological Laboratories, Harvard University, Cambridge, Massachusetts 02138* (97)

HIDDE L. PLOEGH, *Biological Laboratories, Harvard University, Cambridge, Massachusetts 02138* (97)

JORDAN S. POBER, *Biological Laboratories, Harvard University, Cambridge, Massachusetts 02138* (97)

THOMAS D. POLLARD, *Department of Cell Biology and Anatomy, The Johns Hopkins University School of Medicine, Baltimore, Maryland 21205* (271)

FRANK H. RUDDLE, *Department of Biology, Yale University, New Haven, Connecticut 06520* (59)

NANCY B. SCHWARTZ, *Departments of Pediatrics and Biochemistry, Joseph P. Kennedy, Jr., Mental Retardation Research Center, Pritzker School of Medicine, University of Chicago, Chicago, Illinois 60637* (169)

RICHARD C. STROHMAN, *Department of Zoology, University of California, Berkeley, California 94720* (297)

JACK L. STROMINGER, *Biological Laboratories, Harvard University, Cambridge, Massachusetts 02138* (97)

ARON E. SZULMAN, *Department of Pathology, Magee-Womens Hospital, University of Pittsburgh, School of Medicine, Pittsburgh, Pennsylvania 15213* (127)

BARBARA M. VERTEL,* *Departments of Pediatrics and Biochemistry, Joseph P. Kennedy, Jr., Mental Retardation Research Center, Pritz-

* Present address: Department of Biology, Syracuse University, Syracuse, New York 13210.

ker School of Medicine, University of Chicago, Chicago, Illinois 60637 (169)

KLAUS VON DER MARK, *Max-Planck-Institut für Biochemie, D-8033 Martinsried bei München, Federal Republic of Germany* (199)

R. J. WINCHESTER, *The Rockefeller University, New York, New York 10021 and Hospital for Joint Diseases, New York, New York 10035* (115)

PREFACE

The most fundamental processes underlying the orderly progression from a single, fertilized egg to a complex, multicellular organism remain largely unknown today, in spite of significant progress in many areas of developmental biology. Several recurring themes have emerged from a plethora of information generated by recent studies of developing systems. Cellular differentiation is frequently preceded by division and proliferation within cell sets, although the precise relationship between mitotic events and molecular specialization remains unknown. The transduction of metabolic (and developmental) cues from the environment to the level of the genome is probably mediated by the cell surface and may involve subplasmalemmal complexes that somehow join membrane receptors with nuclear components. The basis for the extensive repertoires of selective cell associations and morphogenetic patterns observed during development may arise from the assembly of basic molecular or cellular components into informational mosaics. While impressive strides have been made toward understanding the fundamental questions and theories set forth by classical embryology, it is only recently that we have been able to understand the molecular mechanisms underlying basic developmental events. The approaches to these problems have been greatly facilitated by the interaction of cell, developmental, and molecular biology at both the conceptual and methodological levels. A common denominator has been the exquisitely sensitive technical achievements and elegant conceptual frameworks provided by work in the field of immunology.

The objective of Volumes 13 and 14 of *Current Topics in Developmental Biology* is to provide a survey of concepts, achievements, and prospects concerning the application of immunological methodologies to the analysis of various aspects of cell differentiation and morphogenesis—molecular, cellular, and histogenic—in embryonic, fetal, and postnatal development. Contributions to Volume 13 focus on early embryonic development, the nervous system, and the structural and conceptual basis of transmembrane signaling. The contents of Volume 14 include studies of the immune system, connective tissue, non-muscle contractile proteins, muscle, lens, and slime mold. Thus, the important feature of these volumes is the diversity of research interests unified by the theme of immunological approaches to the analysis of development and differentiation. It is certain that such approaches will be useful in continued investigations; the intent of these volumes is to focus attention on, and stimulate interest in, the many problems of development that may be studied by the application of immunological techniques and concepts. As Dr. Boyse observes in his conspectus to Volume 13, the field of immunology provides far more than methodological resources for students of development. As an "exemplar of ontogeny," the immune system should prove a rich conceptual resource as well.

We could not hope to provide contributions from every laboratory active in the research areas discussed in this volume. Rather, representative work was solicited and, in several areas, manuscripts from two or three laboratories in the same field were brought together to provide a broader perspective. Nearly half the contributions to this volume focus on the immune system as an "exemplar of ontogeny." Cell surface antigens may serve as specific markers of differentiation and/or as recognition molecules that distinguish self from nonself during routine immune surveillance. Immunological probes specific for such membrane macromolecules may be generated from batteries of hybridomas. The technology of preparing monoclonal antibodies and their use in studying surface changes during development of lymphoid cells are discussed by Lennox and Milstein. Lymphocyte developmental biology is described in the chapter by Goldschneider; antigenic markers are used to trace cell lineages during early stages of lymphocyte differentiation. The divergence of T and B cells from a common progenitor cell may be mapped by serological methodologies; as the cells of each subset are purified and characterized, their role in lymphopoiesis should become more apparent.

Gene map assignments for specific surface macromolecules and the analysis of the fine structure of the relevant regions of the eukaryotic genome will facilitate our understanding of how genomic expression affects cell–cell interactions. D'Eustachio and Ruddle discuss the application of somatic cell genetics to the analysis of the developing immune system. Strominger and his colleagues describe, from a molecular perspective, the structural relatedness of histocompatibility antigens and other recognition molecules of the immune system. Sequence homologies between histocompatibility antigens, immunoglobulins, and β_2-microglobulin suggest functional analogies as well, and such an approach should prove illuminating in determining the role of such molecules in biological recognition.

Blood cell surface antigens have long been used as model systems for studying the biochemistry of cell membrane molecules. The expression of Ia antigens during hematopoietic cell membrane differentiation is detailed in the chapter by Winchester. The ABH blood groups may serve not only to distinguish different serotypes, but also to regulate developmental events of various organ systems in the embryo. Szulman describes the distribution of these antigens and the Forssman antigens during morphological differentiation of various embryonic chick tissues, as well as during the maternal–fetal placental relationship. Ostrand-Rosenberg discusses the use of sensitized lymphocytes in the detection of embryonic cell surface antigens of the early mouse embryo.

It has become increasingly obvious that the role of the extracellular matrix during embryogenesis is considerably more than that of a passive structural element. Two major components of this matrix, the proteoglycans and collagens, have been subjected to extensive biochemical and morphological analysis. Dorfman, Schwartz, and Vertel describe the use of specific antibodies in the analysis of the biosynthesis and distribution of chondroitin sulfate proteoglycans. Collagen deposition during chondrogenesis may be visualized by immunofluorescence, and the dynamic aspects of fiber type transition become apparent as described in the chapter by von der Mark.

The development of slime molds provides a useful model system in which to analyze cell surface changes that may accompany differentiation. Burridge and Jordan outline the use of gel overlay techniques in the analysis of cell surface glycoprotein changes in *Dictyostelium discoideum* as well as embryonic skeletal muscle. Gerisch describes the use of monovalent Fab fragments in an analysis of the role of adhesive sites during specific cell–cell associations observed in the morphogenesis of slime molds.

The localization of intracellular proteins and their rearrangements in distribution with cellular differentiation are amenable to analysis by immunohistochemical techniques. Fujiwara and Pollard have used specific immunological probes to analyze subcellular distribution of various contractile proteins. At the level of molecular biosynthesis, Strohman, Moss, and Micou-Eastwood have used antibodies specific to a single contractile protein, myosin, to measure the rate of synthesis and accumulation during myodifferentiation. Friedlander describes changes in cell surface antigens that accompany myogenesis in the embryonic chick and also discusses the use of antibodies specific to the major intrinsic protein of the lens as a means to analyze specific cell–cell interactions that occur via intercellular junctions. The final chapter by Hay provides an overview of the two volumes, as well as a brief report of the ultrastructural immunocytochemical localization of fibronectin in the extracellular matrix of early embryos.

In many respects, problems of development and differentiation are just beginning to yield to immunological approaches. By gathering 28 diverse reports into these two volumes we hope to provide a broad perspective on such studies. The use of monoclonal antibodies should resolve much of the ambiguity involved in characterizing heterologous antisera. The consistent identification of specific molecules, or even individual molecular conformations, should become routine with the availability of standard immunological reagents. Fluorescence-activated cell sorting will permit the separation of specific subsets of cells based on defined antigenic properties. Intracellular injection of immunological probes may allow an assessment of the role of specific molecules in normal cellular metabolic events. Such immunological techniques are becoming established in the repertoire of many laboratories for the study of biological development. Certainly, immunological probes provide the degree of sensitivity and specificity required for the analysis of molecular events during differentiation. The immune system itself is a prime "exemplar of ontogeny," and the gap between developmental biology and immunology is not so much a conceptual one as it is of technical diversion. Cell–cell and cell–molecule interactions form the basis for clonal selection, gene expression, and eventually cell death in the immune response, as they do for the differentiation of every cell type in the developing embryo. These two volumes provide conceptual and methodological bridges that serve to unify the study of biological development. Further technical advances in the application of monoclonal antibodies, fluorescence-activated cell sorting, gene mapping, and gene cloning should extend these bridges and resolve many problems in our understanding of the relationship between gene expression, cell biosynthetic events, and abnormal metabolic conditions. At present, the use of highly specific antibodies in the identification of gene products holds the promise of unambiguously tracing the responsible genes and elucidating the biosynthesis, turnover, and distribution of these molecules. Function may also be assessed directly by specifically interfering with gene product expression, either at the level of translation or display.

I would like to express my gratitude to the many contributors in these two volumes without whose cooperation and enthusiasm such an effort would never have come to fruition. The Editors, Aron Moscona and Alberto Monroy, provided experienced guidance in the development of these volumes. Many colleagues at the University of Chicago and The Rockefeller University contributed ideas and criticism throughout the course of publication. I am grateful to have had the pleasure of working with the staff at Academic Press, without whose expertise and hard work these pages would probably still be on this Editor's desk. I would like to thank Mrs. Violette Carasso in Chicago and Mrs. Madeleine Naylor in New York for their excellent assistance in the preparation of these volumes. I am also very grateful to my wife Sheila for her encouragement of and contributions to this project.

Martin Friedlander

CHAPTER 1

THE USE OF MONOCLONAL ANTIBODY TECHNIQUES IN THE STUDY OF DEVELOPING CELL SURFACES

C. Milstein and E. Lennox

MRC LABORATORY OF MOLECULAR BIOLOGY
UNIVERSITY MEDICAL SCHOOL
CAMBRIDGE, ENGLAND

I. Introduction

The use of serological reagents is one way of examining changes in surfaces of cells undergoing or having undergone differentiation steps. For example, in the adult, not only are there easily recognized tissue-specific antigens, but proximal stages in a cell lineage can show surface antigenic changes. In addition, during embryogenesis, antisera can reveal surface changes. For the purpose of this chapter we label all such antigens "differentiation antigens," although the term does not denote how or whether they function in differentiation or what functional aspects of differentiation they reflect. Here they are markers only, seen through the filters and distortion of an immune response. There is no doubt that seeing cell surfaces through an immune response is a distortion, for a number of reasons, but mainly because

1

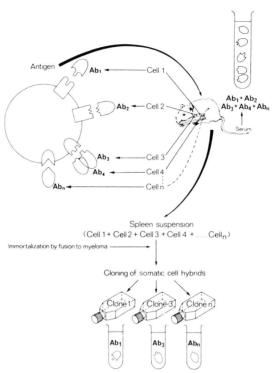

FIG. 1. Pure antibodies from impure antigens. The schematic diagram shows that different antigens on a cell surface are recognized by different antibodies. Single antigens can be recognized by different antibodies (Ab_3 and Ab_4) and the overlap in the antigenic determinant could be such that *different* antibody molecules recognize exactly the *same* determinant. Each antibody is made by a cell but the products are all mixed in the serum, so that the antiserum of an immune animal is a very heterogeneous mixture of antibody molecules. The hybrid myeloma method permits the separation of each antibody molecule by immortilization of antibody-producing cells and fractionation of clones as shown in Fig. 2.

many important changes may occur that cannot be detected by an immune response in the animal chosen for immunization. Nonetheless, antibodies are very useful to indicate change and in some systems may reveal function by interfering with further steps of differentiation. Monoclonal antibodies (McAb) are uniquely suited to the detection of antigenic changes in cell surfaces during differentiation, although they do introduce their own distortion. Both of these aspects will be discussed here.

Conventional antisera against cell surface antigens are usually prepared against cells or cell membranes, that is, an ensemble of possible antigenic components. Each antiserum is a complex mixture of antibodies, not only against the many immunogenic molecules on the cells used but also (Fig. 1) against different determinants on the same molecule, and may even include a collection of different antibodies all directed against the same determinant. The use of such complex antisera is severely restricted and requires extensive purification; moreover, the ability to make a serum specific for a given surface molecule is limited by the availability of cells suitable for absorbing the unwanted antibodies. This is becuse, as will be seen in Section III, antigens are shared by different cell types in an unpredictable way, thus affecting the possible availability of cells with the desired set of antigens for absorption. Even then, what remains is a complex mixture of an-

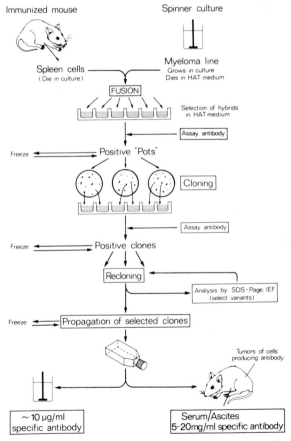

FIG. 2. Immortalization of antibody-producing cells, cloning, and preparation of monoclonal antibodies.

tibodies of various classes and affinities, and specific for a variety of determinants on the molecule examined. The complexity of an antiserum is the result of the expression of an equivalent complex set of clones of cells each committed to the synthesis of a single antibody species (Fig. 1). The immortalization of the transient phenotypic expression of such cells permits their separation into the different clonal derivatives and, from the isolated clones, the preparation of unlimited quantities of each separated monoclonal (i.e., derived from a single clone) antibody species (Fig. 2).

With regard to cross-reactions, monoclonal antibodies are different from conventional—even purified—antibodies. Because each McAb has a unique combining site, any cross-reaction observed cannot be due, as may be the case with conventional sera, to contaminating antibodies, but must be due to a real structural similarity in the recognized antigen(s). One must, however, be cautious about the meaning of such putative structural similarity in terms of gene expression, for this meaning depends on whether the recognized structure is coded directly by the structural gene or is a post-translation addition, e.g., carbohydrate. This applies to conventional sera as well. There is no substitute for analyzing the recognized molecular species by various biochemical means, e.g., gels, stability to heat, proteolytic enzymes, and ultimately structural analysis. It is in the isolation of the surface antigen recognized by the antibody [for instance by antibody precipitation (Springer *et al.*, 1978) or affinity chromatography (Sunderland *et al.*, 1979)] that McAb excel, for they are very noise-free compared to conventional antisera.

II. The Hybrid Myeloma Technique and the Production and Use of Monoclonal Antibodies

The production of monoclonal antibodies is based on the codominant expression of antibody secretion in somatic myeloma cell hybrids (Cotton and Milstein, 1973) and on the immortalization of the antibody-producing cells from the spleen of a suitable immunized animal. This can be achieved by fusion of spleen immunocytes with myeloma cells adapted to grow in tissue culture (Köhler and Milstein, 1975). In general, myeloma cells have been of mouse origin, but a new line of myeloma cells of rat origin permits the growth of rat splenocyte-myeloma hybrids in rats with considerable increase in productive capacity per animal (Galfrè *et al.*, 1979). Suitable mutants of the parental myeloma cell deficient in the enzymes thymidine kinase or HGPRT (hypoxanthine guanine phosphoribosyltransferase) can be killed in appropriate selective medium (Fig. 2). The usual strategy is to subdivide the initial fused population into a large number of cultures so that lines arising in each of them are the result of independent fusion events (Köhler and Milstein, 1976; Galfrè *et al.*, 1977). The hybrid cell lines arising from fusions of this type do not equally represent the different phenotypes of the heterogeneous mixture of cells comprising the normal spleen. A fortunate and useful aspect of the procedure is that the majority of the hybrids established in culture secrete large amounts of immunoglobulin, different from that of the parental myeloma and which is, in turn, the product of a very small proportion of the parental spleen cells (Köhler and Milstein, 1976). Other cells, for instance T cells, present in the spleen in large quantities, do not appear to give established hybrids when a myeloma cell is used as the fusion partner (Köhler *et al.*, 1977a). When a lymphoma of T-cell origin is used, the situation is completely reversed (Goldsby *et al.*, 1977; Hämmerling, 1977; Köhler *et al.*, 1977b). In other words, the use of a myeloma immortalizes preferentially the phenotype of antibody-producing cells (Köhler *et al.*, 1977a; Milstein *et al.*, 1978). On the other hand, in terms of the antibody produced, the population of hybrid cells in a general way appears to be a random representation of the population of antibody-producing cells present in the immunized spleen (Koprowski *et al.*, 1978a; Springer *et al.*, 1978). However, there are likely to be nonrandom selective pressures in certain cases. For instance, the production of antibodies recognizing the parental myeloma line has not been observed, although they were strongly expressed in the animal contributing the spleen to both rat anti-mouse and rat anti-rat hybrid myelomas (Springer *et al.*, 1978; G. Galfrè and G. W. Butcher, unpublished observations). In general, however, the degree of difficulty in obtaining a hybrid clone producing a desired antibody is directly correlated with the frequency of occurrence, in the immune spleen, of cells producing antibody identical to that of the corresponding hybrid clone. In the case of very strong immunogens, this frequency is quite high, and screening for antibody activity of randomly chosen spleen-myeloma hybrid clones is adequate to obtain a collection of antibody specificities directed against the immunogen (Galfrè *et al.*, 1977). When the particular antibody-producing clone being sought is represented at a much lower frequency in the immunized spleen, the problem of finding the desired hybrid becomes more complicated. First, after fusion, that clone usually occurs with unwanted clones present in the same culture. These undesired clones and their faster growing derivatives, which occur at random, eventually compete with and overgrow the clones sought. Second, during this process, which occurs rapidly in the early stages after fusion, a considerable reduction in the number of chromosomes takes place. This renders the active clones unstable and leads to gradual loss of antibody activity due to the overgrowth by inactive variants. Early cloning avoids this but may require previous enrichment of active clones. This can be achieved by using multiple dilution methods (Williams *et al.*, 1977; Herzenberg *et al.*, 1978; Yelton *et al.*, 1978). However, this is quite laborious and not always successful. Methods for direct selection (either before or after fusion) based on the production of a particular antibody will be important in this area. One example is selection, after fusion, of clones that produce hemolytic plaques (Köhler and Milstein, 1975).

A. SEGREGATION OF VARIANTS AND BULK PREPARATION OF ANTIBODIES

Hybrid clones secreting the desired antibody, once purified, can be kept indefinitely. However, as with all permanent cell lines, chromosome changes do take place and variants appear on continued passage. With hybrid myelomas, variants arise which no longer produce or secrete the desired antibody. In our laboratory it is routine to clone at least twice from the cultures with desired activity. Occasional recloning and checks for clonal stability are standard over longer growth periods. In addition to the heavy and light chains of the antibody molecule, the hybrid expresses the chain(s) from the parental myeloma. This is a source of heterogeneity which is best avoided because of the unpredictable properties of the hybrid molecules. This is achieved by segregation of variants or by fusion with nonproducing myelomas (see the following).

The chain composition of the secreted products can be easily analyzed by radioactive tracer methods and by isoelectric focusing and SDS gel electrophoresis of the reduced products. Such checks and the derivation of variants in which the myeloma chains have been eliminated from the hybrid clone are important routine procedures for establishing stable clones of known activity. The order in which chains are lost is not random. Generally, one of the heavy chains is lost first while light chains are lost when only one heavy chain is expressed (Margulies *et al.*, 1976; Köhler *et al.*, 1978). The presence of the four chains, two heavy and two light, is symbolized as HLGK: H and L for the heavy and light chains of the specific antibody and G and K for those of the myeloma. The loss of one of the two heavy chains gives rise to a clone expressing HLK with antibody activity but lacking the myeloma heavy chain, or to one with GLK where the antibody activity and the antibody heavy chain disappear together.

Using cultures after suitable numbers of passages and random screening methods, it is possible to segregate the HL and HK forms, the first active and the second usually inactive but sometimes retaining some activity (Milstein *et al.*, 1976). All these derivatives can be prepared as by-products of the purification of subclones leading to the stabilization of the most desired one which is the one expressing HL. Apart from the obvious immunological interest of the artificial combinations HK and GL, such derivatives could have some practical value as either controls or to raise and test anti-idiotypic antibodies to the separate chains.

The use of variants of the parental myeloma which do not express the myeloma heavy chain (Köhler *et al.*, 1976; Köhler and Milstein, 1976) or either the heavy or the light chains (Shulman *et al.*, 1978) obviates the need for the derivation of segregant hybrids since the fused heterokaryons will be of the HL type. This simplifies the problems but does not eliminate the need for repeated cloning to achieve optimum purity and stability. The penalty for the simplification is the loss of valuable markers and of potentially useful derivatives particularly those expressing HK. The ability to generate hybrid myelomas depends upon the myeloma parental line used, and this should also be taken into consideration before using new variants (Yelton *et al.*, 1978).

To make large amounts of monoclonal antibody, the purified clones are injected into the appropriate animal strain where it usually develops a tumor. In our laboratory we grow these clones in the ascites of animals which have been previously injected intraperitoneally with pristane (Potter, 1972). The serum from the combined blood and ascitic fluid usually contains between 5 and 20 mg/ml of antibody. Variations mainly depend on the tumor but, in particular, the IgM antibodies may give much lower values.

In tumor-bearing mice the antibodies occur at a much higher concentration than in culture supernatants but are contaminated by normal mouse immunoglobulins, whereas in the culture supernatants they are truly monoclonal in the sense that no other mouse immunoglobulins are present. Contaminating proteins are from the tissue culture medium and from cell debris or other secreted products. It is important to keep these differences in mind when deciding which of the reagents should be used in each specific case. For example, the serum may be preferred when immunoabsorbent columns are to be made while the tissue culture fluid is probably a better source for indirect binding studies.

B. Immunizations and Assays

The induction and selection of monoclonal antibodies is dependent on suitable immunization and assays. With regard to immunization there are two main approaches. One is to seek response to a particular immunogen; the other is to "shotgun"—that is, to immunize with a particular material and take whatever turns up when screening with the adopted assays. Both ways can be fruitful and the one to use depends on the problem to be solved.

To seek McAb to a particular immunogen, either purified material and/or a highly selective screening procedure is needed. For developmental surface antigens, the purified material is seldom available, and thus selective screening would be chosen if reagents to a particular immunogen were desired.

It is known with partially purified soluble antigens that there are immunodominant components that contribute disproportionally to the antibody response. Similarly with heterogeneous cell populations, while the major response and the bulk of hybrid myelomas are directed against the majority of the cells, some striking exceptions occur. In these cases the McAb are unexpected in recognizing what is quantitatively a minor immunogen. An example of this is the M1 series of hybrid clones (discussed in more detail in the following) derived with the spleen from a rat immunized with mouse T cells partially purified by removal of the bulk of non-T cells (Springer *et al.*, 1978). Two clones producing different antibodies would have been missed in the binding tests with the original immunogen, but were detected by their cross-reaction with sheep erythrocytes which, for technical reasons, had been added to the cells used in the screening assay. In subsequent analyses, these antibodies, M1/22.25 and M1/87.27, were seen to recognize a subpopulation of cells comprising about 3% of an adult spleen. Moreover, on screening with a panel of tumor cell lines, comprising various lymphoid lines, sarcomas, macrophage lines, and teratocarcinomas, M1/22.25 recognized only the teratocarcinomas (Stern *et al.*, 1978).

Another example of response to a minor subset of the immunizing heterogeneous cell populations revealed by a particular screening procedure is that of a response in mice to multiple injection of allogeneic spleen cells, which is the conventional schedule to raise alloantisera. In this case, to produce McAb against H2, the major histocompatibility antigens, C57BL/10 spleens were injected repeatedly into C3H mice. It was noted that, as the immunization continued, the serum titer began to fall and, in a series of fusions, the frequency of hybrid cultures producing antibody to spleen cells became very low. Clones derived from them do not recognize antigens of the major histocompatibility region but others associated with minor subpopulations of peripheral lymphocytes (see Section III, A). In summary, it is advisable to test different immunization schedules, especially ones of very brief or very long duration.

So far, the major assay employed for screening has been indirect binding of radiolabeled antibody (Williams, 1977). Others, like cytotoxicity or fluorescence assays, have also been used but will not be discussed here. In the binding assay, the target cells are incubated with the supernatants to be tested and after suitable washes further incubated with an appropriate ^{125}I-labeled antibody that binds to immunoglobulins of the immuinized animal (Fig. 3). If the target cells used for screening are a pure population, then the limitation of the assay is determined by the number of antibody molecules specifically bound and is a function of the number of antigen molecules/cell compared to the nonspecific uptake of the supernatants or the developing ^{125}I-labeled antibody. If the screening is with a mixed population of cells, the limit of the assay is in addition determined by the proportion of cells that carry the recognized antigen.

So far most assays have used tissue cell suspensions as targets, but there is no reason why tissue slices or other suitable preparations cannot be used, provided the quantity and availability allow keeping up with the fusion products as they are ready for testing.

C. Use of Panels of Tumor Cell Lines

We mentioned in Section II, B the use of tumors as aids for the detection of McAb that recognize differentiation antigens and we want to expand on this here. Insofar as tumors are monoclonal derivatives of complex differentiated tissue, they are particularly suited to this task. For this reason they have been used as immunogens to raise and test conventional antisera as well as absorbers to remove unwanted cross-reactions. For McAb, they remain useful for the first two functions.

With conventional antisera, tumor cell surfaces have been shown to carry a wide variety of antigens including ones that mark stages of differentiation. Among them are normal antigens of the major histocompatibility complex, viral components of the RNA tumor viruses,

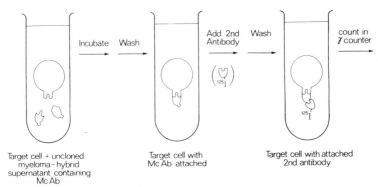

FIG. 3. Binding assay to detect the presence of Ab to cell surface antigens.

nonvirion transformation products of RNA and DNA tumor viruses, tissue (and subset)-specific antigens, "embryonic" antigens, and "tumor-specific" antigens. Even antigens of the major histocompatibility complex (MHC), though widespread on tumors and normal cells, are differentiation antigens in the sense we defined them (Section I), for the K and D end antigens are not found on all cells of all tissues in the adult and are not expressed in certain cells in early stages of differentiation (Erikson, 1977; see also Section III, D). Moreover, the antigens of the I region distinguish two major pathways of differentiation in the lymphoid system, the T and B cells (for review, see Waldmann and Howard, 1979).

Many of the antigens that tumors bear are easy to identify on normal cells and even the quantitative associations of several antigens can be found in what must be normal counterparts of the tumor cells; e.g., many thymic lymphomas correspond in antigenic properties to what seem to be early stages of T-cell differentiation (Old and Stockert, 1977). A word of caution is needed here, however, because tumors are notorious for seemingly anomalous expression of cytoplasmic products (Merrill and De Wys, 1978) and there is beginning to be evidence that the same is true for surface antigens (Akeson, 1977; Nelson-Rees, 1978). Also, some tumors are difficult to place in a differentiation pathway, e.g., the Abelson virus-induced lymphoid tumors. They are clearly not T-cell tumors but have been difficult to place along the B-cell pathway (Risser et al., 1978). As we will discuss in more detail in Section III, A, certain monoclonal antibodies show that Abelson tumors share an antigen (H9/25) with plasma cells, the terminal state of B-cell differentiation, yet they do not secrete immunoglobulins.

Even more difficult to place in a differentiation scheme are the "embryonic" and "tumor-specific" antigens characteristic of many tumors, but known best for the chemically induced sarcomas of the mouse and rat (Baldwin, 1978; Baldwin et al., 1974). The embryonic antigens are defined by serological means as those on the tumors that cross-react with mid-term embryos, using sera either from multiparous females or raised by injection of adults with embryos. Since these are usually very weak antisera, precise embryonic localization of the recognized antigens or their identification with known differentiation pathways has not been possible. Nor has it been possible to show how many different molecules contribute to the antigenic specificities detected.

The description of antigens as "tumor-specific" is used in two senses: as characterizing a particular kind of tumor or as characterizing malignant transformation. In the first sense, these antigens, common to many similar tumors, e.g., specific for a mammary cell carcinoma, may well be antigens that occur on subpopulations of normal tissue, and hence reflecting the tissue of origin, are differentiation antigens. In this connection, there are mouse McAb against human melanomas that do not cross-react with human lymphoid lines (Koprowski et al., 1978b). While the antigens recognized may turn out to be tumor-specific, i.e., to depend on malignant transformation, it is also possible that they will recognize a normal subset, e.g., melanocytes. Immunization of rabbits with epithelial cell membranes from human milk globules generates antisera that recognize normal mammary epithelium and certain (but not all) mammary epithelial carcinomas (Ceriani et al., 1977). Reciprocally, had the mammary epithelial carcinomas been used as immunogens, one might expect that the sera raised would recognize normal mammary epithelium via a tissue-specific differentiation antigen.

The tumor-specific antigens of the chemically induced murine sarcomas (Baldwin, 1973) seem different for they appear to be unique to each independently induced tumor. Up to now, these antigens have been defined principally by transplantation assays. Sera have been too weak for chemical characterization and these antigens remain unplaced in the ensemble of normal antigens. Whether they are antigens expressed elsewhere as normal differentiation antigens or even as variants of ones found in normal cells, or are unique to transformed cells, remains to be seen.

Even with their severe limitations, conventional antisera allow fine specifications of different kinds of leukemias (Greaves et al., 1977). McAb are expected to have an enormous impact here and an example of a T-cell leukemia antigen is already in use (see Section III, D). McAb are also likely to be very useful for a wide variety of tumors. Thus we should, at the same time, be able to mark them as carrying antigens restricted to certain differentiated tissue and use them as fine discriminants in tumor diagnosis and detection (Koprowski et al., 1978b).

It would be useful to identify tumor lines as examples of cells frozen at a normal stage of differentiation. By assigning an antigen "fingerprint" to each such line, a panel of monoclonal might make such analysis possible. We must, however, be cautious in too literal interpretation of such a fingerprint, for, as we mentioned previously, tumor cells may be anomalous in their expression of cytoplasmic products and membrane antigens.

There are enormous advantages to the use of tumor cell lines as immunogens or as cells for screening the myeloma fusion products derived from an immunization with a heterogeneous tissue. They have already been used in this way for the production and/or analysis of conventional antisera against a wide variety of normal differentiation antigens, e.g., the lymphocyte antigens (Old and Stockert, 1977), the antigens on teratocarcinomas (Jacob, 1977), and neural tissue (e.g., Chaffee and Schachner, 1978) to mention only a few in the mouse.

As probes to analyze McAb following immunization with heterogeneous tissue, tumor panels are proving invaluable. Examples of these in our laboratory come from hybrids prepared following alloimmunization of C3H mice with B10 spleens. In one of the fusions, several of the "pot" supernatants (see Fig. 2) had activities marginally above background when assayed on B10 spleens. Assayed on a panel of lymphoid tumor cells, the activities of these cultures against some lines were as much as 30-fold amplified, which allowed easy assay. It was then possible in subsequent fusions to use the tumors as assay targets and isolate many more clones, some of which detected lymphoid subpopulations with different functions in the immune response (see Section III, A).

It is obvious that the use of tumor panels—both as probes and immunogens—to derive McAb should encompass an assortment of tumors as varied as possible in terms of their origins. There are, of course, practical limits on the number that can be handled. Moreover, cells in culture are better for assay purposes than ones taken from an animal, for the latter often carry antibodies that complicate or interfere with the binding assays. When fixed cells are as good, or almost as good, as untreated ones (as is often the case), they can be prepared in large numbers and stored for later use.

D. INTERPRETATION OF RESULTS

The interpretation of results obtained with monoclonal antibodies, although simple in theory, can give rise to a number of complications, especially when thinking in terms of conventional antisera. For instance, unless the antigen contains multiple identical subunits, the monoclonal antibodies are unlikely to give precipitating reactions because no three-dimensional lattices are likely to be produced. Cytotoxicity reactions are affected not only by the class of the monoclonal antibody but also by the density of the antigenic determinants it recognizes and even by the local distribution of the determinants of the cell surface. For instance, in the case of two monoclonal antibodies recognizing rat histocompatibility antigens, neither alone is cytotoxic but the mixture is strongly cytotoxic (Howard et al., 1978). Although these types of synergistic effects can sometimes be confusing, they can also become very useful tools, for instance to develop anti-MHC plaque-forming cells using sublytic sensitized red cells (Howard et al.,

1978). Indirect hemagglutination by a monoclonal anti-IgG is unexpectedly different when the sheep red cells are coated with two different monoclonal anti-sheep red cells. It is negative when the cells are coated with the antibody recognizing a *high*-density determinant but positive when the monoclonal antibody coating the red cells recognizes a *much lower* density determinant (Galfrè et al., 1979).

The fine recognition of McAb may introduce serious complications under certain circumstances, for example, when a given determinant is exposed in one environment but hidden in others. The wrong prima facie conclusion would be that the antigenic molecule is absent in the latter.

The use of monoclonal antibodies obviously eliminates the problem of multiple antigenic recognition by a mixed antibody population, but it does not completely eliminate the problem of cross-reactions resulting from antigenic similarities, for instance, in evolutionarily related proteins. Completely unexpected types of cross-reactions due to antibody multispecificity, an unlikely event in polyclonal antisera, can occur with monoclonal antibodies. Multispecific myeloma proteins have been described (Richards et al., 1975; Tolleshang and Hannestad, 1975) and, although they usually display low association constants, they serve as a warning of a type of phenomenon which may be observed using monoclonal antibodies. So far in our experience this type of cross-reaction (multispecific recognitions), if it occurs at all, is not common enough to blur the recognition of individual differentiation antigens. Apart from these exceptional circumstances, the presence of a particular antigen as recognized by a monoclonal antibody is significant even at very low values. Fairly accurate determinations of average antigen density (Williams et al., 1977) are now possible, adding a new dimension to our understanding of quantitative aspects of antigen expression of cell surfaces (see Section V). Nonspecific absorption onto cell surfaces through, for instance, the Fc portion rather than the combining site remains as an important background noise. This is, of course, much diminished, but not totally eliminated by the use of the highly purified monoclonal antibodies, which provide Ig of higher specific activity than conventional antibodies. Pretreatment of cells with inactive derivatives, for instance of the HK type, may be a very good way of minimizing this effect.

III. Use of Monoclonal Antibodies to Define Differentiation Antigens of Cells of the Immune System and to Characterize Their Subsets

The immune system consists of a very heterogeneous collection of cells involved in complex interactions leading to induction or suppres-

14   C. MILSTEIN AND E. LENNOX

sion of specific immune responses. In these interactions morphologically identical types of cells may perform quite distinct functions. Such
cells have as their major distinctive structural feature the differential
expression of various surface antigens. For instance, antibody precursor cells differ one from another only in the fine structure of the antibody V regions defining the specificity of the antigen receptor. A major
advance in modern cellular immunology has been to recognize and
separate these cell subpopulations and to use them as pieces to reconstitute the puzzle of cell interactions in immune function.

Until the advent of monoclonal antibodies the major tool in the
preparation of reagents capable of recognizing such subpopulations of
cells was the immunization of mice from one strain with cells from
mice of another inbred strain. Thus antibody responses were limited to
those polymorphic antigens differing between the two strains. This
gave rise to the very useful series of Ly antisera, for instance (Boyse *et
al.*, 1971; for a review, see Waldmann and Howard, 1979). With other
animals, particularly humans, such methods were much more difficult
or impossible. Alternative procedures using heterologous immunization and selective absorption were attempted. These gave very heterogeneous antisera from which cell subpopulation-specific reagents can
be prepared (Williams, 1977) only with considerable difficulty. The
introduction of the hybrid myeloma technique has considerably
simplified the search for such specific reagents.

A. ALLOANTIBODIES TO MOUSE LYMPHOCYTES

The availability of a large number of well-characterized inbred
strains of mice and the possibility of preparing congeneic strains differing in the desired markers permitted the characterization, by conventional allogeneic immunizations, of a number of differentiation
antigens. Because of the difficulties in preparing, standardizing, and
maintaining a supply of such precious reagents, it is obviously urgent to
prepare the corresponding hybrid myelomas. Some have already been
derived (see Table I). However, it is quite possible, or indeed very
likely, that as such monoclonal antibodies are developed, problems will
arise in attempting to make correspondences between the McAb and
the conventional antibodies. These problems have been discussed previously and are inherent to the class restriction of the monoclonal antibody as well as to the likely antigenic heterogeneity recognized by the
conventional antibodies. The latter problem may be particularly acute
for antigens which are the expression, on similar subpopulations of
cells, of closely linked genes.

TABLE I

MONOCLONAL ANTIBODIES TO MOUSE ALLOANTIGENS

Cells for immunization	Recipient mouse	Specificity of McAb	Reference
1. T-cell leukemia (ASL-1)	(A × AKR/H-2^b(F1	Thy-1.2	Hämmerling et al. (1978)
2. Spleen A/TL	A/TH	Ia.7	Hämmerling et al. (1978)
3. B leukemia (I29)	(C57BL/6 × C3H/H2^l)F1	Lyb-2.1	Hämmerling et al. (1978)
4. Thymocytes, A/J	(C57BL/6 × A/TL$^-$)F1	TL	Hämmerling et al. (1978)
5. Spleen AKR	BALB/c	Ia-A^k	Hämmerling et al. (1978)
6. Spleen B10	BALB/c	Ig5.C3(H6/31)	Pearson et al. (1977)
7. Spleen CKB or spleen C3H	BALB/c	I-A^k, H-2K^k, Ig	Oi et al. (1978)
8. Spleen B10	C3H	^{2}(H9/25) Plaque-forming cells, T killer cells	Takei et al. (1980a)
		Most Abelson virus induced tumors	Takei et al. (1980b)

The first mouse monoclonal alloantibody, H6/31, defined a new allotype specificity which was genetically mapped in the Ig region and immunochemically located in the delta heavy chain of immunoglobulins (Pearson et al., 1977). It has been confirmed as a specific surface marker for most if not all the B cells of mouse strains carrying the Ig locus haplotypes b or e (A. Zeigler, T. Pearson, and C. Milstein, unpublished). The reagent is at present being extensively used, particularly in attempts to understand the functional significance of IgD-bearing cells. Monoclonal antibodies to other IgD allotypes are now also available (Oi et al., 1978).

In attempting to make McAb to MHC antigens, using as targets a panel of lymphoid tumor cells (see Section II, B), we purified clones producing McAb with strong cytolytic activities to a B10A Abelson tumor and strong binding activity to AKR thymus lymphoma BW5147. Two of them recognize a differentiation antigen(s) appearing in both the B-cell and T-cell lineages. For example, H9/25 antigen appears on cytotoxic T killer cells and their precursors but not on T helper cells. On the other hand it appears on the terminal stage of B-cell differentiation (plaque-forming cells) but not on most or all unprimed or memory B cells (Takei *et al.*, 1980b). Even more startling is its appearance on about half the cells in adult bone marrow. This type of result confronts us with a phenomenon that we will discuss further in connection with other McAb, concerning appearance and disappearance of surface antigenic determinants and with the problem of accounting for the regulation of expression of such "jumping" specificities.

The appearance of the H9/25 antigen on the AKR thymoma is perhaps a reflection of its correspondence to a precursor of a cytotoxic lymphocyte. The presence of the antigen on Abelson lymphomas is harder to rationalize if they correspond to early stages of B-cell differentiation. No problem arises, however, if Abelson lymphomas correspond to pre-B cells and are included among the 50% of the marrow cells that are H9/25-positive.

Other monoclonal alloantibodies to mouse differentiation antigens have been reported (Table I). Of particular interest are those reported by Hämmerling *et al.* (1978) and Oi *et al.* (1978) and derived by immunization of mice with normal cells from spleen, thymus, and leukemias, in several strain combinations. A variety of clones were derived which produce McAb to the Thy-1.2 antigen, a marker widely used to characterize and separate T cells. Other McAb seem to recognize certain specificities on the Ia antigens, which are controlled by the *H2* region and expressed on most, if not all, B cells but not on T cells.

B. XENOANTIBODIES TO MOUSE LEUKOCYTES

In addition to allogeneic McAb, xenogeneic McAb to mouse differentiation antigens have also been prepared. Anti-mouse differentiation antigens were raised by immunizing rats with mouse spleen cells which had been enriched in T cells by concanavalin A stimulation and passage through nylon wool (Springer *et al.*, 1978). The unpredictability of the derivation of hybrid myelomas following this type of stimulation is well exemplified by the specificities of 10 randomly selected McAb producing clones (Table II), namely: (*a*) one recognizing macrophages and precursor cells; (*b*) five detecting determinants of a heat-stable antigen, probably a glycolipid, displaying different degrees of cross-competition. At least one of them was expressed on all the spleen cells *except* T cells; (*c*) two detecting an antigen common to all leukocytes, but not to other cells and tissues (see also Trowbridge, 1978); (*d*) finally, two detecting Forssman antigen specificity present in normoblasts in spleen and later found in teratocarcinomas, preimplantation

TABLE II

RAT MONOCLONAL ANTIBODIES RECOGNIZING MOUSE CELLS[a]

Clone	Antibody	Cellular recognition	Antigen[b]
M1/9.3	IgG	White cells	210,000 MW unstable
M1/89.18	IgG	White cells	
M1/70	IgG	Macrophages and precursors	190,000 MW 105,000 MW unstable
M1/75	IgG	Red cells not on thymocytes	
M1/69	IgG	Red cells and most	No iodinated
M1/22.54	IgG	leukocytes	component[b,c]
M1/89.1	IgG	Thymocytes but not	Stable
M1/9.47	IgG	peripheral T cells	
M1/22.25	IgM	Mouse teratocarcinomas;	Forssman
M1/87	IgM	normoblasts; also testes and other adult tissues; early embryonic cells	Stable

[a] Data from Springer et al. (1978, 1979), Milstein et al. (1978), Stern et al. (1978), and Willison and Stern (1978).

[b] The immunoprecipitates were analyzed by SDS–PAGE. Stability refers to heating at 120°C for 15 minutes.

[c] In this group, antibodies compete among themselves for binding to mouse red blood cells.

mouse embryo, inner cell masses, and, in adults, in testes and, more weakly expressed, in kidney, bone marrow, and lymph nodes (Stern et al., 1978), but not in thymocytes or liver.

The expression of the antigens detected by these antibodies has been studied in some detail by means of the fluorescence-activated cell sorter (FACS). In some cases the quantitative expression appears to be a distinct characteristic of the subpopulations of cells of a given tissue (Fig. 4).

The expression of M1/69 and of M1/70 seems to be inversely proportional to each other in the cells of the macrophage lineage (Springer et al., 1979). The more interesting appears to be M1/70 which is found only in these cells and appears to be correlated with macrophage maturation. It is weakly expressed in bone marrow cells and slightly stronger in blood or spleen cells. It is stronger still in 18-hour stimulated peritoneal cells to increase to its highest concentration in the large peritoneal macrophages following 4 days of stimulation. It is also expressed on a macrophage tumor line in an amount similar to that on the large peritoneal macrophages.

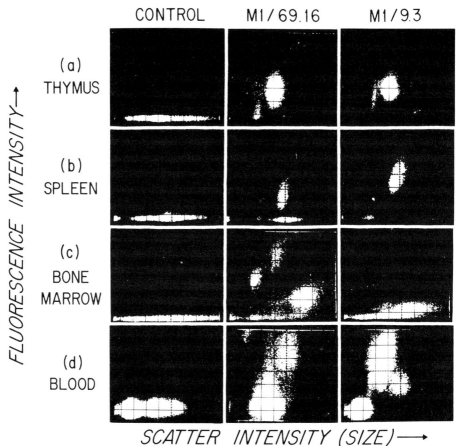

FIG. 4. Cell fingerprints obtained by fluorescence-activated cell sorter (FACS) two-dimensional display of lymphoid tissues labeled by monoclonal antibodies. Dots represent the fluorescent and scatter intensity of individual cells. Cells were labeled first with McAb (see Table II), then with fluoresceinated anti-rat IgG. Scatter gains are the same for blood and bone marrow but differ on other tissues. From Milstein *et al.* (1978); reproduced from *Excerpta Medica* with permission from Elsevier.

Other xenogeneic immunizations have been performed and their products are being investigated. A preliminary report suggests that one of them (R3-1 may recognize T cells (but not B cells) of all mouse strains (Hämmerling *et al.*, 1978).

C. XENOANTIBODIES TO RAT LYMPHOCYTE SUBSETS

In comparison with studies in the mouse, the study of rat lymphocyte antigens using conventional antibodies is much less developed.

Rat Thy-1 antigen had been purified and specific rabbit antibodies prepared (Williams *et al.*, 1976). But unlike mouse lymphocytes, rat peripheral lymphocytes did not express Thy-1; thus this marker could not be used to explore T-cell function, as was done with the mouse. Moreover in bone marrow it was found in the lymphoid cells but, unlike the case of mice, Thy-1 was not a marker of T-cell precursors (Hunt *et al.*, 1977). The hybrid myeloma technique was first applied to this problem as a test case for the preparation of specific reagents to discriminate cell subpopulations (Williams *et al.*, 1977). These and subsequent investigations have already produced a host of specific McAb (Table III) which make the rat system a good experimental alternative to the mouse system in a variety of antigenic and biochemical studies.

From a xenoimmunization of mice with rat thymocyte membranes two particularly interesting monoclonal reagents have been defined: W3/13 and W3/25. The first recognizes most, if not all, the peripheral T cells as well as the majority of cells in the thymus. A striking feature of expression of W3/13 antigen is that, although it is absent from B cells, it is present in plaque-forming cells (D. S. Secher, unpublished). Thus, at some unknown stage during differentiation from B cells to plaque-forming cells (cells actively secreting antibody), the antigen recognized by W3/13 and expressed at several stages of T-cell differentiation becomes expressed and is found on the terminal cells of B-cell differentiation (another example of a "jumping specificity"). W3/13 recognizes a glycoprotein (Standring *et al.*, 1979), but it is still unclear whether the actual determinant is on the carbohydrate or on the protein part.

While W3/13 recognizes all or most T cells, W3/25 appears to be specific for a subset of T cells which comprises about 80% of the T cells of the thoracic duct lymphocytes (TDL) and can carry out at least two essential functions of the T cells: helper function and graft-versus-host reactivity. The other 10% of T cells of the TDL, the W3/25 negative cells, includes allogeneic suppressor cells (White *et al.*, 1978). The general properties of W3/25 rat antigen correlate with the properties of the previously described murine Ly-1 antigen (see Cantor and Boyse, 1977) except that the latter, prepared by alloimmunization, recognizes a polymorphism while the former does not.

The way in which the monoclonal antibodies are used to define the functional properties of subpopulations is illustrated by these studies (Table IV). The McAb act as markers of cell subpopulations which thus can be fractionated for instance by the fluorescence-activated cell sorter. The use of xeno- rather than alloimmunization avoids a major source of noise in the indirect binding studies (Fig. 3). In using rat lymphoid cells as the target, some of which themselves carry Ig, it is an

TABLE III

Monoclonal Antibodies to Rat Differentiation Antigens

Clone	Antigen[a]	Cell recognition[b]	Antibody	References
W3/13	GP-95,000	T cells; plaque formers; myeloid (?) cells in BM; brain	IgG1	Williams et al. (1977); D. S. Secher (personal communication)
W3/25		T-cell subset with helper and GVH functions	IgG1	Williams et al. (1977); White et al. (1978)
W3/15 HLK		Red cells; erythroid (?) cells in BM	IgG	Williams et al. (1977)
W3/4 HLK		Mostly B cells	IgM	Williams et al. (1977)
MRC OX1	Leukocyte common Gp-150,000/200,000	All leukocytes	IgG	Sunderland et al. (1979); Standring et al. (1979)
MRC OX2	Thy-brain Gp3 60,000	Thymocytes; B (but not T) lympho-cytes–brain	IgG	McMaster and Williams (1979)
MRC OX3	Ia polymorphism (also in mouse and human)—32,000 and 28,000	20% Thymocytes; B (but not T) lymphocytes	IgG	McMaster and Williams (1979)
MRC OX4 MRC OX5 MRC OX6	Ia polymorphic in mouse—32,000 and 28,000		IgG	McMaster and Williams (1979)
MRC OX7	Thy-1 (Thy-1.1 in mice)	Different in mouse and rat (see Williams et al., 1976; Hunt et al., 1977)	Ig	Mason and Williams (1980)

[a] Gp, glycoproteins; numbers refer to apparent MW in SDS–PAGE after reduction.
[b] BM, bone marrow; GVH, graft versus host.

advantage that the specific monoclonal antibodies (which are recognized by the second antibody) are of mouse origin while the Ig carried by the target cells are of rat origin. Indirect immunofluorescent staining can be done using fluoresceinated anti-mouse immunoglobulin made specific by absorption with rat cells including those carrying rat Ig. A further development could be the use of suitable anti-mouse Ig McAb of rat origin.

Other McAb which recognize rat lymphocyte subsets have been developed from xenogeneic immunizations and permit the recognition of peripheral B lymphocytes (Table III). Thus in thoracic duct lymphocytes, W3/13 positive cells are MRC OX2, OX3, and OX4 negative. The converse is also true. Both populations together make up over 95% of the cells of the TDL. But overlaps of subsets comprising small number of cells (like plasma cells) are not excluded and may be functionally very important. MRC OX2 is absent from peripheral T cells but is expressed on thymocytes and also in brain while OX3 (and also, 4, 5, and 6) are on all B lymphocytes and 20% of thymocytes, but not on T lymphocytes (McMaster and Williams, 1979). They provide new examples of what we referred to before as "jumping" antigenic determinants, with the additional fact that the last three seem to recognize Ia antigens and OX3, a polymorphic form of it. All four recognize in addition mouse Ia polymorphisms (see Section III, A).

A set of monoclonal antibodies to rat cells offers some unique opportunities for ontogenic studies. A mixture of anti-Thy-1 (OX7 of Table III is probably a better alternative than the previous conventional anti-Thy-1), W3/15, and W3/13 antibodies recognize about 100% of the bone marrow cells. The majority of the cells of the bone marrow seem to be separately recognized by these three reagents, the anti-Thy-1 recognizing the lymphoid population, W3/13 the myeloid population, and

TABLE IV

CELLS WITH SURFACE ANTIGEN RECOGNIZED BY McAb W3/25 (80% OF T CELLS) INCLUDE THE HELPER ACTIVITY[a,b]

TDL transferred	Type of cells transferred	PFC/ spleen in recipient
None		<100
Unseparated	All T and B	~150,000
W3/25+ fraction	W3/25+ T and 5% of B	~15,000
W3/25- fraction	W3/25- T and B	<100
W3/25+ + Ig+ fraction	W3/25+ T and B	~200,000

[a] Thoracic duct lymphocytes were taken from suitably immunized rats. After indirect labeling with W3/25 McAb (labels 80% T cells) and/or anti-rat immunoglobulin (labels all B cells) and fluorescent second antibody cells were separated in the FACS II and transferred to irradiated recipients together with antigen. Plaque-forming cells (PFC) were determined in the spleen after 7 days, using an allotype method to discriminate donor and recipient cells.

[b] This table shows a simplified version of the data described by White et al. (1978).

W3/15 the erythroid population (Williams *et al.*, 1977). But the sum of the number of cells recognized by each of these individual reagents is over 100% (Table V) suggesting overlapping subpopulation(s) of cells recognized by more than one reagent. Thy-1 may be expressed on stem cells (Hunt *et al.*, 1977) and it is tempting to speculate that the overlaps between pairs of these reagents constitute stem cells becoming increasingly specialized and to ask whether there are stem cells which are recognized by all three reagents. Ontogenic modulation of these antigens could be investigated since it is clear that for instance W3/13 antigen is lost at some stage between the bone marrow myeloid precursor and the more mature forms in the peripheral tissues (see Table III and preceding).

D. XENOANTIBODIES AS MARKERS OF HUMAN LYMPHOCYTES

Efforts to dissect the subpopulations of human cells of the immune system have so far proved more elusive, but this has been, at least partly, due to the distracting effect introduced by the detection of other no less interesting specificities (Barnstable *et al.*, 1978). Recently a clone has been isolated which heralds a large series of new reagents to come (McMichael *et al.*, 1979). This monoclonal antibody NA/1.34 detects an antigen so far found only on thymocytes (see Fig. 5). Within the thymus not all cells express this antigen and the proportion that does seems to vary from 40% in fetal to over 90% in adult thymuses (Janossy *et al.*, 1980). An interesting observation has been the inverse correlation of the expression of this particular antigen HTA1

TABLE V

SUBPOPULATIONS OF BONE MARROW CELLS[a,b]

Developing specificity	Percentage of labeled cells	Arithmetic addition	Overlap
W3/13	44	44	—
W3/15	24	24	—
Anti-Thy-1	42	42	—
W3/13 + W3/15	61	68	7
W3/13 + anti-Thy-1	83	86	3
W3/15 + anti-Thy-1	56	66	10
W3/13 + W3/15 + anti-Thy-1	97	110	13

[a] Data from Williams *et al.* (1977).
[b] Fluorescent cells analyzed in the fluorescence-activated cell sorter. The results are the average of the three experiments described in the original paper (Williams *et al.*, 1977).

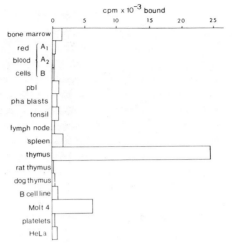

FIG. 5. Specificity of binding of McAb NAI/34. Indirect binding was measured using 2.5×10^6 cells of each source: pbl, peripheral blood lymphocytes; pha, phytohemagglutinin. From McMichael *et al.* (1979); reproduced from *European Journal of Immunology* with permission from Verlag-Chemie, GmbH.

(recognized by NA/1.34) with the expression of the HLA-A,B,C specificity recognized by antibody W6/32: cells which are positive for one are negative for the other and vice versa (Bradstock *et al.*, 1980). The expression of these two specificities is also correlated with a separate histological localization of the two types of cells within the thymus (Janossy *et al.*, 1980), the first in the cortex and Hassal's corpuscles, the second in the medulla. It is not known whether the expression of HTA1 is functionally correlated with entrance into, or exit from, the thymus. Outside the thymus, HTA-positive cells have been found in the periphery, only in certain types of T-cell leukemias. HTA1 antigen appears to contain a chain of apparent molecular weight of about 45,000, probably associated with another of about 12,000 (A. Ziegler *et al.*, unpublished). In most of these properties HTA1 resembles the mouse TL or thymus leukemia antigen (Konda *et al.*, 1973).

Two independent clones secreting antibody specific for subpopulations of B cells have been isolated by Trucco *et al.* (1978). These antibodies may recognize the human Ia antigens. Some of the mouse anti-rat Ia McAb described in Table III also seem able to recognize human Ia.

IV. Other Systems

So far we have concentrated our discussion of McAb to surface antigens which recognized subpopulations of lymphoid cells since it includes the more elaborate set of data. This is not surprising as, in the short time since the hybrid myeloma procedure was developed, attention has been focused on differentiation of the cells involved in the antibody response. But monoclonal antibodies to other surface antigens have already been developed and are being used. Indeed, the first monoclonal antibodies were against sheep red blood cell (SRBC) membrane antigens (Köhler and Milstein, 1975, 1976).

In Section III we have discussed McAb to MHC antigens defining lymphocyte subpopulations. But these antigens are themselves emerging as of interest in differentiation, since they are undetectable in some embryonic cells (for a review, see Erikson, 1977) and in a subset of thymic cells (McMichael et al., 1979). McAb to the large (A, B, and C) and small (β_2m) chains of HLA are now available (Barnstable et al., 1978; Trucco et al., 1978; Parham and Bodmer, 1978) as are McAb to rat (Galfrè et al., 1977; McKearn et al., 1978) and mouse (Hämmerling et al., 1978; Oi et al., 1978) MHC antigens.

Of special interest to developmental biology are the embryonic antigens expressed on mouse teratocarcinomas and early embryos (Jacob, 1977; Graham, 1977; Hogan, 1978). Conventional mouse antisera prepared against F9 teratocarcinoma have been used to follow expression of the F9 antigen at various stages in embryogenesis and in adult tissue (Babinet et al., 1975; Buc-Caron et al., 1978). A rabbit antiteratocarcinoma serum was used in similar studies (Edidin and Gooding, 1975; Gooding et al., 1976).

More recently two monoclonal antibodies have come on the scene. One of these, mentioned in Section II, B, recognizes a Forssman antigen specificity present on a minor subpopulation of spleen cells (the actual immunogen) and is also present in the adult testes, kidney, and brain (Stern et al., 1978). It is present on teratocarcinomas but absent on differentiated derivatives.

In the preimplantation embryo (Willison and Stern, 1978) it first appears on the trophectoderm of the blastocyst where its expression is transient. On the inner cell mass its expression persists up to implantation. In postimplantation embryos (Evans et al., 1979), expression on ectoderm is transient and endoderm is positive at least until day $7\frac{3}{4}$. Germ cells presumably derived from ectoderm are positive at least to 16 days; germ cells of the adult male are negative. The Forssman antigen represents another example of the "jumping" specificities previously discussed and emphasizes the danger of using a single differentiation antigen to follow cell lineages.

The other McAb (Solter and Knowles, 1978) was derived from an immunization of a mouse with a teratocarcinoma line. It is striking that it also apparently recognizes a glycolipid, but not the Forssman specificity. Its distribution on preimplantation embryos, while somewhat different in timing, is very similar to that of the Forssman specificity.

In addition, normal and tumor cells of neural and muscle origin are being examined for differentiation antigens (Schubert, 1973; Schubert *et al.*, 1974; Chaffee and Schachner, 1978; Imada and Sueoka, 1978; Imada *et al.*, 1978), and represent an area of potential importance for the application of monoclonal antibodies. Cuello *et al.* (1979) have prepared a monoclonal antibody to the transmitter-like substance P. The culture fluid of the cloned cell line NC1/34 does not cross-react with other brain peptides tested and can be used for radioimmunoassays down to about 50 fmole of substance P. By indirect immunofluorescence, the antibody binds to nerve terminals and cell bodies located in defined nuclear organizations of the rat central nervous system.

So far we have concentrated on surface antigens. There are several reasons to do so, the most important being the difficulty of dealing with surface components in other ways and the extensive preliminary work done on them by conventional immunological procedures. Intracellular components often have enzymatic activities and their expression is therefore easier to follow. But for certain purposes and in cases in which the biological activity is not easy to visualize or measure *in situ,* the use of McAb could prove of great value. McAb to all the antigenic

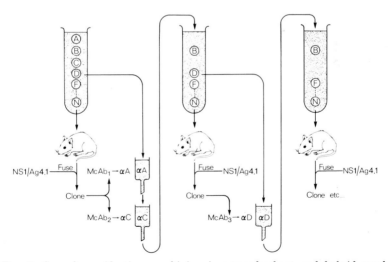

Fig. 6. Cascade purification: combining immunoadsorbent and hybrid myeloma methods to derive a complete set of specific antibodies to a heterogeneous population of antigens.

components of the intracellular fluid could be made by a "cascade purification" procedure. By this we mean that a set of Mcab is first prepared to the bulk of intracellular material with no previous purification. With this set, immunoadsorbent columns can be prepared to remove the recognized antigens. A new set of monoclonal antibodies can now be raised using this partially purified mixture of antigens. This allows new immunoadsorbents to be prepared to further remove antigens to repeat new immunizations (Fig. 6).

V. Future Prospects

The hybrid myeloma technique for the preparation of monoclonal antibodies has proved very valuable in the characterization of differentiation antigens. The results have been very encouraging but they have also been somewhat surprising in a variety of ways, in particular the persistent involvement of carbohydrates (lipopolysaccharides and glycoproteins) and the frequent recognition of common antigenic determinants on subpopulations of cells that have developed along different differentiation pathways. We have pointed out the individual cases and referred to them as "jumping" antigens. "Jumping" differentiation antigens had been described before. For instance, the Thy-1 antigen was known to be expressed in T cells and in brain (Reif and Allen, 1966; Raff, 1971; Williams et al., 1976). But the expression of these "jumping" antigens appears to be more common than we suspected. To what extent this property is due to the same carbohydrate determinants expressed on different protein antigens or in different lipopolysaccharide molecules remains to be seen.

While the possible carbohydrate involvement in antibody recognition remains to be elucidated for each individual case, the few experiments performed so far have generally failed to disclose differences between molecules carrying the common determinants recognized on different cell types. Thus, the determinant recognized by antibody M1/22.25 appeared to be on a similar kind of molecule when studied on teratocarcinoma lines and sheep red cells and in both cases are compatible with a Forssman antigen specificity carried on glycolipid molecules (Stern et al., 1978). But these are rather early experiments and it remains to be seen whether in some cases the common recognition of different cell types may not indeed be the result of the presence of similar or identical carbohydrate structures attached to different proteins or other components. Indeed different molecular weight polypeptides have been precipitated from thymus and spleen using an Mcab which recognizes a common leukocyte antigen in mice (Trowbridge,

1978). This could add a considerable degree of flexibility to the diversity of the cell surface. Such combinatorial complexity would make our effort to understand their regulation that much more difficult.

McAb offer the possibility not only of characterization and purification of antigens but also a reagent for functional studies. We discussed one such example in which cells carrying a given antigen are separated from others lacking it by a FACS, so that the function of the separated subsets of cells can be studied (Section III, C). Other sorting procedures or cell killing can also be used to the same effect. Another way in which antibodies have been used in functional studies is to block and interfere with the system under study. For example, the Fab fragment of anti-F9 retards development of early embryos and this effect can be reversed by removal of the antibody Fab (Kemler et al., 1977). Monoclonal antibodies to specific components of the MHC have also been used in studies of prolonged survival (passive enhancement) of renal allografts in rats (Gallico et al., 1979; McKearn et al., 1978).

Among the total population of cell surface antigens of an individual, some antigens will be expressed in a very large proportion, perhaps even in all its cells, while others will be expressed in restricted subsets. The majority of the cell surface antigens are probably somewhere in between. The important parameters to define this mosaic pattern are (a) the presence of absence of each surface antigen in all the differentiated cells of the individual and (b) the quantitative expression of all the antigens which are detectable in each cell or cell subpopulation. The dynamics of the changes in these two parameters will define the dynamics of the cell surface development. This will require, of course, the organization of a huge collection of monoclonal antibodies capable of recognizing all the antigens of a given species, preferably independent of the polymorphic derivatives. The recognition of polymorphic forms essential for a variety of functional and genetic studies will require separate sets of reagents.

A complete collection of reagents of that type will, of course, be a task of many years to come by many different laboratories. Easy access to the available reagents and to storage of information about them will be essential. To this effect, it is essential to make easily available the products of all isolated clones within a reasonable period (say a year) of the publication reporting them. Cataloging and easy access to the information is also critical.

But even before a large number of such reagents are prepared, a very modest collection will provide considerable information. The combination of the use of monoclonal antibodies in conjunction with the analytical power of modern cytofluorimeters is full of potential. Such instruments permit the simultaneous measurement of parameters such as cell size and fluorescence intensity at different wavelengths in a large number of individual cells and in an extremely short time. Two-dimensional displays of cell size and fluorescence intensity of a given cell population following reaction with fluoresceinated monoclonal antibodies, produces characteristic patterns of "cellular fingerprints" such as those illustrated in Fig. 4. These displays can be accurately quantitated and computer stored. With proper instrumentation cells can be sorted and used for functional analysis (Herzenberg and Herzenberg, 1978). The approach offers, therefore, the possibility of a massive, frontal attack to the problem of antigenic modulation and changes of the surfaces of cells during ontogenic development as well as variations in the steady state of the cell populations themselves.

VI. Concluding Remarks

Serological techniques are useful to study changes in cell surfaces during development and also to identify differentiated subsets of cells as well as to attempt the definition of cell lineages. Conventional antisera have several limitations: it is almost impossible to make them specific for individual components and the amounts produced are small and preparations are difficult to reproduce. Monoclonal antibodies (McAb) derived by fusion of myeloma cells to spleen cells of immunized animals are ideally suited to avoid these difficulties. Once clones are purified and stabilized by repeated subculture, they form a permanent source of antibody specific for a unique determinant. As a general rule hybrid myelomas are capable of producing any of the antibody specificities expressed by an immunized animal. But the practical ease with which individual specificities can be obtained is primarily determined by the immunogenicity of the antigen carrying that specificity compared with other antigens presented at the same time. A careful choice of immunization schedules and assay procedures is also important for getting antibodies of desired specificities. For antibodies to differentiation antigens, panels of tumor cell lines have been very useful, both for immunization and for screening.

McAb have now been prepared to a variety of cell surface differentiation antigens. Even at this early stage in the utilization of the technique, reagents recognizing new, hitherto undefined, antigens have been produced. The most extensive results have been obtained with cells of the immune system: xenogeneic antibodies recognizing specific subpopulations of rat, mouse, and human lymphoid cells and allogeneic or xenogeneic antibodies recognizing polymorphic specificities in those same three species. These reagents have also been used for the isolation and biochemical characterization of the antigens and to isolate cell subpopulations, using sorting techniques, to study their functional properties.

Early applications of the technique to the study of developing cell surfaces in other systems indicate its potential in areas such as embryology, neurobiology, and tumor biology as well as in biochemical characterization and purification of cell surface molecules, as the same McAb used to recognize a new antigenic specificity can also be used for the preparation of affinity columns for the large-scale isolation of the antigen in question. Among the antigenic structures recognized so far, some are protein molecules and a high proportion are glycoproteins or lipopolysaccharides. Antigens expressed in more than one population of cell have not been uncommon. In some cases these populations may belong to a single differentiation pathway. However, in other cases quite unrelated cell populations express the same antigenic determinant. An interesting example of such a "jumping" specificity is that of McAb W3/13 which occurs in brain, myeloid cells of the bone marrow, in T cells, and in plasma cells but not in their immediate precursors, B cells. This result indicates that great care is required in the use of individual antigens or specificities in drawing conclusions about the relationship and origins of individual cell lines, or in defining cell lineages. With McAb this could be further complicated because the same specificity could detect products of unrelated genes. But the day is now near when a multiplicity of reagents will be available to study the patterns of antigenic expression in different cell lineages. This will not only be more reliable but will also permit the study of the dynamics of the expression of the developing cell surfaces. In turn, this could help to clarify the extent to which tumor-specific antigens can be accounted for by the illegitimate expression of normal differentiation antigens.

NOTE ADDED IN PROOF

A large number of papers dealing with the subject have been published since this manuscript was prepared. It is impossible to refer to them at this late stage without redoing the tables and large sections of the text. We apologize to the reader for omitting these publications, which in general do not modify but rather reinforce our main conclusions and ideas. The use of monoclonal Ab to affect the surface development during differentiation is nicely illustrated by the work of Dulbecco *et al.* (1979).

REFERENCES

Akeson, R. (1977). *J. Natl. Cancer Inst.* **58**, 863–869.
Babinet, C., Condamine, H., Fellous, M., Gachelin, G., Kemler, R., and Jacob, F. (1975). *In* "Teratomas and Differentiation" (M. I. Sherman and D. Solter, eds.), pp. 101–107. Academic Press, New York.

Baldwin, R. W. (1973). *Adv. Cancer Res.* **18,** 1–75.
Baldwin, R. W., Embleton, M. J., Price, M. R., and Vose, B. M. (1974). *Transplant. Rev.* **20,** 77–99.
Barnstable, C. J., Bodmer, W. F., Brown, G., Galfrè, G. Milstein, C., Williams, A. F., and Ziegler, A. (1978). *Cell* **14,** 9–20.
Boyse, E. A., Itakura, K., Stockert, E., Iritani, C., and Miura, M. (1971). *Transplantation* **11,** 351–352.
Bradstock, K. F., Janossy, G., Bollum, F. J., and Milstein, C. (1980). *Nature (London)* (in press).
Buc-Caron, H. M., Condamine, H., and Jacob, F. (1978). *J. Embryol. Exp. Morphol.* **47,** 149–160.
Cantor, H., and Boyse, E. A. (1977). *Immunol. Rev.* **33,** 105–124.
Ceriani, R. L., Thompson, K., Peterson, J. A., and Abraham, S. (1977). *Proc. Natl. Acad. Sci. U.S.A.* **74,** 582–586.
Chaffee, J. K., and Schachner, M. (1978). *Dev. Biol.* **62,** 185–192.
Cotton, R. G. H., and Milstein, C. (1973). *Nature (London)* **244,** 42–43.
Cuello, C., Galfrè, G., and Milstein, C. (1979). *Proc. Natl. Acad. Sci. U.S.A.* **76,** 3532–3536.
Dulbecco, R., Bologna, M., and Unger, M. (1979). *Proc. Natl. Acad. Sci. U.S.A.* **76,** 1848–1852.
Edidin, M., and Gooding, L. R. (1975). *In* "Teratomas and Differentiation" (M. I. Sherman and D. Solter, eds.), pp. 109–121. Academic Press, New York.
Erikson, R. P. (1977). *In* "Immunobiology and Gametes" (M. Johnson and M. Edidin, eds.), pp. 85–114. Cambridge University Press, London and New York.
Evans, M. J., Lovell-Badge, R. H., Stern, P. L., and Stinnakre, M. G. (1979). *In* "Cell Lineage, Stem Cells and Cell Determination" (N. Le Douarin, ed.), pp. 115–130. Elsevier, Amsterdam.
Galfrè, G., Howe, S. C., Milstein, C., Butcher, G. W., and Howard, J. C. (1977). *Nature (London)* **266,** 550–552.
Galfrè, G., Milstein, C., and Wright, B. (1979). *Nature (London)* **277,** 131–133.
Gallico, G. G., Butcher, G. W., and Howard, J. C. (1979). *J. Exp. Med.* **149,** 244–253.
Goldsby, R. A., Osborne, B. A., Simpson, E., and Herzenberg, L. A. (1977). *Nature (London)* **267,** 707–708.
Gooding, L. R., Hsu, Y.-C., and Edidin, M. (1976). *Dev. Biol.* **49,** 479–486.
Graham, C. F. (1977). *In* "Concepts in Mammalian Embryogenesis" (M. I. Sherman, ed.), pp. 315–394. MIT Press, Cambridge, Massachusetts.
Greaves, M. F., Janossy, G., Roberts, M., Rapson, N., Ellis, R. B., Chessels, J., Lister, T. A., and Catowsky, D. (1977). *In* "Immunological Diagnosis of Leukemias and Lymphomas" (S. Theirfelder, H. Rodt, and E. Thiel, eds.), pp. 61–75. Springer-Verlag, Berlin and New York.
Hämmerling, G. J. (1977). *Eur. J. Immunol.* **7,** 743–746.
Hämmerling, G. J., Lemke, H., Hämmerling, U., Höhmann, C., Wallich, R. and Rajewsky, K. (1978). *Curr. Top. Microbiol. Immunol.* **81,** 100–106.
Herzenberg, L. A., Herzenberg, L. A., and Milstein, C. (1978). *In* "Handbook of Experimental Immunology" (D. M. Weir, ed.), 3rd ed., pp. 25.1–25.7. Blackwell, Oxford.
Herzenberg, L. A., and Herzenberg, L. A. (1978). *In* "Handbook of Experimental Immunology" (D. M. Weir, ed.), pp. 22.7–22.21. Blackwell, Oxford.
Hogan, B. L. M. (1978). *In* "Biochemistry of Cell Differentiation II" (J. Paul, ed.), pp. 333–376. Univ. Park Press, Baltimore, Maryland.
Howard, J. C., Butcher, G. W., Galfrè, G., and Milstein, C. (1978). *Curr. Top. Microbiol. Immunol.* **81,** 54–60.

Hunt, S. V., Mason, D. W., and Williams, A. F. (1977). *Eur. J. Immunol.* **7**, 817–823.
Imada, M., and Sueoka, N. (1978). *Dev. Biol.* **66**, 97–108.
Imada, M., Sueoka, N., and Rifkin, D. B. (1978). *Dev. Biol.* **66**, 109–116.
Jacob, F. (1977). *Immunol. Rev.* **33**, 3–32.
Janossy, G., Thoma, A. J., Bollum, F. J., Mattingly, S., Pizzolo, G., Bradstock, K. F., Wong, L., Ganeshaguru, K., and Hoffbrand, A. V. (1980). *J. Immunol.* (in press).
Kemler, R., Babinet, C., Eisen, H., and Jacob, F. (1977). *Proc. Natl. Acad. Sci. U.S.A.* **74**, 4449–4452.
Köhler, G., and Milstein, C. (1975). *Nature (London)* **256**, 495–497.
Köhler, G., and Milstein, C. (1976). *Eur. J. Immunol.* **6**, 511–519.
Köhler, G., Howe, S. C., and Milstein, C. (1976). *Eur. J. Immunol.* **6**, 292–295.
Köhler, G., Pearson, T., and Milstein, C. (1977a). *Somatic Cell Genet.* **3**, 303–312.
Köhler, G., Lefkovitz, I., Elliot, B., and Coutinho, A. (1977b). *Eur. J. Immunol.* **7**, 758–760.
Köhler, G., Hengartner, H., and Milstein, C. (1978). *Protides Bio. Fluids, Proc. Colloq.* **25**, 545–549.
Konda, S., Stockert, E., and Smith, R. T. (1973). *Cell. Immunol.* **7**, 275–289.
Koprowski, H., Gerhard, W., Wiktor, T., Martinis, J., Shander, M., and Croce, C. M. (1978a). *Curr. Top. Microbiol. Immunol.* **81**, 8–19.
Koprowski, H., Steplewski, Z., Herlyn, D., and Herlyn, M. (1978b). *Proc. Natl. Acad. Sci. U.S.A.* **75**, 3405–3409.
McKearn, T. J., Sarmiento, M., Weiss, A., Stuart, F. P., and Fitch, F. W. (1978). *Contemp. Top. Immunol. Microbiol.* **81**, 61–65.
McMaster, W. R., and Williams, A. F. (1979). *Eur. J. Immunol.* **9**, 426–433.
McMichael, A. J., Pilch, J. R., Galfrè, G., Mason, D. Y., Fabre, J. W., and Milstein, C. (1979). *Eur. J. Immunol.* (in press).
Margulies, D. H., Kuehl, W. M., and Scharff, M.D. (1976). *Cell* **8**, 405–415.
Mason, D. W., and Williams, A. F. (1980). *Biochem. J.* (in press).
Merrill, J. M., and De Wys, W. (1978). *In* "Clinical Oncology for Medical Students and Physicians—A Multidisciplinary Approach" (P. Rubin and R. F. Bakemeier, eds.), pp. 56–62. Am. Cancer Soc.
Milstein, C., Adetugbo, K., Cowan, N. J., Köhler, G., Secher, D. S., and Wilde, D. C. (1976). *Cold Spring Harbor Symp. Quant. Biol.* **41**, 793–803.
Milstein, C., Galfrè, G., Secher, D. S., and Springer, T. (1978). *Excerpta Med., Ciba Found. Symp.* **66**, 251–266.
Nelson-Rees, W. A. (1978). *J. Natl. Cancer Inst.* **60**, 1205–1206.
Oi, V. T., Jones, P. P., Goding, J. W., Herzenberg, L. A., and Herzenberg, L. A. (1978). *Contemp. Top. Microbiol. Immunol.* **81**, 115–129.
Old, L. J., and Stockert, E. (1977). *Annu. Rev. Genet.* **11**, 127–160.
Parham, P., and Bodmer, W. F. (1978). *Nature (London)* **276**, 397–398.
Pearson, T., Galfrè, G., Ziegler, A., and Milstein, C. (1977). *Eur. J. Immunol.* **7**, 684–690.
Potter, M. (1972). *Physiol. Rev.* **52**, 631–719.
Raff, M. C. (1971). *Transplant. Rev.* **6**, 52–80.
Reif, A. E., and Allen, J. M. (1966). *Nature (London)* **209**, 521–523.
Richards, F. F., Konigsberg, W. H., Rosenstein, R. W., and Varga, J. M. (1975). *Science* **187**, 130–137.
Risser, R., Stockert, E., and Old, L. J. (1978). *Proc. Natl. Acad. Sci. U.S.A.* **75**, 3918–3922.
Schubert, D. (1973). *In* "Tissue Culture of the Nervous System" (G. Sato, ed.), pp. 55–86. Plenum, New York.

Schubert, D., Heinemann, S., Carlisle, W., Tarikas, H., Kimes, B., Patrick, J., Steinbach, J. H., Culp, W., and Brandt, B. L. (1974). *Nature (London)* **249**, 224–227.

Shulman, M., Wilde, C. D., and Köhler, G. (1978). *Nature (London)* **276**, 269–270.

Solter, D., and Knowles, B. B. (1978). *Proc. Natl. Acad. Sci. U.S.A.* **75**, 5565–5569.

Springer, T., Galfrè, G., Secher, D. S., and Milstein, C. (1978). *Eur. J. Immunol.* **8**, 539–551.

Springer, T., Galfrè, G., Secher, D. A., and Milstein, C. (1979). *Eur. J. Immunol.* **9**, 301–306.

Standring, R., McMaster, W. R., Sunderland, C. A., and Williams, A. F. (1979). *Eur. J. Immunol.* **8**, 832–839.

Stern, P., Willison, K., Lennox, E., Galfrè, G., Milstein, C., Secher, D. S., Ziegler, A., and Springer, T. (1978). *Cell* **14**, 775–783.

Sunderland, C. A., McMaster, W. R., and Williams, A. F. (1979). *Eur. J. Immunol.* **9**, 155–159.

Takei, F., Galfrè, G., Alderson, T., Lennox, E., and Milstein, C. (1980a). *Eur. J. Immunol.* (in press).

Takei, F., Waldmann, H., Lennox, E., and Milstein, C. (1980b). *Eur. J. Immunol.* (in press).

Tolleshang, H., and Hannestad, K. (1975). *Immunochemistry* **12**, 173–182.

Trowbridge, I. S. (1978). *J. Exp. Med.* **148**, 313–323.

Trucco, M. M., Stocker, J. W., and Ceppellini, R. (1978). *Curr. Top. Microbiol. Immunol.* **81**, 66.

Waldmann, H., and Howard, J. C. (1979). *In* "Defense and Recognition IIA" (E. S. Lennox, ed), pp. 29–95. Univ. Park Press, Baltimore, Maryland.

White, R. A. H., Mason, D. W., Williams, A. F., Galfrè, G. and Milstein, C. (1978). *J. Exp. Med.* **148**, 664–673.

Williams, A. F. (1977). *Contemp. Top. Mol. Immunol.* **6**, 83–116.

Williams, A. F., Barclay, A. N., Letarte-Muirhead, M., and Morris, R. J. (1976). *Cold Spring Harbor Symp. Quant. Biol.* **41**, 51–61.

Williams, A. F., Galfrè, G., and Milstein, C. (1977). *Cell* **12**, 663–673.

Willison, K. R., and Stern, P. L. (1978). *Cell* **14**, 785–793.

Yelton, D. E., Diamond, B. A., Kwan, S. P., and Schaff, M. D. (1978). *Curr. Top. Microbiol. Immunol.* **81**, 1–7.

CHAPTER 2

EARLY STAGES OF LYMPHOCYTE DEVELOPMENT[1]

Irving Goldschneider

DEPARTMENT OF PATHOLOGY
UNIVERSITY OF CONNECTICUT HEALTH CENTER
FARMINGTON, CONNECTICUT

I. Organization of the Lymphoid System: Overview

The lymphocyte system in higher vertebrates is divided developmentally along two major pathways. Lymphocytes which differentiate in the thymus before emigrating to peripheral lymphoid tissues are referred to as T lymphocytes or T cells. Lymphocytes which differentiate in the bursa of Fabricius in birds or in the bone marrow and fetal liver in mammals are referred to as B lymphocytes or B cells. Mature T and B cells are functionally heterogeneous populations of lymphocytes which exhibit complex migratory patterns and which occupy discrete anatomical compartments within lymph nodes, spleen, and other lymphoid tissues. T lymphocytes initiate cell-mediated immunological reactions (e.g., delayed-type hypersensitivity reactions, allograft rejection, immunity to intracellular parasites). B lymphocytes

[1] Supported in part by NIH grants AI-09649 and AI-14743. Part of the work reported in this chapter was undertaken during the tenure of an American Cancer Society–Eleanor Roosevelt–International Cancer Fellowship awarded by the International Union against Cancer.

33

initiate antibody-mediated immunological reactions. Cooperative interactions between T cells, B cells, and macrophages are necessary for most immunological reactions to occur; and complex systems for modulating immunological responses have been described.

Like all hemopoietic cells, T and B lymphocytes originate from pluripotent hemopoietic stem cells in yolk sac, liver, spleen, and bone marrow. The complex series of proliferative and differentiative events which constitutes lymphocyte development is poorly understood, but operationally it can be divided into two sequential stages, antigen-independent and antigen-dependent (Burnet, 1959). Antigen-independent development occurs in hemopoietic tissues and primary lymphoid tissues (thymus, bursa), and to a lesser extent in secondary (peripheral) lymphoid tissues. As in other hemopoietic cell systems, differentiation and proliferation are regulated by a combination of microenvironmental and hormonal influences. However, prior exposure of lymphocyte precursors to endogenous antigens, especially histocompatibility antigens, may be crucial in determining the receptor repertoire to self- and nonself-antigens. The products of this stage of development are immature lymphocytes, which may undergo further differentiation and clonal expansion upon stimulation with exogenous antigens, mitogens, and inflammatory reactants. This latter, antigen-dependent, stage of lymphocyte development occurs mainly in the secondary lymphoid tissues and results in the production of functionally mature lymphocytes, including memory cells, effector cells, and modulator cells.

Many of the major differentiative events of functional consequence occur prior to the migration of lymphocytes to the peripheral lymphoid tissues. These events include: (a) the generation of immunological diversity; (b) the expression of the antigen receptor repertoire; (c) the establishment of self-tolerance, at least by T cells; (d) the development of functional heterogeneity; and (e) the acquisition of specific migratory properties. Here we will summarize the results of recent work on the nature of the cell types which characterize the early stages of lymphocyte development. The discussion will be limited for the most part to considerations of T-lymphocyte generation within the general context of normal hemopoiesis. Special emphasis will be given to the use of cell surface antigens as markers with which to identify and isolate pluripotent hemopoietic stem cells, thymocyte progenitors, and immature (subcapsular) thymocytes. The reader is referred to other reviews for a more global treatment of lymphocyte development (e.g., Greaves *et al.,* 1973; Goldschneider and Barton, 1976; Cantor and Weissman, 1976; *Cold Spring Harbor Symposia on Quantitative Biology,* 1977; Nossal *et al.,* 1977; Katz, 1977).

II. Hemopoiesis: Definitions and Basic Considerations

As in all renewing cell systems, generation of differentiated hemopoietic cells is the province of a minor population of primitive stem cells and their immediate descendents, the committed progenitor cells. Inasmuch as these and other terms used to designate the stages of hemopoiesis are loosely applied, it is necessary to define them for the purposes of the present discussion.

Hemopoiesis may be considered to progress through four major developmental stages or cellular hierarchies: stem cells → progenitor cells → immature cells → mature cells. The hallmarks of these cellular compartments are self-renewal, commitment, differentiation, and function, respectively. Because of the multipotentiality of hemopoietic stem cells, each compartment has horizontal as well as vertical subcompartments. Unfortunately, these operationally defined compartments and subcompartments do not have anatomically defined correlates. Rather, cells of various developmental stages and lineages are admixed in hemopoietic tissues; and stem and progenitor cells migrate widely throughout the hemopoietic system. These factors have greatly complicated the study of hemopoiesis in general, and are particularly evident in the study of the early stages of lymphopoiesis.

Pluripotent hemopoietic stem cells are defined as the least mature members of the hemopoietic system from which all erythroid, myeloid, and lymphoid cells are derived. Not only can they give rise to committed progenitors of the various hemopoietic cell lines, but they have an extensive capacity for self-replication as well.

Hemopoietic progenitor cells are committed to the production of differentiated members of one or more hemopoietic cell lines. By definition, they are more restricted in their developmental potential than are stem cells, and they lack the ability to self-replicate to any significant extent.

Both hemopoietic stem and progenitor cells have extensive proliferative capacities. However, most stem cells normally are in G_0, whereas most progenitor cells are in active cell cycle. Neither cell type has morphological characteristics which would enable it to be associated with a particular hemopoietic cell line. Differentiation and proliferation of hemopoietic stem cells appear to be at least partly under the control of microenvironmental factors; that of hemopoietic progenitor cells appears to be strongly influenced by specific humoral factors. Several models have been proposed to explain how these multipotent cells become committed to differentiation within a single hemopoietic cell lineage. These topics are extensively reviewed elsewhere (e.g., Metcalf and Moore, 1971; Cronkite, 1975; Till, 1976; Metcalf, 1977).

Immature hemopoietic cells are defined as differentiating cells which are derived from progenitor cells and which generate mature hemopoietic cells. Immature cells have a more restricted proliferative capacity than progenitor cells and are readily identifiable as belonging to a specific hemopoietic cell lineage.

The term hemopoietic precursor cells will be used in a nondiscriminating manner to designate stem, progenitor, and/or immature hemopoietic cells when the stage of development is in doubt.

Mature hemopoietic cells are the final products of hemopoiesis and, with the exception of lymphocytes and macrophages, are fully differentiated, end-stage cells. Lymphocytes and macrophages retain the capacity to undergo further proliferation and differentiation when appropriately stimulated during inflammatory or immunological reactions.

III. Hemopoietic Stem Cells

The existence of pluripotent hemopoietic stem cells was firmly established by Till and McCulloch (1961), who demonstrated that a small population of bone marrow cells was able to form macroscopically visible colonies of mature hemopoietic cells in spleens of lethally irradiated mice. These colonies themselves contained pluripotent stem cells which could give rise to additional hemopoietic colonies, so that the progeny of a single stem cell could effectively reconstitute all members of the myeloid and erythroid cell series in a lethally irradiated recipient. The clonal nature of this repopulation was demonstrated by Wu et al., (1967) and Nowell et al. (1970), who examined the progeny of hemopoietic cells which contained radiation-induced chromosomal markers. These studies and a recent study by Abramson et al. (1977) demonstrated that T and B lymphocytes, which are not normally produced in spleen colonies, also are derived from the same stem cells which produce myeloid and erythroid cells. Again it has been calculated that the progeny of a single hemopoietic stem cell can repopulate the lymphoid system of a lethally irradiated host (Phillips et al., 1977).

Subsequent efforts to study hemopoietic stem cells have been seriously hindered by their small numbers in hemopoietic tissues and by the absence of suitable assays in species other than the rat and mouse. Estimates of the frequency of stem cells in hemopoietic tissues vary from 0.05 to 0.8% of nucleated cells depending on the method that is used to calculate the seeding efficiency ("f" factor) in the spleen colony-forming-unit assay (van Bekkum, 1977). Attempts to enlarge the stem cell compartment by perturbations of hemopoiesis or to isolate stem cells on the basis of their physical properties have produced only modest enrichment of these cells (Cronkite, 1975; van Bekkum, 1977). Techniques for selectively growing stem cells *in vitro* are not yet available, although proliferation of stem cells has been demonstrated in suspension cultures of bone marrow cells (Dexter *et al.*, 1977) and in semisolid agar cultures of fetal liver cells (Johnson and Metcalf, 1977; also personal communications). While numerous candidates have been proposed, there are no known morphological criteria by which hemopoietic stem cells can be unequivocally identified (Yoffey, 1973; Cronkite, 1975; van Bekkum, 1977).

A. DIFFERENTIATION ANTIGENS ON STEM CELLS

One of the most promising new approaches to the study of hemopoiesis is the development of antisera to antigenic determinants on hemopoietic stem cells. Few such antigens have been identified thus far, but one of these, the Thy-1 antigen, has already permitted the identification and isolation of hemopoietic stem cells in the rat (see Section III, C). Till (1976) has postulated that, in addition to stem cell-specific antigens, multiply marked stem cells may display a repertoire of antigens which separately characterize individual hemopoietic cell lineages. One of the major predictions of this hypothesis is that mature hemopoietic cells of one lineage will share certain antigenic specificities with hemopoietic stem cells but not with mature hemopoietic cells of another lineage. Davis (1975) on the other hand has postulated that hemopoietic stem cells are essentially "null" cells which lack differentiation antigens that are expressed by more mature hemopoietic cell types, at least insofar as lymphoid differentiation is concerned. These are not mutually exclusive positions but differences in emphasis. Indeed it is likely that the study of the patterns formed by the selective loss or retention of stem cell-associated antigens and by the acquisition of new antigens during hemopoiesis will provide more insights into the developmental relationships of hemopoietic cells than would the study of either class of antigen alone.

1. *Lymphocyte-Associated Stem Cell Antigens*

More is known about the plasma membrane antigens of lymphocytes than of any other cell type. Inasmuch as lymphocyte precursors seem to diverge from pluripotent stem cells early in hemopoiesis (see Section IV), the chances that these two populations have overlapping antigenic profiles would seem to be great. This presumption is given credence by numerous reports of anti-stem cell activity in anti-lymphocyte sera (e.g., Gallagher *et al.*, 1972; Ledney, 1972; Mookerjee and Poulter, 1974; Mosedale *et al.*, 1976). However, none of the well-characterized T-cell alloantigens (Thy-1, TL, G_{IX}, Ly-1,2,3,5) or B-cell alloantigens (PC-1, Ly-4,6,7) in the mouse and none of the heteroantigens specific for medullary thymocytes, plasma cells, and peripheral T and B cells in rat and mouse have been found on hemopoietic stem cells (reviewed by Schlesinger, 1972; Goldschneider and Barton, 1976; Katz, 1977). The recently described rat T-cell alloantigens (A.R.T.-1, A.R.T.-2, RT-Ly-1, RT-Ly-2, Pta, Ag-F) have not yet been characterized with respect to anti-stem cell activity (Lubaroff *et al.*, 1979). Hemopoietic stem cells also appear to lack surface immunoglobulin and receptors for complement components and for the Fc portion of immunoglobulin molecules, all of which are represented on members of the B-cell series. It should be noted that in a few instances the absence of lymphocyte-associated antigens from hemopoietic stem cells has not been determined directly, but has been inferred, perhaps invalidly, from the absence of these markers on lymphocyte precursors.

What then is the source of the anti-stem cell activity that is commonly present in anti-lymphocyte sera? No single answer is possible because the method for preparing these heterologous antisera is not standardized, the lymphocyte inocula (peripheral lymphocytes, thymocytes, leukemic cells) are frequently heterogeneous, and the absorption procedures for rendering the antisera specific are often inadequate (Lance *et al.*, 1973). Hence it is not clear in most instances whether the anti-stem cell and the anti-lymphocyte activities are directed against the same antigens. Leaving aside the possible presence of naturally occurring cross-reactive antibodies or of antibodies formed against contaminating nonlymphocytic cells, three sources of anti-stem cell antibodies have been identified in anti-lymphocyte sera: (*a*) antibodies to histocompatibility antigens; (*b*) antibodies to antigens on immature lymphocytes, especially cortical thymocytes; and (*c*) antibodies to C-type leukemia virus antigens.

a. Histocompatibility Antigens. Histocompatibility antigens are well represented on hemopoietic stem cells, being one of the major obstacles to successful transplantation of bone marrow between members of outbred species. Both major and minor histocompatibility antigens have been implicated in rejection of bone marrow grafts (Jeannet and Speck, 1978). The genetics of the major histocompatibility complex of the mouse (*H-2* locus) has been extensively studied and many of the antigenic products have been identified (reviewed by Klein, 1975; Shreffler and David, 1975; Katz, 1977). Of these, the H-2D and H-2K antigens, the major antigens involved in the effector limb of allograft rejection, have been detected on hemopoietic stem cells (van den Engh, 1978). This is not surprising inasmuch as these antigens are present on most cell types in the adult and the embryo (Edidin, 1972).

Cudkowicz (1975) has described another series of histocompatibility antigens that are important in hemopoietic graft rejection between inbred strains of mice, including rejection of parental bone marrow cells by F_1 hybrid recipients. These antigens are coded by the $H-2$ complex but differ from classical histocompatibility antigens in two ways. First, they appear to be restricted to hemopoietic cell precursors, presumably including stem cells. Second, they are noncodominantly expressed. The nature of these "hemopoietic histocompatibility (Hh) factors" and the mechanism by which they elicit graft rejection are unknown.

There is controversy as to the presence of Ia antigens on hemopoietic stem cells. These antigens are coded by genes in the I region of the $H-2$ complex and are thought to be involved as recognition sites in cellular interactions involving T cells, B cells, and macrophages (Katz and Benacerraf, 1975). They are absent from most other cell types, apparently including murine hemopoietic stem cells and myeloid progenitor cells (Basch et al., 1977; van den Engh et al., 1978). However, antisera with anti-Ia activity have been found to react with human myeloid and erythroid progenitor cells and with undifferentiated leukemic cells (Winchester et al., 1978). This raises the possibility that Ia antigens also may be present on human hemopoietic stem cells. Unfortunately, a direct assay for human stem cells does not exist. Theoretically at least, the presence of Ia or Ia-like antigens on stem cells might offer a mechanism by which stem cells could interact with regulatory cells in the microenvironment (Wiktor-Jedrzejczak et al., 1977; Shinpock and Goodman, 1977; Till, 1976).

b. *Cell Line or Cell Stage Specific Antigens.* There is considerable evidence to suggest that lymphocytes in the thymus cortex are more recently derived from progenitor cells in bone marrow than are lymphocytes in the thymus medulla (see Section V, A). This may account for the tendency of heterologous antisera to cortical, but not medullary, thymocytes to inhibit hemopoietic stem cell activity in rat bone marrow. Two antigens have been operationally defined which are shared by cortical thymocytes and by stem cells: the rat cortical thymocyte antigen (RCTA) (Goldschneider and Barton, 1976), and the rat low electrophoretic mobility thymocyte antigen (RLTA) (Zeiller and Dolan, 1972). Antiserum to RCTA was raised in rabbits against density gradient purified cortical thymocytes; antiserum to RLTA was raised against cortical thymocytes isolated by cell electrophoresis. The nature and relationship (if any) of these two antigens are unknown, but they do not appear to be present on more mature members of the T-cell series. Thus, rabbit antisera to rat medullary thymocytes (Goldschneider, 1975) and to thoracic duct lymphocytes (Goldschneider and McGregor, 1973) have not been found to have anti-stem cell activity.

Another antiserum which reacts with cortical thymocytes and hemopoietic stem cells was prepared against a population of lymphocyte-like "null" cells in adult rat bone marrow (Goldschneider, 1976). The "null" cells were obtained by a combination of buoyant density centrifugation, glass bead filtration, and complement-dependent lysis with anti-T and anti-B cell sera. This antiserum abrogated hemopoietic stem cell activity in rat bone marrow, and appeared to affect erythroid, myeloid, and lymphoid progenitor cells as well (Goldschneider, 1977). The rat bone marrow "lymphocyte" antigen (RBMLA) detected by this antiserum subsequently has been shown to be part of the Thy-1 antigen molecule of the rat (Goldschneider et al., 1978; see Section III, A, 3).

In the mouse the Th-B heteroantigen is present in high concentrations on cortical thymocytes and immature B cells and in low concentrations on mature B cells (Stout et al., 1975). The level of expression of this antigen on B cells is under the control of a single genetic locus and is abnormal in certain immunologically deficient strains of mice (Herzenberg et al., 1977). Although the distribution of Th-B antigen on other hemopoietic cell types has not yet been reported, it is possible that this antigen may provide evidence for the existence of a common precursor for T and B cells, be it a bipotential lymphopoietic progenitor cell or the hemopoietic stem cell itself.

The mouse-specific B lymphocyte antigen (MBLA) appears to be present at all stages of B-cell development, including B-cell precursors which lack detectable surface immunoglobulin (Raff et al., 1971; Rysser and Vassali, 1974). It is not known whether some of the latter cells are true B-cell progenitors or whether they are immature forms of differentiating B cells which contain small amounts of cytoplasmic immunoglobulin, the so-called "pre-B" cells (Raff et al., 1976). Inasmuch as MBLA-positive cells appear to develop from MBLA-negative cells (Rysser and Vassali, 1974), it is unlikely that this antigen is present on hemopoietic stem cells. This is of interest in view of the contrary prediction of the multiply marked stem cell hypothesis (Till, 1976) and the contention that B-cell precursors are descended directly from hemopoietic stem cells (Abramson et al., 1977).

c. Viral Antigens. A novel approach to the identification of lymphocyte-associated stem cell antigens has been described by Staber *et al.* (1978), who used antiserum specific for antigens coded by xenotropic C-type virus to inhibit B lymphocyte and hemopoietic stem cell activities in mice. The antiserum did not affect myeloid or erythroid progenitor cell activity and could be neutralized by xenotropic BALB/c virus and Friend leukemia virus. It is not known whether the differential expression of viral antigen represents selective infectivity of target cells or selective production of viral antigen by infected cells (Bloom *et al.*, 1977). The latter mechanism has been implicated in the highly restricted expression of the G_{IX} alloantigen in mice (Stockert *et al.*, 1971). The G_{IX} antigen, which is identical to the major envelope glycoprotein of the murine leukemia virus, is expressed only on cortical thymocytes even though lymphocytes at other stages of development contain the viral genome (Obata *et al.*, 1975). A similar mechanism has been postulated for the expression of the TL alloantigens on cortical thymocytes (Boyse *et al.*, 1971). It is possible that other virally coded antigens, in addition to the one described by Staber *et al.* (1978), are selectively displayed on hemopoietic stem cells and on various members of the hemopoietic cell series.

2. Brain-Associated Stem Cell Antigens

Rabbit antiserum to the neuronal fraction of mouse brain homogenate contains antibodies to a series of antigens that are present on hemopoietic cells (Golub and Day, 1975). The major antigens detected are the Thy-1 or theta antigen (Reif and Allen, 1964) and the brain-associated stem cell antigen (Golub, 1972). The Thy-1 antigen is discussed in Section III, A, 3. The brain-associated stem cell antigen is present on hemopoietic stem cells (Golub, 1972) and on thymocyte progenitors (Basch and Kadish, 1977) but not on the vast majority of thymocytes or B lymphocytes. It also may be present on myeloid progenitor cells (Mayer-Hamme and Bluestein, 1978).

Recently, Basch *et al.* (1978) have identified a Thy-1-negative variant of T-cell lymphoma that is able to absorb the anti-stem cell antibodies from anti-mouse brain serum. Antiserum to this tumor cell variant has anti-stem cell activity, whereas antisera to other antigenic variants of this cell line do not. The antigen in question has been designated the stem cell antigen, SC-1.

The propensity of anti-brain sera to react with hemopoietic stem cells is not restricted to the mouse. Antisera to rat brain Thy-1 antigen reacts with hemopoietic stem cells in that species (Goldschneider *et al.*,

1978; see Section III, A, 3); and antisera to human, rat, and hamster brain homogenates react with mouse hemopoietic stem cells and can be neutralized with mouse brain (Krogsrud *et al.*, 1977; Filppi *et al.*, 1976). These observations are of interest because they suggest that only a small number of brain-associated stem cell antigens exist in the mouse, and that homologous antigens are displayed on brain and possibly on hemopoietic stem cells of phylogenetically diverse species. It is also possible that similar antigens are present on other types of pluripotent cells as well. Thus, it has been observed that antigens on human sperm cells and possibly human teratocarcinoma cells cross-react with mouse brain and hemopoietic stem cells (Krogsrud *et al.*, 1977). The relationship between these immature cell types and brain is unlikely to be fortuitous inasmuch as other "early" antigens, including the *T/t* gene product, have been found in brain (Stern *et al.*, 1975).

B. THY-1 ANTIGENS ON RAT STEM CELLS

Thy-1 (theta) antgen is a cell surface antigen which has been described in brain and thymus of mouse (Reif and Allen, 1964) and rat (Douglas, 1972). Two allelic forms of the molecule, Thy-1.1 and Thy-1.2, exist in the mouse; only one form, Thy-1.1, has been found in the rat. In addition, Thy-1 antigen in the mouse and rat share a xenoantigenic determinant that is recognized by rabbit antiserum (Morris and Williams, 1975). In both species, Thy-1 antigen is a glycoprotein of approximately 25,000 daltons (Letarte-Muirhead *et al.*, 1975).

Despite these similarities, there are striking differences in the distribution of Thy-1 antigen in the mouse and rat. Thy-1 is present on essentially all peripheral T cells in the mouse (Raff, 1971), but on fewer than 10% of peripheral T cells in the rat (Acton *et al.*, 1974). Conversely, Thy-1 is present on as many as 45% of nucleated bone marrow cells in the rat (Williams, 1976), but fewer than 5% of bone marrow cells in the mouse. Most Thy-1-positive cells in mouse bone marrow are mature T cells, whereas those in rat bone marrow are immature members of the hemopoietic system, including B-lymphocyte precursors, presumptive thymocyte progenitors, and members of the myeloid cell series (Hunt *et al.*, 1977; Gregoire *et al.*, 1977; Ritter *et al.*, 1978). Indeed, our studies have shown that Thy-1 antigen appears on hemopoietic cells in fetal rat liver at least 4 days before it appears on fetal rat thymocytes (Ritter *et al.*, 1978).

It is not clear why the distribution of Thy-1 antigen should vary so greatly between the rat and mouse and between these and other mammalian species (Dalchau and Fabre, 1979). The question is important because Thy-1 antigen has proved to be a valuable marker for the identification and isolation of hemopoietic stem cells in the rat (Goldschneider *et al.,* 1978; also Section III, B) but not in the mouse (El-Arini and Osoba, 1973; Tyan, 1975; Thierfelder, 1977; however, see Ritter *et al.,* 1979).

We have used several approaches to demonstrate that Thy-1 antigen is present on the surface of hemopoietic stem cells in the rat (Goldschneider *et al.,* 1978). In one, the Thy-1 antigen and the rat bone marrow lymphocyte antigen (RBMLA) were shown to be parts of the same molecule, sharing both alloantigenic and xenoantigenic determinants. The bone marrow lymphocyte antigen previously had been shown to be on hemopoietic stem cells (Goldschneider, 1976, 1977; see Section III, A, 1, b).

In another approach, hemopoietic stem cell activity in fetal liver, neonatal spleen, and adult bone marrow was abrogated by incubation with antibodies to Thy-1 antigen. Both heteroantisera and alloantisera to Thy-1 antigen were effective, and the reaction could be completely neutralized by addition of purified Thy-1 antigen. The results indicate that both "embryonic-type" and "adult-type" stem cells are Thy-1 positive. This is of interest because these two stem cell populations differ considerably with respect to their physical characteristics and proliferative capacities. "Embryonic-type" stem cells are large low-density cells with extensive proliferative capacities, whereas "adult-type" stem cells are smaller, higher density cells with more limited proliferative capacities (Metcalf and Moore, 1971). The presence of Thy-1 antigens on both of these populations is consistent with other evidence which suggests that they bear a precursor–product relationship.

Direct evidence that Thy-1 antigen is present on hemopoietic stem cells in rats was provided by experiments in which Thy-1-positive and Thy-1-negative cells were separated on the fluorescence-activated cell sorter. All stem cell activity was recovered in the Thy-1-positive cell fraction.

C. ISOLATION OF STEM CELLS

Further analysis of rat bone marrow cells with the fluorescence-activated cell sorter indicated that it was possible to isolate highly enriched populations of hemopoietic stem cells on the basis of three parameters: (a) fluorescence intensity for Thy-1 antigen; (b) low-angle light scatter, a function of cell size; and (c) resistance to cortisone (Goldschneider *et al.,* 1979a). Approximately 95% of stem cells were present in the upper tenth percentile of Thy-1-positive cells as judged by relative fluorescence intensity. The stem cells had intermediate light scattering properties as compared to small lymphocytes on the one hand and members of the myeloid and erythroid cell series, including myeloid progenitor cells, on the other. Separation according to these two parameters resulted in an approximately 150-fold enrichment of hemopoietic stem cell activity. Pretreatment of the bone marrow donor with cortisone produced on additional 2-fold enrichment, presumably by destroying putative thymocyte progenitor cells which otherwise were coisolated with the stem cells (see Section IV, B).

Two cell populations were present in the stem cell-rich fraction: an 8- to 12-μm-diameter undifferentiated cell type with abundant basophilic cytoplasm surrounding a round-to-oval multinucleolated leptochromatic nucleus; and a mixed population of 8- to 9-μm-diameter cells, most of which were erythroblasts. We propose that the former cell type, which comprises approximately 75% of the cells in this fraction and is not present in other fractions, is the pluripotent stem cell. Dividing 75% by 300, the enrichment value, it can be calculated that approximately 0.25% of nucleated cells in normal rat bone marrow are hemopoietic stem cells. This is in agreement with the estimated values of most authors.

Comparable enrichment of rat hemopoietic stem cells has been obtained by Gong (1978) who mechanically separated endosteal marrow from the more centrally located red marrow. Stem cells in endosteal marrow appear to be a subset of hemopoietic stem cells (Lord et al., 1975) and may not have been well represented in the marrow samples that we obtained by perfusion of the marrow cavity. It will therefore be of interest to determine whether endosteal hemopoietic stem cells also are Thy-1 positive.

IV. Thymocyte Progenitor Cells

Although most schemes of hemopoiesis envision the existence of discrete lymphoid stem and/or progenitor cells, there is no direct evidence in the literature that such cells occur. In the final analysis, the properties that have been attributed to presumptive lymphoid progenitor cells can be explained by the presence of pluripotent hemopoietic stem cells or, in some instances, immature lymphocytes. Thus, assay systems which measure T- and B-cell generation in vivo or in vitro do not intrinsically distinguish between the activities of hemopoietic stem cells and lymphoid progenitor cells (Kadish and Basch, 1976; Miller, 1976), and protocols designed to isolate lymphoid progenitor cells on the basis of their physical properties show considerable overlap with hemopoietic stem cells (El-Arini and Osoba, 1973; Lafleur et al., 1972). In vitro colony-forming unit assays (reviewed by Metcalf, 1977), which have established the existence of myeloid and erythroid progenitor cells, have not proved helpful in identifying lymphoid progenitors. Most clones of lymphocytes that are generated in these systems appear to arise from immature cells which have already expressed T- or B-cell markers (Andersson *et al.*, 1977; Metcalf, 1977). The occurrence of congenital or acquired deficiencies in T- and/or B-cell production (reviewed by Rosen, 1979) is frequently used as evidence for the existence of lymphoid progenitor cells. However, these deficiencies have diverse etiologies which could equally well affect other stages in the developmental pathway of lymphocytes.

It does seem likely that lymphoid precursors, whatever their nature, diverge early from myeloid and erythroid precursors during hemopoiesis. For example, Abramson *et al.* (1977) have identified hemopoietic stem cells of restricted potential in mouse bone marrow that can selectively regenerate the erythroid and myeloid cell series of irradiated recipients, and Johnson and Metcalf (1977) have cultured cells with similar attributes from fetal liver. Comparable findings have been obtained in neoplastic disorders involving multipotent hemopoietic cells in man. Thus in polycythmia vera, the malignant cells of the granulocytic, megakaryocytic, and erythrocytic series in females heterozygous for the X-linked gene *G6PD* express only one *G6PD* allele, suggesting that they are clonally derived (Adamson *et al.*, 1976). The lymphocytes in these patients are heterozygous for the *G6PD* gene. In chronic myelogenous leukemia, the Ph[1] chromosomal marker is usually represented in the leukemic granulocytes and the apparently normal populations of erythrocytes and megakaryocytes, but not in lymphocytes (Nowell and Hungerford, 1961; Whang *et al.*, 1963). Although alternative explanations of these findings are possible, the simplest interpretation is that lymphocyte precursors develop from pluripotent hemopoietic stem cells contemporaneously with but independently of a common erythroid–myeloid stem cell.

Exceptions do exist to this scheme of early divergence of lymphoid precursors and myeloid–erythroid precursors during hemopoiesis. Thus Fialkow (1977) has reported that in some patients with chronic myelogenous leukemia, B lymphocytes but not T lymphocytes probably arise from the neoplastic clone; Kaplan *et al.* (1978) have noted that human B lymphocytes but not T lymphocytes share an antigen with myeloid progenitor cells. Superficially at least, these observations suggest that T-cell precursors may diverge from B-cell precursors before the latter diverge from myeloid–erythroid cell precursors.

Attempts to identify a common precursor of T and B cells or a discrete B-cell progenitor in mouse bone marrow have not been successful thus far (Abramson *et al.*, 1977). The earliest stage of B-cell development that has been described is the "pre-B" cell, which contains small amounts of cytoplasmic immunoglobulin but no detectable surface immunoglobulin (Raff et al., 1976). The situation is more encouraging with respect to the identification of a T-cell progenitor, as indicated by the following observations. (a) Clones of hemopoietic cells bearing radiation-induced chromosomal markers are able to regenerate selectively the T-cell system of recipient irradiated mice (Abramson et al., 1977). (b) The thymus factor, thymopoietin, is able to induce rapidly the expression of the mouse T-cell differentiation antigens Thy-1, TL, G_{IX}, LY-1,2,3, and 5 on a subset of hemopoietic cells which have the capacity to repopulate the thymus of irradiated recipients (Komura et al., 1975). (c) The thymus factor, thymosin (Goldstein et al., 1972), is able to induce simultaneously the expression of Ly-1,2,3 alloantigens and terminal deoxynucleotidyl transferase (TdT) on a subset of mouse hemopoietic cells (Goldschneider et al., 1979b). Each of these markers is normally associated with immature members of the T-cell series (Cantor and Boyse, 1977; Gregoire et al., 1977). (d) Putative T-cell progenitors in rat bone marrow can be physically separated from hemopoietic stem cells and from myeloid progenitor cells by the fluorescence-activated cell sorter (Goldschneider et al., 1979a; see Section IV, B for details).

A. TERMINAL DEOXYNUCLEOTIDYL TRANSFERASE (TdT)

Our working hypothesis is that thymocyte progenitors contain or can be induced to express the enzyme terminal deoxynucleotidyl transferase. This enzyme has the unique property of adding monodeoxyribonucleotides at random to any 3'-OH-terminal segment of DNA in cell-free systems without template direction (Bollum, 1978). It has been identified by enzymatic and immunofluorescent techniques in thymus from birds and mammals and in bone marrow from rodents and human beings (Chang, 1971; Coleman et al., 1974; Kung et al., 1975; Barton et al., 1976; Goldschneider et al., 1977; Gregoire et al., 1977). It is also present in prepubertal spleen from rats and mice (Gregoire et al., 1979). Terminal transferase has not been found in mature T and B cells in rodents or in avian bone marrow or bursa of Fabricius (Sugimoto and Bollum, 1979). Among neoplasms of the hemopoietic system, terminal transferase is commonly found in acute lymphoblastic leukemias of the T cell and "null" cell varieties, but only occasionally in B cell and nonlymphocytic leukemias of mouse and man (Hutton et al., 1979). Because of its restricted cellular distribution and because of its unusual biochemical properties, it has been postulated that TdT may act as a somatic mutagen in the early stages of T-cell differentiation, perhaps in the generation of immunological diversity (Bollum, 1974; Baltimore, 1974).

We have used a highly specific antiserum to homogeneous calf terminal transferase (Bollum, 1975) to study the ontogeny of TdT-positive cells in rats and mice. The results further strengthen the argument that TdT-positive hemopoietic cells are thymocyte progenitors. In summary, we have found that:

1. TdT is restricted to cortical thymocytes and to a subset of "null" cells in bone marrow and spleen (Barton et al., 1976; Goldschneider et al., 1977).

2. TdT-positive bone marrow cells are indistinguishable morphologically from the least mature thymocytes in the subcapsular region of the thymus cortex (Gregoire et al., 1977). In the mouse, both cell types have strong H-2, weak (or negative) Thy-1 antigenic phenotypes and exclusively nuclear TdT (Goldschneider et al., unpublished). In contrast, more mature cortical thymocytes have weak H-2, strong Thy-1 phenotypes and combined nuclear and cytoplasmic TdT distributions (see Section V).

3. TdT-positive cells are maximally represented in spleen and bone marrow approximately 3–4 weeks after birth, after which they decline rapidly in spleen and gradually in bone marrow (Gregoire et al., 1979). Similar kinetics have been observed in assays for thymocyte progenitor cells, but not for hemopoietic stem cells or for precursors of myeloid, erythroid, or B cells (Kadish and Basch, 1976; Tyan, 1977).

4. TdT-positive bone marrow and spleen cells (Bollum, 1975; Gregoire et al., 1979) and thymocyte progenitors (Basch and Kadish, 1977) are relatively sensitive to cortisone, whereas hemopoietic stem cells and myeloid progenitor cells are not (Goldschneider et al., 1979a).

5. TdT-positive cells are present in bone marrow of congenitally athymic (nu/nu) mice and neonatally thymectomized rats (Gregoire et al., 1979), and they can be generated in vitro in cultures of bone marrow (Schrader et al., 1979), indicating that they are not derived from the thymus. However, the thymus may affect the kinetics of generation of TdT-positive cells in bone marrow, possibly by a humoral factor (Pazmino et al., 1978; Goldschneider et al., 1979b).

6. TdT-positive bone marrow and spleen cells from athymic mice can be induced to express T cell-specific Ly-1,2,3 antigens in vitro by brief incubation with thymosin or the purified α_1 peptide therefrom (Goldschneider et al., 1979b). Thymosin also can induce some TdT-

negative hemopoietic cells to express TdT and/or Ly-1,2,3 antigens. The Ly-1$^+$2$^+$3$^+$ antigenic phenotype is normally associated with cortical thymocytes and immature T cells (Cantor and Boyse, 1977). Other authors (Silverstone et al., 1976) have induced Thy-1 antigen on TdT-positive mouse bone marrow cells by treatment with thymopoietin.

B. Isolation of Thymocyte Progenitors

In its aggregate, the evidence strongly indicates that many TdT-positive cells can serve as precursors of thymocytes. The question remains as to whether these cells are thymocyte progenitors or pluripotent hemopoietic stem cells. Four observations appear to exclude the stem cell alternative. First, TdT-positive cells themselves arise from TdT-negative precursors in fetal mouse thymus and in postnatal bone marrow. Second, TdT-positive cells have not been detected in chicken bone marrow, although hemopoietic stem cells obviously are present. Third, TdT-positive cells are more sensitive to cortisone than are hemopoietic stem cells. Fourth, TdT-positive cells can be physically separated from hemopoietic stem cells using the fluorescence-activated cell sorter. This latter observation has made it possible to obtain highly enriched suspensions of TdT-positive cells (Goldschneider et al., 1979a).

The scheme for isolating viable TdT-positive bone marrow cells is based on the observations that TdT-positive cells in the rat are strongly positive for Thy-1 antigen and that they have a characteristic size distribution as judged by low-angle light scatter. There is some overlap of these parameters with hemopoietic stem cells, but stem cell-free fractions can be obtained by selecting the appropriate limits on the cell sorter (TdT-positive cells have lower mean fluorescence intensity for Thy-1 antigen and lesser light scattering properties than do hemopoietic stem cells). The resulting cell suspensions contain approximately 85% TdT-positive cells.

TdT-positive cells have a characteristic morphological appearance by light and electron microscopy. Although superficially resembling medium-size lymphocytes, they have abundant basophilic cytoplasm containing numerous free polyribosomes, a prominant Golgi zone, and a slightly eccentric, leptochromatic nucleus with several nucleoli.

Studies are in progress to assess directly the developmental potential of TdT-positive cells in in vivo and in vitro systems. It will be of especial importance to determine whether they are wholly committed to T-cell differentiation or whether some are B-cell progenitors or common precursors of T and B cells.

V. Thymocytopoiesis

Upon reaching the thymus, thymocyte progenitors undergo a series of differentiative events that result in the production of several subsets of T-cell precursors (reviewed by Goldschneider and Barton 1976; Cantor and Weissman, 1976). This process takes approximately 3 days, during which time thymocyte progenitors undergo six to eight divisions. It is likely that these events are regulated by the thymus epithelial parenchyma, which has been implicated in the production of several soluble inducing factors. The thymus epithelium has also been implicated in the selection process by which self-tolerance is established and the immunological repertoire of the T-cell system is defined (Zinkernagel et al., 1978). Remarkably, the vast majority of thymocytes that are produced appear to die in situ or shortly after release from the thymus (Bryant, 1971; Shortman, 1977). This is consistent with Jerne's hypothesis (1971) that the thymus serves as a mutant-breeding organ in the generation of immunological diversity.

A. CORTICAL AND MEDULLARY THYMOCYTES

Two major populations of thymocytes coexist in anatomically discrete areas within the thymus: a cortisone-resistant, low Thy-1, high H-2 population in the thymus medulla; and a cortisone-sensitive, high Thy-1, low H-2 population in the thymus cortex. Medullary thymocytes account for 5 to 15% of thymocytes. They are long-lived, immunologically competent, and able to migrate to classical T-cell regions in lymph node (paracortex) and spleen (periarteriolar lymphoid sheath) (Goldschneider and McGregor, 1968; Anderson and Blomgren, 1970). Cortical thymocytes are short-lived cells which are generally considered to be functionally incompetent and incapable of migrating to peripheral lymphoid tissues. However, evidence is available which indicates that there is a major migration pathway from thymus cortex primarily to red pulp of spleen (Goldschneider and McGregor, 1968; Zatz and Lance, 1970; Chanana and Cronkite, 1971; Durkin et al., 1978) and to Peyer's patches of intestine (Durkin et al., 1978). The fate of these immunologically virginal T cells is unknown, but it is possible that some are stimulated by antigen in the presence of circulating thymus hormone to differentiate into long-lived, functionally mature T cells (Cantor, 1972; Stutman, 1977; Weissman et al., 1977).

In studies in the rat, we have identified two populations of peripheral T cells, one of which is cortisone resistant and has the antigenic phenotype of medullary thymocytes, the other of which is cortisone sensitive and has the antigenic phenotype of cortical thymocytes

(Goldschneider, 1975, 1976). Preliminary data suggest that some of the cortical-thymocyte-like T cells have the ability to modulate the responses of other lymphocytes to antigens and mitogens. This is not surprising, inasmuch as other investigators have found that the unusually high percentage of suppressor T cells in spleen of neonatal mouse and chicken correlates with the presence of suppressor cells in thymus cortex of these animals (reviewed by Droege and Zucker, 1975). Moreover, Durkin *et al.* (1978) have described an increased flow of cells from thymus cortex to spleen of rats after the administration of a tolerogenic dose of antigen.

There is controvery concerning the relationship of cortical and medullary thymocytes. Initial autoradiographic studies by Weissman (1973), in which [^{3}H]thymidine was applied topically to the thymus capsule, suggested that medullary thymocytes were the direct descendents of cortical thymocytes. In those experiments, a wave of labeled cells was observed to proceed with time from the subcapsular region of the thymus cortex to the deep cortex and ultimately to the thymus medulla. However, Shortman and Jackson (1974) found that cortical and medullary thymocytes had independent generative kinetics. In their experiments, [^{3}H]thymidine was administered parenterally, and cortical and medullary thymocytes were distinguished by their relative sensitivities to lysis with anti-Thy-1 serum and complement. More recently, Fathman *et al.* (1975) separated high and low Thy-1-positive thymocytes on the fluorescence-activated cell sorter at timed intervals after topical application of [^{3}H]thymidine. They confirmed the observation that cortical and medullary thymocytes had independent generative kinetics and suggested that both were descended from a population of high Thy-1 cells in the subcapsular region of the thymus cortex.

B. SUBCAPSULAR THYMOCYTES

We have identified two subsets of subcapsular thymocytes which we propose are the most ancestral members of the thymocyte series (Goldschneider and Shortman, unpublished). These cells have a low Thy-1, high H-2 antigenic phenotype, similar to presumptive thymocyte progenitors in mouse bone marrow. One subset contains terminal deoxynucleotidyl transferase (TdT) (see Section IV, A), the other does not. In aggregate these cells constitute fewer than 1% of total thymocytes. They have not been distinguished previously from medullary thymocytes because of their low Thy-1 phenotype and low buoyant density. However, they are larger than most medullary thymocytes and can be enriched more than 70-fold by velocity sedimentation.

Results of studies in which 14-day fetal mouse thymi were cultured *in vitro* for 4 weeks suggest that the TdT-positive subset of subcapsular thymocytes generates TdT-positive cortical thymocytes, and that these in turn generate TdT-negative thymocytes (Goldschneider and Mandel, unpublished). This developmental cycle is repeated at 48- to 72-hour intervals. Inasmuch as total cell numbers per culture remains essentially constant after the first week *in vitro,* it is likely that most of the TdT-negative thymocytes die shortly after they are formed.

The origin of medullary thymocytes is not clear from any of the preceding experiments. The simplest explanation is that they are direct descendents of the TdT-negative subset of subcapsular thymocytes, inasmuch as both cell populations have low Thy-1, high H-2 antigenic phenotypes and low buoyant densities. Support for this notion of a separate origin of cortical and medullary thymocyte may also be found in the studies of Droege and Zucker (1975) and Pazmino *et al.* (1978). However, medullary thymocytes are a heterogeneous population of cells, and it is possible that some are descended from TdT-positive thymocytes. It may be possible to test these developmental relationships directly if one or both subsets of subcapsular thymocytes can selectively migrate to thymus after adoptive transfer to intermediate hosts (Kadish and Basch, 1977).

C. Scheme of T-Cell Development

A hypothetical scheme of the early stages of T lymphocyte development in mice is presented in Fig. 1. In this scheme, self-renewing populations of pluripotent hemopoietic stem cells (HSC) are induced by unknown microenvironmental and/or humoral mechanisms to generate thymocyte progenitors (P_T). The latter cells have been identified by their ability to express terminal transferase and/or Ly-1,2,3 antigens after incubation *in vitro* with the thymus factor thymosin. However, the possibility has not been excluded that P_T are common progenitors of T and B lymphocytes.

In fetal life, P_T migrate to the thymus anlage, where they are induced by the epithelial parenchymal cells to generate TdT-positive cortical thymocytes and, directly or indirectly, TdT-negative medullary thymocytes. In postnatal life, P_T give rise to TdT-positive thymocyte progenitors (P_T') and to TdT-negative thymocyte progenitors (P_T'') in bone marrow and spleen. These two subsets of thymocyte progenitors have been identified by their ability to express Ly-1,2,3 antigens and Thy-1 antigen after incubation *in vitro* with the thymus factors thymosin and thymopoietin, respectively. It is unlikely that P_T' and P_T'' are

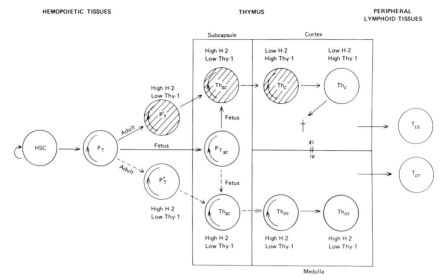

FIG. 1. Hypothetical scheme of T lymphocyte development. Solid arrow, major developmental pathway; broken arrow, minor developmental pathway; curved arrow (extracellular), self-replication; curved arrow (intracellular), many members in mitotic cycle; hatched lines, terminal deoxynucleotidyl transferase (TdT); †, cell death. See text Section V, C for details.

identical inasmuch as thymopoietin does not seem to affect P_T cells, at least as judged by its failure to induce the appearance of P'_T cells. Thymic influence is not a prerequisite for the appearance of thymocyte progenitors in postnatal life, although it may affect the relative proportions of P'_T and P''_T cells.

In the scheme depicted in Fig. 1, P'_T and P''_T and/or P_T migrate to the thymus, where they appear as actively proliferating, high H-2, low (or negative) Thy-1 cells (Th_{sc}) in the subcapsular region of the thymus cortex. It is presumed that P'_T cells form TdT-positive Th_{sc} and P''_T cells form TdT-negative Th_{sc}. The TdT-positive Th_{sc} give rise to TdT-positive cortical thymocytes (Th_c) through a series of differentiative steps that include decreased expression of H-2 antigens, increased expression of Thy-1 and other differentiation antigens, and decrease in cell size. During this process TdT shifts from an exclusively nuclear to a predominantly cytoplasmic intracellular location. Ultimately synthesis of TdT ceases, resulting in a population of TdT-negative cortical thymocytes, most of which are apparently programmed to die within the thymus. Despite this, some cortical thymocytes seed to peripheral lymphoid tissues where they form a pool of short-lived, cortisone-sensitive T cells

(T_{cs}). Although T_{cs} constitute a minority of peripheral T cells, they probably represent the major subset of emigrating thymocytes.

The fate of the TdT-negative subset of subcapsular thymocytes (Th_{sc}) is not known. It is suggested that they may be immediate precursors of medullary thymocytes (Th_m), which they closely resemble. However, the possibility that some medullary thymocytes are derived from TdT-positive precursors in the thymus cortex has not been excluded. Th_m which migrate from the thymus form a pool of long-lived, immunologically competent, cortisone-resistant T cells (T_{cr}) in peripheral lymphoid tissues. In addition, some T_{cr} probably are derived from antigen-stimulated T_{cs}.

VI. Concluding Remarks

The early (antigen-independent) stages of lymphocyte development are discussed within the context of normal hemopoiesis. Emphasis is given to identification of the most ancestral members of the T lymphocyte series using cell surface "differentiation" antigens as markers. Of the various precursor cell populations that are described, the following have been purified sufficiently to warrant definitive analysis of their respective roles in lymphopoiesis: (a) pluripotent hemopoietic stem cells from rat bone marrow; (b) thymocyte progenitors from rat bone marrow; and (c) T-cell precursors from the subcapsular region of mouse thymus. Each of these cell types has been identified in part by the relative concentration of Thy-1 (theta) antigen on its surface and by the presence or absence of the enzyme, terminal deoxynucleotidyl transferase (TdT). Isolation of these cell types has been achieved with the aid of the fluorescence-activated cell sorter (FACS).

Further, analysis of these precursor cell populations has revealed the existence of at least two and possibly three subsets of thymocyte progenitors based on their ability to express Thy-1, Ly-1,2,3, and/or TdT antigens after induction with thymus factors. Evidence favoring the independent development of cortical and medullary thymocytes from precursors in the subcapsular cortex is also reviewed. Based on these observations, a hypothetical scheme is presented in which the thymus functions as a compound organ to govern the development of a dual system of T lymphocytes.

REFERENCES

Abramson, S., Miller, R. G., and Phillips, R. A. (1977). J. Exp. Med. 145, 1567–1579.
Acton, R. T., Morris, R. J., and Williams, A. F. (1974). Eur. J. Immunol. 4, 598–602.
Adamson, J. W., Fialkow, P. J., Murphy, S., Perchal, J. F., and Steinman, L. (1976). N. Engl. J. Med. 295, 913–916.

Andersson, B., and Blomgren, H. (1970). *Cell. Immunol.* **1**, 362–371.
Andersson, J., Coutinho, A., Melchers, F., and Watanabe, T. (1977). *Cold Spring Harbor Symp. Quant. Biol.* **41**, 227–236.
Baltimore, D. (1974). *Nature (London)* **248**, 409–411.
Barton, R., Goldschneider, I., and Bollum, F. J. (1976). *J. Immunol.* **116**, 462–468.
Basch, R. S., and Kadish, J. L. (1977). *J. Exp. Med.* **145**, 405–419.
Basch, R. S., Janossy, G., and Greaves, M. F. (1977). *Nature (London)* **270**, 520–522.
Basch, R. S., Panagiotatos, T., and Buxbaum, J. (1978). *J. Supramol. Struct., Suppl.* **2**, 176.
Bloom, B. R., Senik, A., Stoner, G., Ju, G., Nowakowski, M., Kano, S., and Jimenez, L. (1977). *Cold Spring Harbor Symp. Quant. Biol.* **41**, 73–83.
Bollum, F. J. (1974). *In* "The Enzymes" (P. D. Boyer, ed.), 3rd ed., vol. 10, pp. 145–171. Academic Press, New York.
Bollum, F. J. (1975). *Proc. Natl. Acad. Sci. U.S.A.* **72**, 4119–4122.
Bollum, F. J. (1978). *Adv. Enzymol.* **47**, 347–374.
Boyse, E. A., Old, L. J., and Stockert, E. (1971). *In* "RNA Viruses and Host Genome in Oncogenesis" (P. Emmelot and P. Bentvelzen, eds.), pp. 171–185. North-Holland Publ., Amsterdam.
Bryant, B. J. (1971). *Adv. Exp. Med. Biol.* **12**, 103–112.
Burnet, F. M. (1959). "The Clonal Selection Theory of Acquired Immunity." Cambridge Univ. Press, London and New York.
Cantor, H. (1972). *In* "Cell Interactions" (L. G. Silvestri, ed.), pp. 172–182. North-Holland Publ., Amsterdam.
Cantor, H., and Boyse, E. A. (1977). *Immunol. Rev.* **33**, 105–124.
Cantor, H., and Weissman, I. (1976). *Prog. Allergy* **20**, 1–64.
Chanana, A. D., and Cronkite, E. P. (1971). *Adv. Exp. Med. Biol.* **12**, 113–118.
Chang, L. M. S. (1971). *Biochem. Biophys. Res. Commun.* **44**, 124–131.
Cold Spring Harbor Symposia on Quantitative Biology (1977). Vol. 41, Part 1 (multiple authors).
Coleman, M. S., Hutton, J. J., DeSimone, P., and Bollum, F. J. (1974). *Proc. Natl. Acad. Sci. U.S.A.* **71**, 4404–4408.
Cronkite, E. P. (1975). *In* "Immunopathology Annual—1975," pp. 35–69. Appleton, New York.
Cudkowicz, G. (1975). *Transplant. Proc.* **7**, 155–159.
Dalchau, R., and Fabre, J. W. (1979). *J. Exp. Med.* **149**, 576–591.
Davis, S. (1975). *Blood* **45**, 871–880.
Dexter, T. M., Allen, T. D., and Lajtha, L. G. (1977). *J. Cell. Physiol.* **91**, 335–344.
Douglas, T. C. (1972). *J. Exp. Med.* **135**, 1054–1062.
Droege, W., and Zucker, R. (1975). *Transplant. Rev.* **25**, 3–25.
Durkin, H. G., Carboni, J. M., and Waksman, B. H. (1978). *J. Immunol.* **121**, 1075–1081.
Edidin, M. (1972). *In* "Transplantation Antigens" (B. D. Kahan and R. A. Reisfeld, eds.), pp. 125–140. Academic Press, New York.
El-Arini, M. O., and Osoba, D. (1973). *J. Exp. Med.* **137**, 821–837.
Fathman, C. G., Small, M., Herzenberg, L. A., and Weissman, I. L. (1975). *Cell. Immunol.* **15**, 109–128.
Fialkow, P. J. (1977). *Haematol. Bluttransfus.* **20**, 297–305.
Filppi, J. A., Rheins, M. S., and Nyerges, C. A. (1976). *Transplantation* **21**, 124–128.
Gallagher, M. T., Richie, E. R., Heim, L. R., Judd, K. P., and Trentin, J. J. (1972). *Transplantation* **14**, 597–602.
Goldschneider, I. (1975). *Cell. Immunol.* **16**, 269–284.

Goldschneider, I. (1976). *Cell. Immunol.* **24**, 289–307.
Goldschneider, I. (1977). *J. Immunol.* **118**, 2040–2046.
Goldschneider, I., and Barton, R. W. (1976). *In* "The Cell Surface in Animal Embryogenesis and Development" (G. Poste and G. L. Nicolson, eds.), pp. 599–695. Elsevier, Amsterdam.
Goldschneider, I., and McGregor, D. D. (1968). *J. Exp. Med.* **127**, 155–168.
Goldschneider, I., and McGregor, D. D. (1973). *J. Exp. Med.* **138**, 1443–1465.
Goldschneider, I., Gregoire, K. E., Barton, R. W., and Bollum, F. J. (1977). *Proc. Natl. Acad. Sci. U.S.A.* **74**, 734–738.
Goldschneider, I., Gordon, L. K., and Morris, R. J. (1978). *J. Exp. Med.* **148**, 1351–1366.
Goldschneider, I., Metcalf, D., Battye, F., Mandel, T., and Bollum, F. J. (1979a). *J. Exp. Med.* (in press).
Goldschneider, I., Ahmed, A., Bollum, F. J., and Goldstein, A. L. (1979b). Submitted for publication.
Goldstein, A. L., Guha, A., Zatz, M. M., Hardy, M. A., and White, A. (1972). *Proc. Natl. Acad. Sci. U.S.A.* **69**, 1800–1803.
Golub, E. S. (1972). *J. Exp. Med.* **136**, 369–374.
Golub, E. S., and Day, E. D. (1975). *Cell. Immunol.* **16**, 427–431.
Gong, J. K. (1978). *Science* **199**, 1443–1445.
Greaves, M. F., Owen, J. J. T., and Raff, M. C. (1973). "T and B Lymphocytes." Am. Elsevier, New York.
Gregoire, K. E., Goldschneider, I., Barton, R. W., and Bollum, F. J. (1977). *Proc. Natl. Acad. Sci. U.S.A.* **74**, 3993–3996.
Gregoire, K. E., Goldschneider, I., Barton, R. W., and Bollum, F. J. (1979). *J. Immunol.* **123**, 1347–1352.
Herzenberg, L. A., Herzenberg, L. A., Black, S. J., Loken, M. R., Okumura, K., van der Loo, W., Osborne, B. A., Hewgill, D., Goding, J. W., Gutman, G., and Warner, N. L. (1977). *Cold Spring Harbor Symp. Quant. Biol.* **41**, 33–45.
Hunt, S. V., Mason, D. W., and Williams, A. F. (1977). *Eur. J. Immunol.* **7**, 817–823.
Hutton, J. J., Coleman, M. S., Keniklis, T. P., and Bollum, F. J. (1979). *In* "Tumor Markers" (E. Mihich and R. Baserga, eds.). Pergamon, Oxford.
Jeannet, M., and Speck, B. (1978). *In* "Experimental Hematology Today 1978" (J. Baum and G. D. Ledney, eds.), pp. 163–169. Springer-Verlag, Berlin and New York.
Jerne, N. K. (1971). *Eur. J. Immunol.* **1**, 1–9.
Johnson, G. R., and Metcalf, D. (1977). *Proc. Natl. Acad. Sci. U.S.A.* **74**, 3879–3882.
Kadish, J. L., and Basch, R. S. (1976). *J. Exp. Med.* **143**, 1082–1099.
Kadish, J. L., and Basch, R. S. (1977). *Cell. Immunol.* **30**, 12–24.
Kaplan, J., Inoue, S., and Ottenbreit, M. J. (1978). *Nature (London)* **271**, 458–459.
Katz, D. H. (1977). "Lymphocyte Differentiation, Recognition, and Regulation." Academic Press, New York.
Katz, D. H., and Benacerraf, B. (1975). *Transplant. Rev.* **22**, 175–195.
Klein, J. (1975). "Biology of the Mouse Histocompatibility—2 Complex." Springer-Verlag, Berlin and New York.
Komuro, K., Goldstein, G., and Boyse, E. A. (1975). *J. Immunol.* **115**, 195–198.
Krogsrud, R. L., Bain, J., and Price, G. B. (1977). *J. Immunol.* **119**, 1486–1492.
Kung, P. C., Silverstone, A. E., McCaffrey, R. P., and Baltimore, D. (1975). *J. Exp. Med.* **141**, 855–865.
Lafleur, L., Miller, R. G., and Phillips, R. A. (1972). *J. Exp. Med.* **135**, 1363–1374.
Lance, E. M., Medawar, P. B., and Taub, R. N. (1973). *Adv. Immunol.* **17**, 1–92.
Ledney, G. D. (1972). *Transplantation* **13**, 558–569.

Letarte-Muirhead, M., Barclay, A. N., and Williams, A. F. (1975). *Biochem. J.* **151,** 685–697.

Lord, B. I., Testa, N. G., and Hendry, J. H. (1975). *Blood* **46,** 65–72.

Lubaroff, D. M., Rasmussen, G. T., and Hunt, H. D. (1979). *Transplant Proc.* **11,** 1642–1645.

Metcalf, D. (1977). "Haemopoietic Colonies. In Vitro Cloning of Normal and Leukaemic Cells." Springer-Verlag, Berlin and New York.

Metcalf, D., and Moore, M. A. S. (1971). "Haemopoietic Cells." North-Holland Publ., Amsterdam.

Mayer-Hamme, S., and Bluestein, H. G. (1978). *J. Cell. Physiol.* **94,** 47–56.

Miller, R. G. (1976). *In* "Stem Cells of Renewing Cell Populations" (A. B. Cairnie, P. K. Lala, and D. G. Osmond, eds.), pp. 211–219. Acadmic Press, New York.

Mookerjee, B. K., and Poulter, L. (1974). *Immunology* **27,** 601–607.

Morris, R. J., and Williams, A. F. (1975). *Eur. J. Immunol.* **5,** 274–284.

Mosedale, B., Smith, M. A., and Courtenay, J. S. (1976). *Transplantation* **22,** 122–131.

Nossal, G. J. V., Shortman, K., Howard, M., and Pike, B. L. (1977). *Immunol. Rev.* **37,** 187–209.

Nowell, P. C., and Hungerford, D. A. (1961). *J. Natl. Cancer Inst.* **27,** 1013–1035.

Nowell, P. C., Hirsch, B. E., Fox, D. H., and Wilson, D. B. (1970). *J. Cell. Physiol.* **75,** 151–158.

Obata, Y., Ikeda, H., Stockert, E., and Boyse, E. A. (1975). *J. Exp. Med.* **141,** 188–197.

Pazmino, N. H., Ihle, J. N., and Goldstein, A. L. (1978). *J. Exp. Med.* **147,** 708–718.

Pazmino, N. H., McEwan, R., and Ihle, J. N. (1978). *J. Exp. Med.* **148,** 1330.

Phillips, R. A., Melchers, F., and Miller, R. G. (1977). *Prog. Immunol.* **3,** 155–161.

Raff, M. C. (1971). *Transplant. Rev.* **6,** 52–80.

Raff, M. C. (1977). *Cold Spring Harbor Symp. Quant. Biol.* **41,** 159–173.

Raff, M. C., Nase, S., and Mitchison, N. A. (1971). *Nature (London)* **230,** 50–51.

Raff, M. D., Megson, M., Owen, J. J. T., and Cooper, M. D. (1976). *Nature (London)* **259,** 224–226.

Reif, A. E., and Allen, J. M. (1964). *J. Exp. Med.* **120,** 413–433.

Ritter, M. A., Gordon, L. K., and Goldschneider, I. (1978). *J. Immunol.* **121,** 2463–2471.

Ritter, M. A., Morris, R. J., and Goldschneider, I. (1979). *Immunology* (in press).

Rosen, F. S. (1979). *In* "Immunopathology" (S. Cohen, ed.), Chapter 15. Wiley, New York.

Rysser, J. E., and Vassalli, P. (1974). *J. Immunol.* **113,** 719–728.

Schlesinger, M. (1972). *Prog. Allergy* **16,** 214–299.

Schrader, J. W., Goldschneider, I., Bollum, F. J., and Schrader, S. (1979). *J. Immunol.* **122,** 2337–2339.

Shinpock, S. C., and Goodman, J. W. (1977). *Exp. Hematol.* **5,** Suppl. 2, 36.

Shortman, K. (1977). *Prog. Immunol.* **3,** 197–205.

Shortman, K., and Jackson, H. (1974). *Cell. Immunol:* **12,** 230–255.

Shreffler, D. C., and David, C. S. (1975). *Adv. Immunol.* **20,** 125–196.

Silverstone, A., Cantor, H., Goldstein, G., and Baltimore, D. (1976). *J. Exp. Med.* **144,** 453–548.

Staber, F. G., Schlafi, E., and Moroni, C. (1978). *Nature (London)* **275,** 669–671.

Stern, P. L., Martin, G. R., and Evans, M. J. (1975) *Cell* **6,** 455–465.

Stockert, E., Old, L. J., and Boyse, E. A. (1971). *J. Exp. Med.* **133,** 1334–1335.

Stout, R. D., Yutoku, M., Grossberg, A., Pressman, D., and Herzenberg, L. A. (1975). *J. Immunol.* **115,** 507–512.

Stutman, O. (1977). *Contemp. Immunobiol.* **7,** 1–46.

Sugimoto, M., and Bollum, F. J. (1979). *J. Immunol.* **122,** 392–397.

Thierfelder, S. (1977). *Nature (London)* **269,** 691–693.

Till, J. E. (1976). *In* "Stem Cells of Renewing Cell Populations" (A. B. Cairnie, P. K. Lala, and D. G. Osmond, eds.), pp. 143–155. Academic Press, New York.

Till, J. E., and McCulloch, E. A. (1961). *Radiat. Res.* **14,** 213–222.

Tyan, M. L. (1975). *Transplantation* **19,** 326–334.

Tyan, M. L. (1977). *J. Immunol.* **118,** 846–851.

van Bekkum, D. W. (1977). *In* "Experimental Hematology Today" (S. J. Baum and G. D. Ledney, eds.), pp. 3–10. Springer-Verlag, Berlin and New York.

van den Engh, (1978). *In* "Experimental Hematology Today" (S. J. Baum and G. D. Ledney, eds.), pp. 9–15. Springer-Verlag, Berlin and New York.

Weissman, I. L. (1973). *J. Exp. Med.* **137,** 504–510.

Weissman, I. L., Papaioannou, V. E., and Gardner, R. L. (1977). *Cold Spring Harbor Symp. Quant. Biol.* **41,** 9–15.

Whang, J., Frei, E., Tjio, J. H., Carbone, P. P., and Brecher, G. (1963). *Blood* **22,** 664–673.

Wiktor-Jedrzejczak, W., Sharkis, S., Ahmed, A., Sell, K., and Santos, G. W. (1977). *Science* **196,** 313–315.

Williams, A. F. (1976). *Eur. J. Immunol.* **6,** 526–528.

Winchester, R. J. Meyers, P. A., Broxmeyer, H. E., Wang, C. Y., Moore, M. A. S., and Kunkel, H. G. (1978) *J. Exp. Med.* **148,** 613–618.

Wu, A. M., Till, J. E., Siminovitch, L., and McCulloch, E. A. (1967). *J. Cell. Physiol.* **69,** 177–184.

Yoffey, J. M. (1973). *In* "Haemopoietic Stem Cells" (G. E. W. Wolstenholme and M. O'Connor, eds.), pp. 5–45. Am. Elsevier, New York.

Zatz, M. M., and Lance, E. M. (1970). *Cell Immunol.* **1,** 3–17.

Zeiller, K., and Dolan, L. (1972). *Eur. J. Immunol.* **2,** 439–444.

Zinkernagel, R. M., Callahan, G. N., Althage, A., Cooper, S., Klein, P. A., and Klein, J. (1978). *J. Exp. Med.* **147,** 882–896.

CHAPTER 3

SOMATIC CELL GENETICS AND THE DEVELOPMENT OF THE IMMUNE SYSTEM[1]

Peter D'Eustachio and Frank H. Ruddle

DEPARTMENT OF BIOLOGY
YALE UNIVERSITY
NEW HAVEN, CONNECTICUT

During its development, an animal generates a large number of lymphoid cells, each committed to make antibody molecules of a single specificity. Together, these cells constitute a repertoire capable of recognizing and specifically responding to a great variety of foreign antigens. Experimental data accumulated in the past 20 years have made it possible to divide these antigen-specific cells into two large classes, T cells and B cells, to define stages in the maturation of each class of cells, and to analyze their roles in the adult immune response. A large catalog of cell surface markers characteristic of these cells has been developed and it has been possible to correlate the expression of various of these markers with cells at a particular stage of maturation or functional activity.

The genetics of the immune system has likewise been extensively studied. A variety of genetic factors have been defined that affect the development of lymphoid cells, the markers they express, and the ways in which they interact in the course of an immune response. Nevertheless, two classes of problems have so far not been amenable to conventional genetic analysis. First, it has rarely been possible to distinguish clearly between structural genes and regulatory genes. Second, it has

[1] Work of the authors discussed in this paper was supported by U.S.P.H.S. grant GM9966. P. D. was supported by a National Research Service award GM07439.

59

CURRENT TOPICS IN
DEVELOPMENTAL BIOLOGY, VOL. 14

rarely been possible to define the relationship between these genetic markers and factors and the molecular basis of immune function.

The techniques of somatic cell genetics provide a promising new approach to these problems, and the purpose of this chapter is to discuss the application of these techniques to the immune system. To facilitate this discussion, the first part of this chapter will summarize briefly the data that are now available concerning the genetics of the immune system, focusing especially on its development. In the second part of the chapter, we will describe the techniques of somatic cell genetics in detail, concentrating on several recent developments that allow analysis of the fine structure of the eukaryotic genome. Finally, we will discuss two specific problems, the mapping of genes coding for immunoglobulin (Ig) molecules, and the definition and analysis of antigen-specific functions of T cells. Both of these problems are of considerable importance in the development of the immune system, and they provide excellent models for the ways in which somatic cell genetics can be applied to the analysis of specialized cell types and their development.

I. The Major Components of the Immune System

A. THE ANTIBODY MOLECULE

The immunoglobulin, or antibody molecule, is a multichain structure composed of two identical heavy polypeptide chains and two identical light polypeptide chains held together by noncovalent forces and disulfide bonds. Each chain is composed of a variable (V) region whose sequence differs from one Ig molecule to the next, and a constant (C) region, whose sequence is largely conserved. The V regions of the heavy and light polypeptide chains associate to form the antigen-binding site, whose antigen-binding specificity is determined by the amino acid sequences of these V regions (Edelman and Gall, 1969).

On the basis of their amino acid sequences, light chains can be divided into two classes, κ and λ. Within a class, all light chains have the identical C region sequence except for genetic polymorphisms. V region sequences can be divided into subgroups on the basis of "family resemblances" among their sequences. V regions of heavy chains can similarly be classified into subgroups. Heavy chains possess one of eight constant region sequences, γ_1, γ_{2a}, γ_{2b}, γ_3, α, μ, δ, and ε, and differ from light chains in that V region sequences of all subgroups can be found in association with any given class of C region (Gally and Edelman, 1972; Capra and Kehoe, 1975; Kabat et al., 1976; McKean et al., 1978).

Certain variations in the amino acid sequences of these chains are inherited as autosomal Mendelian codominant markers, called allotypes. The patterns of inheritance of these markers in humans (Natvig and Kunkel, 1973) and in rabbits (Kindt, 1975) suggest that the genes coding for Ig molecules fall into three unlinked clusters. One cluster codes for the V and C regions of all heavy chains, a second for the V and C regions of λ light chains, and a third for the V and C regions of κ light chains. Analysis in the mouse has been less extensive, but available data are consistent with this pattern (Laskin *et al.*, 1977).

In no case has any of these genes been mapped unequivocally. In the mouse, a locus very closely linked to the Lyt-2,3 markers on chromosome 6 has been shown to affect the production of a particular group of κ chains (Gottlieb and Durda, 1976). It cannot be determined, however, whether this phenomenon reflects the action of structural Ig genes, or of regulatory genes. In the case of the heavy chain in the mouse, expression of C region polymorphisms has been shown to be closely linked to the gene coding for a serum protein, prealbumin (Taylor *et al.*, 1975). The linkage of prealbumin, however, is not known and again it remains possible that the Ig-related marker is a regulatory gene rather than a structural one.

B. ANTIGEN-SPECIFIC CELLS

The cells directly responsible for the production of antibody molecules are small lymphocytes and their progeny (Gowans and McGregor, 1965). These cells have been extensively characterized, and can be divided into two classes, T cells and B cells, on the basis of their location in the body, their antigenic markers, and a variety of functional properties (reviewed, for example, by Greaves *et al.*, 1973; D'Eustachio *et al.*, 1977; Katz, 1977) (Fig. 1). B cells, when stimulated by antigen, divide and mature further to give rise to clones of antigen-specific memory cells and antibody-producing plasma cells. T cells do not secrete antibodies in response to foreign antigens but instead exhibit an antigen-specific "helper" activity that appears to be necessary for the full stimulation of B cells. Alternatively, they may give rise to antigen-specific suppressor cells, which inhibit the response, or to "killer" cells which directly lyse cells bearing the foreign antigen on their surfaces. Analysis of the development and cell surface markers of T and B cells has so far been limited largely to the mouse, and our discussion here will focus on that species. Nevertheless, to the extent that the human lymphoid system has been studied, surface antigens and differentiation pathways closely analogous to those of the mouse have been found (Gathings *et al.*, 1977).

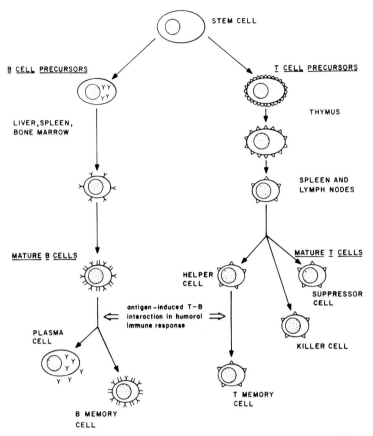

FIG. 1. T and B lymphocytes. B cells are most readily identified and classified according to the amount and cellular distribution of Ig (Y) and of receptors for complement and Fc (‖). T cells can be classified according to the relative amounts of TL (○) and Thy-1 (△) antigens on their surfaces (D'Eustachio *et al.*, 1979).

B cells mature in the liver and spleen of the fetus and in the bone marrow of the adult. In the course of its maturation, each B cell becomes committed to produce a single species of Ig and to express copies of this molecule on its surface. Mature B cells also possess surface receptors for the third component of complement (Bianco *et al.*, 1970) and for the Fc portions of aggregated Ig molecules (Basten *et al.*, 1972). Plasma cells generally lack detectable amounts of these markers. At least in the mouse, they do express the PC-1 surface antigen (Takahashi *et al.*, 1970). The appearance of PC-1 on these cells appears to be very closely associated with the initiation of Ig secretion in the maturing plasma cell. Neither the structural genes coding for these various markers nor the genes responsible for their coordinate expression during B-cell differentiation have been mapped.

T cells mature in the thymus. Cells at different stages of maturation can be distinguished by their differential expression of the Thy-1, TL, Lyt, and G_{IX} surface antigens. Thy-1, which has been mapped to mouse chromosome 9 (Itakura et al., 1971), is found on all T cells as well as some kinds of nonlymphoid cells (Reif and Allen, 1964). It is present in large amounts on cells in the thymus and in smaller amounts on mature T cells (Raff, 1970). TL ("thymus-leukemia") antigens, as their name implies, are present on thymic cells of some strains of mice, are not detectable on mature T cells, but can reappear on T cell-derived leukemic cells (Old and Stockert, 1977). Different TL-positive strains of mice express different combinations of these antigens. Their expression is controlled by a genetic locus closely linked to the major histocompatibility complex on mouse chromosome 17 (Boyse et al., 1964). G_{IX} is a cell surface marker of thymic cells. It is a glycoprotein indistinguishable from the gp69/71 coat protein of murine leukemia viruses (Stockert et al., 1971; Obata et al., 1975; Tung et al., 1975). Expression of G_{IX} on thymocytes appears to be controlled by two unlinked genes in the mouse, neither of which has been mapped (Old and Stockert, 1977). The Lyt antigens (Boyse et al., 1968) first appear on T cells at about the time they leave the thymus, and can be used to distinguish different functional populations of mature T cells (Cantor and Boyse, 1976). "Helper" T cells express the Lyt-1 antigen, which is encoded by a gene on mouse chromosome 19 (Itakura et al., 1971). Killer and suppressor T cells both express the Lyt-2 and Lyt-3 antigens. These two markers are encoded by closely linked genes on mouse chromosome 6 (Itakura et al., 1972). Suppressor cells in addition express the I-J antigen, which is encoded by a locus within the major histocompatibility complex (Murphy et al., 1976). This marker is found both on the cell surface and on soluble factors produced by stimulated suppressor cells (Taniguchi and Miller, 1978a).

In addition, T cells possess a cell-surface receptor for antigen, whose function is closely analogous to that of the Ig molecules found on B cells (Basten et al., 1971; Rutishauser and Edelman, 1972; Cone et al., 1977). This receptor appears to have a number of biochemical properties in common with the Ig molecule, but its isolation has been possible only in a few instances and it is not well characterized (Binz and Wigzell, 1976; Krawinkel et al., 1976; Marchalonis et al., 1976). In particular, the relationship between receptor expression and specialized T-cell function (helper, killer, suppressor) remains entirely unclear. Likewise, although it is attractive to speculate that the T-cell receptor is encoded as a part of the Ig gene clusters (Edelman, 1976), no data at all are available concerning its genetics.

II. Somatic Cell Genetics

Somatic cell genetics provides a new approach to the genetic analysis of the higher eukaryotes. It has the advantages of speed, simplicity, economy, and high resolution. Already in the first decade of its practice well over 200 genes have been mapped in man (Fig. 2, Table I) (McKusick and Ruddle, 1977; Bergsma, 1978). Somatic cell genetics depends on two classes of parasexual events detectable in somatic cells *in vitro*. The first is the transfer of genetic information from a donor cell to a recipient cell; the second is the gradual elimination or modification of this transferred material in the recipient cell and its progeny. The latter permits the dissection of chromosome sets, and the assignment by correlation of gene functions to specific chromosomes.

The transfer of genetic information can now be accomplished in four ways, namely: cell hybridization, microcell-mediated gene transfer, chromosome-mediated gene transfer, and DNA-mediated gene transfer. The four methods differ both in the amount of genetic information transferred and its fate in the recipient cell.

Cell hybridization effects the transfer of an entire nuclear genome. Hybrids can be readily formed by treating cell populations with membrane-fusing agents such as inactivated Sendai virus (Harris and Watkins, 1965) or polyethylene glycol (PEG) (Pontecorvo, 1976). A number of schemes have been developed which permit the efficient selection of heterosynkaryons and the elimination of unfused parental cells and homosynkaryons. The majority of these methods depend on the existence of different recessive, complementing, conditional auxotrophic markers in the contributing parental cells (Littlefield, 1964; DeMars, 1974; Creagan and Ruddle, 1977), but dominant markers may also be used to advantage (Baker *et al.,* 1974; Siminovitch, 1976).

Chromosome elimination occurs spontaneously in interspecific hybrids. In hybrid cells, the recipient parent is represented by, at the least, a complete haploid chromosome set whereas the donor chromosome set is partially monosomic. Donor chromosomes are progressively eliminated, but the rate of elimination tends to decrease progressively as a direct function of generation number, and those hybrids which have retained but a few donor chromosomes are generally stable. Factors which determine the direction of segregation are poorly defined but parental chromosome number, adaptation to growth *in vitro*, epigenetic state, and species origin all appear to play a role. In the case of mouse × hamster hybrids, mouse chromosomes are usually lost. In the case of mouse × human hybrids, human chromosomes are usually but not invariably eliminated. The loss of human chromosomes is not absolutely random, and particular chromosomes are sometimes preferentially retained (Ruddle and Creagan, 1975).

The elimination of donor chromosomes can be regulated experimentally. If a donor chromosome carries a prototrophic gene then under selective conditions only cells retaining that gene and its associated chromosome can survive. A good example involves the gene which codes for the enzyme hypoxanthine guanine phosphoribosyltransferase (HPRT). This gene is X-linked in all mammalian species so far determined. Cells are conditionally dependent on HPRT activity for survival in medium containing hypoxanthine, aminopterin, and thymidine (HAT medium). Thus, mouse × human hybrid cell populations formed between mouse recipient cells deficient in HPRT (mo HPRT$^-$) and human donor cells prototrophic for HPRT (hu HPRT$^+$) and grown in HAT medium, exhibit a preferential retention of the human X chromosome. Hybrid cells which have retained the human X chromosome can be selected against by exposing the cells to toxic metabolic analogs of hypoxanthine such as thioguanine which are metabolically incorporated into cells possessing HPRT activity. Thus in the case of the HPRT system, it is possible to select for and against cells which either possess or lack HPRT activity.

Microcell-mediated gene transfer facilitates the transfer of only one or several "donor" chromosomes into a recipient cell (Fournier and Ruddle, 1977a,b). The donor parent is treated with mitotic blocking agents, which promotes the formation of polykaryocytes in which the chromosomes are divided among a number of micronuclei. When these cells are treated with cytochalasin and subjected to centrifugal force, they are fragmented, yielding microcells. Microcells possess a micronucleus containing only one or several intact chromosomes, plus a rim of cytoplasm and an intact plasma membrane. Microcells are viable for only a few hours, but may be rescued by fusion to intact, viable recipient cells. Sendai virus and PEG have been successfully used as fusion agents. Selection for microcell hybrids is accomplished by incorporating a conditional auxotrophic marker into the recipient parent, and by purifying the microcells to homogeneity, thus eliminating contaminating intact donor cells. In this kind of system, a donor microcell chromosome bearing the complementing prototrophic gene would invariably be present in all hybrids. Other chromosomes will also be present in all permutations. The advantages of the microcell cell system are (a) the incorporation of one or only a few chromosomes, thus simplifying the correlation of donor chromosomes with the expression of donor phenotypes; (b) the

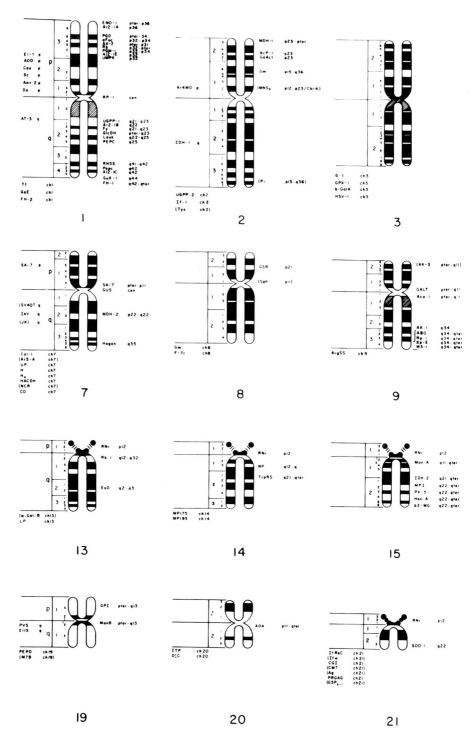

Fig. 2. Schematic diagram of the human gene map. See Table I for an explanation of the gene symbols.

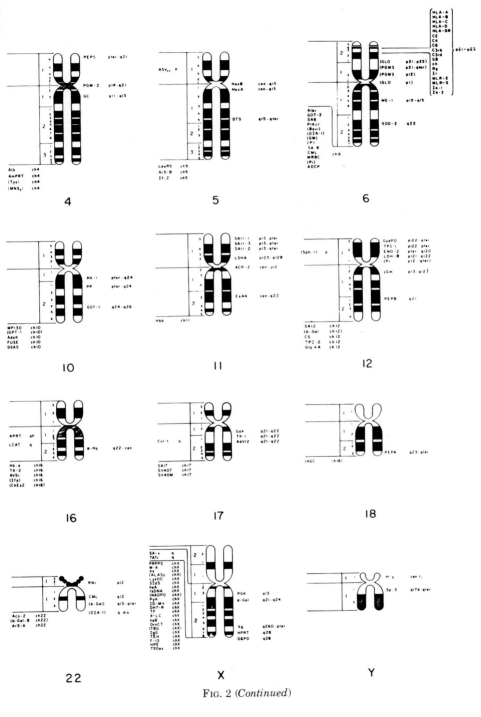

FIG. 2 (Continued)

TABLE I

Human Gene Assignments

Chromosome[a]	Gene symbol	EC number	McKusick number	Status[b]	Gene name
01p360	A12-1A		10292	P	Adenovirus 12 chromosome modification
01q220	A12-1B			P	Adenovirus 12 chromosome modification
01q420	A12-1C			P	Adenovirus 12 chromosome modification
01p320	A12-1E			P	Adenovirus 12 chromosome modification
10	AAT	26 1 1	13818	C	Glutamic-oxaloacetic transaminase-1; Aspartate aminotransferase-1 (GOT-1, GOT-S)
06	AAT	26 1 1	13815	P	Mtch. GOT (GOT-2, GOT-M)
LGg (10?)	AAT	26 1 2	13820	C	Ala aminotransferase (AAT); Aspartate aminotransferase (GTP)
09	ABO		11030	C	Blood group
02	ACE r	31 1 7		P	Acetylcholinesterase derepressor
09 (see 03)	Aco-1	42 1 3	10085	I	Sol. aconitase (s-ACO, ACO-S)
03 (see 22)	Aco-2	42 1 3	10084	C	Mtch. aconitase (m-ACO, ACO-M)
02	AcP-1	31 3 2	17150	C	Acid phosphatase-1
11p110-p120	AcP-2	31 3 2	20095	P	Acid phosphatase-2
03	ACY-1	35 1	10462	P	Aminoacylase-1 (Acy-1)
17	Ad5T			P	(AdV5-T) virus integration site
20q	ADA	35 4 4	10270	I	Adenosine deaminase
06	ADCP	35 4 4	10271	P	Adenosine deaminase complexing prot.
20p	ADA	35 4 4	10270	P	Adenosine deaminase
04 (or 5?)	ade+B		10255	P	Es-Act syntenic (or chm. 5)(FGRAT)(formylglycinamide ribonucleotide amidotransferase)
21	ade+C	63 413	13844	P	Phosphoribosylglycinamide synthetase PRGAS (GAPS, GARS, PRAGL)
10	AdoK	27 120	10275	C	Adenosine kinase (ADSK, AdK, ADK)

Location	Symbol	Method	MIM No.	Status	Disorder / Title
17	AdV12		10297	C	Adenovirus-12 chromosome modification site-17
03	tsAF8		11695	P	Reverses hamster G-1 block (tsAF8)
21	Ag		15200	T	β lipoprotein
06	AH-3	1d9910	20191		Adrenal hyperplasia III (S21HO) (steroid 21-hydroxylase)
06p210-p220	AJ		14284	C	HLA-C (antigen)
09	AK-1	27 4 3	10300	P	Adenylate kinase-1
01	AK-2	27 4 3	10302	C	Adenylate kinase-2 (mtch.)
09	AK-3	27 4 3	10303	P	Adenylate kinase-3 (nucleoside TPase)
11	AL-a		15125 –15127	C	Lethal antigen subtypes 1, 2, and 3 (SA11-1, 2, and 3)
0X	ALASy	23 137	30130	C	δ-Aminolevulinic acid syn. (?) Anemia, hypochromic
04	Alb		10360	P	Albumin
04	Alb r			T	Analbuminemia linked to Gc
06 or LGc	Am-2		1471?	P	Ig heavy chain structure order: G3, G1, G2, A2 (Gm-Hs)
04	AmPRT	24 214	17245	P	Pur-1+, amidophosphoribosyltransferase (PRPPAT)
01	Amy-1	32 1 1	10465	C	Amylase, salivary
01	Amy-2	32 1 1	10470	C	Amylase, pancreatic
01	Anir-2		10620	T	Aniridia, type II Baltimore (An-2)
01	AOD		10900	T	Auriculo-osteodysplasia
16	APRT	24 2 7	10260	C	Adenine phosphoribosyltransferase
02	Ar4MO	1d14 1	10833	P	Aryl hydrocarbon hydroxylase
07pter-q220	ArgSL	43 2 1	20790	P	Arginosuccinate lyase (ASL)
09	ArgSS	63 4 5	21570	P	Arginosuccinate synthetase (ASS) Citrullinemia
22	ArS-A	31 6 1	25010	C	Arylsulfatase-A (ARSA, ARS-A)
05	ArS-B	31 6 1	25320	C	Arylsulfatase B (ARSB, ARS-B)
01	ATh-3		10730	T	Antithrombin III (AT-3)
21	AVS		10745	C	Interferon receptor system (AVS, AVR) Antiviral protein (AVP) (IfRec) Antiviral state depressor (AVr)
16	AVS r			P	Antiviral state
05	AVSrr		10745	P	Regulator(s) of repressor of AVS (AVS = antiviral state)

(Continued)

TABLE I (*Continued*)

Human Gene Assignments

Chromosome[a]	Gene symbol	EC number	McKusick number	Status[b]	Gene name
0Z	AVS s		10745	P	(AVP, antiviral protein) (AVR) stim. (IfRec)
06 or 19	Bevi		10918	I	Baboon type C virus (M7) replic.
06	Bevi		10918	P	Baboon type C virus (M7) integration
06p210-p220	Bf		13847	C	Glycine-rich β-glycoprotein (GB)
15	BVIN			P	BALB virus induction, N-tropic
11	BVIX			P	BALB virus induction, xenotropic
06p210-p220	C2		12060	C	Complement component-2
LGh -1?	C3		12070	C	Complement component-3
06p210-p220	C3 rb		12062	C	Complement component-C3b receptor
06p210-p220	C3 rd		12065	P	Complement component-C3d receptor
06p210-p220	C4		12080	C	Complement component-4 (Ch + Rg)
LGn	C6		21708	T	Complement component-6
LGn	C7		12095	T	Complement component-7
06p210-p220	C8		12095	T	Complement component-8
01	Cae		11620	C	Zonular pulverulent cataract
LGk	Cat-C		21250	C	Congenital cataract
08	CF7		22750	P	Coag. factor VII regulator (F-7 r)
10	hCG-1		11885	P	Chorionic gonadotropin-1 (hGC-1)
18	hCG-2		11885	P	Chorionic gonadotropin-2 (hGC-2)
06p210-p220	Ch		11043	C	Chido blood group (C4S)
01	ChEs1	31 1 8	17740	T	Cholinesterase (E1, E-1)
16	ChEs2	31 1 8	17750	T	Plasma cholinesterase (E2, E-2)
LGh	ChIst		14400	C	Hypercholesterolemia
0X	Chris		30690	C	Factor IX (PTC, plasma thromboplastic component) (Christmas Disease) (heB)

Chrom	Symbol	Map	MIM	Status	Title
07	ChT-N		16282	T	Neutrophil chemotactic response (NCR)
21	CGI			P	Cell growth inhib. by interferon
22	CML		15141	P	Chronic myeloid leukemias (not MHC)
06	CMLy			P	Cell-mediated lympholysis (not MHC)
21	CMT	21 1 6		T	Catechol-O-Me-transferase
07 or LGm	Co		11045	T	Colton blood groups
07 and 17	Col I		12015	P	Collagen I α-1(I) or α-2(I)
			12016		
12	CS	41 3 7	11895	C	Mtch. citrate synthase (condensing enzyme)
LGi	Db		16877	C	Double-band parotid salivary protein
20	D:C		12565	P	Desmosterol to cholesterol conversion (DCE) (presumptive enzyme)
0X	DHT-R		31370	P	Androgen insens., like tfm, receptor
22	Dia-1	16 4 3	25080	C	Diaphorase; see chm. 6
LGa	Dm		16090	C	Myotonic dystrophy
0X	tsDNA			P	Heat-sens. DNA ligation rev. (hrClAGOH)
0Y	DNA-Y			C	Y-specific reiterated DNA
01	Do		11060	T	Dombrock blood group
05	DTS		12615	P	Diphtheria toxin sensitivity
0X	Dunca			P	Duncan's disease (immunodeficiency, progressive combined variable) (lymphoma, etc.) (XLRLS) (X-LC)
01	E1	31 1 8	17740	T	Cholinesterase (ChEs1)
16	E2	31 1 8	17750	T	Plasma cholinesterase (ChEs2)
19	E11S		12915	T	Echo-11 virus sensitivity
14	EBV		13285	P	Epstein–Barr virus integration site
10	EBS-1		13195	C	Epidermolysis bullosa, Ogna type
0X	E-D	1d11 4	30520	P	Lysl oxidase (Ehlers-Danlos syndr. V) (LysDO)
01	E1-1		13050	C	Elliptocytosis-1
10	EMP-130		13371	P	Surface protein MW 130,000 (MP130)
14	EMP-175			P	Surface protein MW 175,000 (MP175)
14	EMP-195		13374	P	Surface protein MW 195,000 (MP195)

(Continued)

TABLE I (Continued)

HUMAN GENE ASSIGNMENTS

Chromosome[a]	Gene symbol	EC number	McKusick number	Status[b]	Gene name
01	ENO-1	42 111	17245	P	Enolase-1 (ENO-1, PPH-1)
12	ENO-2	42 111	13136	C	Enolase, 2nd form (PPH) (ENO-2)
04 or 5	EsAct	31 1 1	13325	P	Esterase activator (Es-Act)
11cen–q22	EsA4	31 1 1	13322		Esterase-A4 (Es-A4)
13	Es-D		13328	P	Esterase D (ESD)
08	F-7 r			P	Coag. factor VII regulator
0X	F-9		30690	C	Factor IX (PTC, plasma thromboplastic component) (Christmas Disease) (heB)
0X	F-13		30550	C	Factor XIII (fibrin stabilizing factor, X-linked form)
0Xq210-q220	Fabry	32 122	30150	P	α-Galactosidase (a-Gal disease)
04 or 5	FGRAT		10255	P	Es-Act syntenic (ade+B) (formylglycinamide ribonucleotide amidotransferase)
01	FH-1	42 1 2	13685	C	Fumarate hydratase-1 (FH-S)
01	FH-2	42 1 2	13686	C	Mtch. fumarate hydratase (FH-M)
06p210-p220	FOUR		14283	C	HLA-B (antigen)
01	a-Fuc	32 151	23000	C	α-L-fucosidase
10	FUSE			P	Surface inducer of rat cell fusion
01	Fy		11070	P	Duffy blood group
03	G-1+		11695	P	Reverses hamster G-1 block (tsAF8)
02	GaAct		13703	P	Galactose enzyme activator (Gal+-Act)
01	GaE	51 3 2	23035	P	UDPGal-4-epimerase (GALE)
01p	GaE	51 3 2	23035	T	UDPGal-4-epimerase (GALE)
0X	a-Gal	32 122	30150	C	α-Galactosidase (a-GAL A)
22 or 13	a-GalB	32 149	10417	I	α-Galactosidase B (a-GALB) N-Ac-a-galactosaminidase (a-NAGA)

12 or 22	b-Gal	I	23020	32 123	β-Galactosidase
03	b-GalA	C	23050	32 123	β-Galactosidase-A (see chm. 12,22)
			23050		GM-1 gangliosidosis; acid liver enz.
17q210-q220	GaK	P	23020	27 1 6	Galactokinase (GALK, GalK, GK)
09(02,03?)	GALT	C	23040	27 712	Hexose-1-phosphate uridylyltransferase (GalT, GallPUT, GaPUT, GAPUT)
12	GAPD	C	13840	12 112	Glyceraldehyde-3-P dehydrogenase,GydPD
21	GAPS	P	13844	63 413	Phosphoribosylglycinamide synthetase ade+C (PRGAS, GARS, PRAGL)
09(02,03?)	GaPUT	C	23040	27 712	Hexose-1-phosphate uridylyltransferase (GalT, GallPUT, GALT, GAPUT)
06p210-p220	GB	C	13847		Glycine-rich β-glycoprotein (Bf)
04q110-q130	Gc	P	13920		Group-specific protein system
10	hGC-1	P	11885		Chorionic gonadotropin-1 (hCG-1)
18	hGC-2	P	11885		Chorionic gonadotropin-2 (hCG-2)
07	b-Gcu	C	25322	32 131	β-Glucuronidase (GUS)
01	GDH	P	13811	11 147	Glucose DH (GlcDH)
17q210-q220	GK	P	23020	27 1 6	Galactokinase (GALK, GalK, GaK)
17	a-Glc	P		32 120	α-Glucosidase (Pompe's disease)
01	GlcDH	P	13811	11 147	Glucose DH (GDH)
06p210-p220	GLO	C	13875	44 1 5	Glyoxalase I (Gx-1, Glo)
12	Gly+A	P	13845	21 2 1	Serine hydroxymethyltransferase (SHMT, SerHMT); glycine A auxotroph
02 or 12	Gm	I	14700 –14719		Immunoglobulin
02	Gm-Ha	I	14710		Ig heavy chain attachment to membrane
02 or 8	Gm-H	I	1471Z		Immunoglobulin heavy chains (14710-14719) (may also req. chm. 6) (see 8)
06 or LGc	Gm-Hs	P	1471?		Ig heavy chain structure order: G3, G1, G2, A2 (Am-2)
LGc	Gml-4	P	1471Z		Immunoglobulins
10	GOT-1	C	13818	26 1 1	Glutamic-oxaloacetic transaminase-1 Aspartate aminotransferase (AAT,GOT-S)

(Continued)

73

TABLE I (*Continued*)

HUMAN GENE ASSIGNMENTS

Chromosome[a]	Gene symbol	EC number	McKusick number	Status[b]	Gene name
06	GOT-2	26 1 1	13815	P	Mtch. GOT (AAT)
0Xq28	G6PD	11 149	30590	P	Glucose-6-phosphate dehydogenase
19	GPI	53 1 9	17240	C	Glucose-6-P isomerase (PHI) Phosphohexose isomerase
10	GPT-1	26 1 2	13820	T	Ala aminotransferase (AAT,GTP)
01q210-q230	GPUT-1	27 7 9	19175	P	Glucose-1-phosphate uridylyltransferase (UDPglucose pyrophosphorylase-1) (UGPP-1)
02	GPUT-2	27 7 9	19176	P	Cathodal, major UGPP (UGPP-2)
03 (21?)	GPX-1	1a 1 9		C	Glutathione peroxidase (GPx,GSPX)
08p21	GR	16 4 2	13830	P	Glutathione reductase (GSR)
10	GSAS		13825	P	Glutamate γ-semiald. synthetase
08p21	GSR	16 4 2	13830	P	Glutathione reductase (GR)
03 (21?)	GSPx-1	1a 1 9		C	Glutathione peroxidase (GPx,GPX)
LGg (10?) 1	GTP	26 1 2	13820	C	Ala aminotransferase (AAT), sol. ??
01q44	GuK-1	27 4 8	13927	I	Guanylate kinase-1
01	GuK-2	27 4 8	13928	C	Guanylate kinase
07cen+-	GUS	32 131	25322	C	β-Glucuronidase (b-Gcu)
06p210-p220	Gx-1	44 1 5	13875	C	Glyoxalase I (GUS, Glo)
12	GydPD	12 112	13840	C	Glyceraldehyde-3-P dehydrogenase, GAPD
07	H			P	Histones (all 5)
07	H4		14275	C	Histone H4
07	HACDH	11 135	14345	P	HydroxyacylCoA-DH (HADH)
07	Hagem		23400	P	Hageman (factor XII, HaF)
02,4,5,11,16	Hb		14180	I	α- or β-Globin
16 ?	Hb-aG		14180	I	Hb α-G and α-A; see chm 4,5,2

Location	Symbol	Description		MIM	
16	Hb-a	α-Globin	I	14180	
11	Hb-b	β-Globin	I	14190	
11	Hb-d	Hemoglobin δ	C	14200	
11	Hb-gA	Hemoglobin γ-A	C	14220	
11	Hb-gG	Hemoglobin γ-G	C	14225	
11	Hb-e	Hemoglobin ε	C	14210	
LGh	HC	Hypercholesterolemia (Chlst)	C	14400	
10	hCG-1	Chorionic gonadotropin-1 (hGC-1)	P	11885	
18	hCG-2	Chorionic gonadotropin-2 (hGC-2)	P	11885	
0X	heA	Hemophilia A (classical hemophilia)	C	30670	
0X	heB	Factor IX (PTC, plasma thromboplastic component) (Christmas Disease)	C	30690	
05	Hex-A	Hexosaminidase-A (1 A subunit) see 15 (β-N-acetyl-glucosaminidase) (HEXB)	C	14265	32 130
15	Hex-A	Hexosaminidase-A (+ part on chr. 5) (β-N-acetyl-glucosaminidase) (HEXA)	P	15455	32 130
05	Hex-B	Hexosaminidase-B (and 1 A subunit) (β-N-acetylglucosaminidase)	C	14265	32 130
10	hGC-1	Chorionic gonadotropin-1 (hCG-1)	P	11885	
18	hGC-2	Chorionic gonadotropin-2 (hCG-2)	P	11885	
10	HK-1	Hexokinase-1	C	14260	27 1 1
06p210-p220	HLA-	Major histocompatibility component	C	(var.)	
06p210-p220	HLA-A	Major histocompatibility component	C	14280	
06p210-p220	HLA-B	FOUR histocompatibility component	C	14283	
06p210-p220	HLA-C	AJ histocompatibility component	C	14284	
06p210-p220	HLA-D	Mixed lymphocyte culture (MLC)	C	15785	
06p210-p220	HLA-DR		C	14286	
16	a-Hp	α-Haptoglobin (Hpa)	C	14010	
0X	HPE	Hypophosphatemia	C	30780	
11	HPFH	Heterocellular hereditary persistence of fetal hemoglobin to Hb-b, thal, or S	T		
0Xq28	HPRT	Hypoxanthine phosphoribosyltransferase	C	30800	24 2 8
03	HSV-1	Herpes simplex virus type 1 suscep. (HVS)	P	14245	

75

(Continued)

TABLE I (Continued)

HUMAN GENE ASSIGNMENTS

Chromosome[a]	Gene symbol	EC number	McKusick number	Status[b]	Gene name
0X	Hunter	31 6--	30990	C	Sulfoiduronate sulfatase (Hunter's, Hurler's, MPS II syndrome) (SIdS)
0X	Hurler	31 6--	30990	C	Sulfoiduronate sulfatase (Hunter's, Hurler's, MPS II syndrome) (SIdS)
0Y[c]	H-Y				"Male-specific" histocompatibility antigen; testis diff'n.
06p210-p220	Ia-1		14686	C	Immune response associated
06p210-p220	Ia-2		14687	C	Immune response associated
02q11	ICD-S	11 142	14770	I	Isocitrate dehydrogenase-1, sol. (IDH-1, IDH-S)
15q2	ICD-M	11 142	14765	P	Mtch. NADP-isocitrate dehydrogenase
02q11	IDH-1	11 142	14770	I	Isocitrate dehydrogenase-1, sol. (ICD-S, IDH-S)
15q2	IDH-2	11 142	14765	P	Mtch. NADP-isocitrate dehydrogenase (ICD-M, IDH-M)
0X	ID-M+		30823	C	Immunodeficiency with increased IgM
02	If-1		14757	P	Interferon-1
05	If-2		14758	C	Interferon-2
16	If p			T	Contr. If prod'n.
21	IfRec		10745	I	Interferon receptor system (AVS, AVR)
0Z	IfRec s		10745	P	Antiviral protein (AVP)
21	If[c]			T	(AVP, antiviral protein) (AVR) stim.
					Lymphoblastogenesis suppr., etc.
02,6,7,8,X	Ig		1471Z	I	Immunoglobulins (and see LGm)
06	Gm-Hs		1471?	P	Ig heavy chain structure order: G3, G1, G2, A2 (Am-2)
07q	Inv		14720	P	κ light chain Ig (Km)
08	Gm-H		14710	P	Ig heavy chain; see chm. 2
0X	ID-M+		30823	C	Immunodeficiency with increased IgM

0X	IgG		30030	C	Agammaglobulinemia, Bruton type
07 or LGm	Inv		14720	P	Immunoglobulin κ light chain (Km)
0X	Ig-M+		30823	C	Immunodeficiency with increased IgM (ID-M+)
LGk	Ii		11080	C	Blood group
21q221	IPO-A	1e 1 1	14745	P	Superoxide dismutase-1, sol., dimeric Indophenol oxidase A (SOD-1)
06	IPO-B	1e 1 1	14746	C	Superoxide dismutase-2, mtch. (SOD-2) (tetrameric)
06p210-p220	Ir		14685	T	Immune response locus (or loci)
20	ITP	36 1 3	14753	C	Inosine triphosphatase
07 or LGm	Jk		11100	T	Kidd blood group
06	JDM		12585	P	Juvenile diabetes mellitus (DMJ)
LGf	K		11090	C	Kell blood group
0X	pre K			P	Blood group antigen Xk, Kell precursor, acanthocytosis, chronic granulomatous disease
07 or LGm	Jk		11100	T	Kidd blood group
06	JDM		12585	P	Juvenile diabetes mellitus (DMJ)
LGf	K		11090	C	Kell blood group
0X	pre K			P	Blood group antigen Xk, Kell precursor, acanthocytosis, chronic granulomatous disease
07 or LGm	Kidd		11100	T	Kidd blood group (Jk)
07	Km		14720	P	κ light chain Ig (Inv)
16	LCAT	23 143	24590	P	Lecithin cholesterol acetyltransferase
11p123-p128	LDH-A	11 127	15000	P	Lactate dehydrogenase-A (LDH A)
12p121-p122	LDH-B	11 127	15010	P	Lactate dehydrogenase-B (LDH B)
LGh	Le		11110	C	Lewis blood group
08	LETS			P	Large extern. transform. sens. prot.
01q230-q250	Leuk			P	Leukemia
05	LeuRS	61 1 4	15135	P	Leu-tRNA Syt. (Leu-RS, hr025Cl)
13	Lp		15220	P	Lipoprotein
LGa	Lu		11120	C	Lutheran blood group
0X	LysDO	1d11 4	30520	P	Lysyl oxidase (Ehlers–Danlos syndr. V)
06 or 19	M7B		10918	I	Baboon type C virus (M7) replic. (Bevi)
15	Man-A	32 124	15458	P	Cytopl. a-mannosidase (a-Man A)

77

(Continued)

TABLE I (*Continued*)

HUMAN GENE ASSIGNMENTS

Chromosome[a]	Gene symbol	EC number	McKusick number	Status[b]	Gene name
19	Man-B	32 124	24850	P	(A-MANN-2) Lysos. a-D-mannosidase; mannosidosis
02	MDH-1	11 137	15420	C	Sol. malate dehydrogenase-1 (MDS-S)
07	MDH-2	11 137	15410	C	Mtch. malate dehydrogenase (MOR-M) (MDH-M)
06p120-q150	ME-1	11 140	15425	S	Malic enzyme, sol. (ME-S)
15	b2-MG		10970	P	β-2-Microglobulin
06p210-p220	MHC				Major histocompatibility complex
06p210-p220	MLC		15785	C	Mixed lymphocyte culture (HLA-D)
06p210-p220	MLC-W		15786	P	Mixed lymphocyte reaction, weak
06p210-p220	MLR-2		15786	P	Mixed lymphocyte reaction, weak
06p210-p220	MLR-S		15786	C	Mixed lymphocyte reaction
LGj	MN		11130	C	Blood group
02 or LGj	MNSs		11130	T	MNSs blood group
10	MP130		13371	P	Surface protein MW 130,000 (EMP-130)
14	MP175			P	Surface protein MW 175,000 (EMP-175)
14	MP195		13374	P	Surface protein MW 195,000 (EMP-195)
15q2	MPI	53 1 8	15455	C	Mannosephosphate isomerase
0X	MPS II	31 6--	30990	C	Sulfoiduronate sulfatase (Hunter's, Hurler's syndrome) (SIdS)
06	MRBC		14686	P	Monkey RBC recep. (B cell-specif.)
22	NADHD	16 2 2	25080	I	(DIA-1, Dia-1) NADH diaphorase
0X	NADPO	16----	30640	T	NADPH oxidase of leukocytes (possibly)
06p	Nb			P	Neuroblastoma
07	NCR		16282	T	Neutrophil chemotactic response (ChT-N)
06	NDF		20270	P	Neutrophil differentiation factor
09	Np		16120	C	Nail-patella syndrome-1 (NPa)

14q	NP	24 2 1	16405	P	Purine nucleoside phosphorylase
0X	OrnCT	21 3 3	23720	C	Ornithine carbamoyltransferase (OTC)
C					
06	P		11140	T	Blood group
LGi	Pa		16873	C	Parotid acidic protein
06	PA		17337	P	Plasminogen activator (PlAct)
18	Pep-A	3411 1	16980	P	Peptidase-A (PEPA)
12q21	Pep-B	3411 1	16990	P	Peptidase-B (PEPB)
01q42	Pep-C	3411 1	17000	P	Peptidase-C (PEPC)
19	Pep-D	3411 1	17010	C	Peptidase-D (PEPD)
04	Pep-S	3411 1	17025	P	Peptidase-S (PEPS)
06	Pg		16970	I	Pepsinogen
01p340-p360	PGD	11 143	17220	P	6-Phosphogluconate dehydrogenase
0Xq130	PGK	27 2 3	31180	S	Phosphoglycerate kinase
01p32	PGM-1	27 5 1	17190	I	Phosphoglucomutase-1
04	PGM-2	27 5 1	17200	P	Phosphoglucomutase-2
06p12	PGM-3	27 5 1	17210	P	Phosphoglucomutase-3
19	PHI	53 1 9	17240	P	Glucose-6-P isomerase (GPI)
02,12,LGc,06	Pi		10740	I	a-1-Antitrypsin (protease inh.)
15q2	PK-3	27 140	17905	C	Pyruvate kinase-3 (PK-M2)
01	PKU		26160	P	Phenylketonuria
06	PlAct		17337	P	Plasminogen activator (PA)
10	PP	36 1 1	17903	C	Pi-pyrophosphatase
01p340-p360	PPH-1	42 111	17245	P	Enolase-1 (ENO-1, Eno-1) Phosphopyruvate hydratase-1
12	PPH-2	42 111	13136	C	Enolase, 2nd form (PPH) (Eno-2, ENO-2)
LGi	Pr		16878	C	Proline-rich parotid salivary protein
21	PRGAS	63 413	13844	P	Phosphoribosylglycinamide synthetase ade+C

(Continued)

TABLE I (*Continued*)

HUMAN GENE ASSIGNMENTS

Chromosome[a]	Gene symbol	EC number	McKusick number	Status[b]	Gene name
0X	PRPPS	27 6 1		P	(RPPPK) PRPP Syt., RP PP-kinase (GAPS, GARS, PRAGL)
0X	PTC		30690	C	Factor IX (heB, plasma thromboplastic component) (Christmas Disease)
04	Pur-1+	24 214	17245	P	AmPRT, amidophosphoribosyltransferase
19	PVS		17385	C	Poliovirus receptor (PVR)
0X	PyK	27 138	30600	C	Glycogen storage disease (VIII)
13	Rb-1		18020	C	Retinoblastoma-1; X-ray sens. (RB-1)
06	RBC r		14686	P	Monkey RBC recep. (B cell-specif.)
06p21-p22	Rg		11171	C	Rodgers blood group (C4F)
01	Rh		11170	C	Rhesus blood group
01q41-q42	RN5S		18042	I	5S rRNA
13p12	RNr		18045	C	Rbs. RNA (rRNA)
14p12	RNr		18045	C	Rbs. RNA (rRNA)
15p12	RNr		18045	C	Rbs. RNA (rRNA)
21p12	RNr		18045	C	Rbs. RNA (rRNA)
22p12	RNr		18045	C	Rbs. RNA (rRNA)
13 or14,15	RNt			T	tRNA (transfer ribonucleic acid)
01c	RP-1		18010	P	Retinitis pigmentosa
0X	RPPPK	27 6 1		P	(PRPPS) PRPP Syt., RP PP-kinase, ribosephosphate pyrophosphokinase
06	S21H0	1d9910	20191		Adrenal hyperplasia III (AH-3) (steroid 21-hydroxylase)
11	SA-1		18555	C	Human species antigen (AL) (SA11)
06	SA6		18551	P	Surface antigen, MW 45,000 (AS6)
07	SA7		18552	P	Species antigen 7 (AS)
11	SA11		18555	C	Human species antigen (AL) (SA-1)

80

Location	Symbol		Code	Type	Description
12	SA12		18556	P	Human species antigen (SA 12)
06	SA-B		14686	P	B-cell antigens
17	SA17		31345	P	Surface antigen 17 (species antigen)
0Xq	SA-X			P	Species antigen-X
0X	SA-X2			P	Surface antigen (= SA-X,SA-X3 ?)(SAX-2)
0X	SA-X3			P	Cell surface antigen (= SA-X,SA-X2 ?)
01p	Sc		11175	P	Scianna blood group
LGa	Se		18210	C	Secretor
12	SHMT	21 2 1	13845	P	Serine hydroxymethyltransferase (Gly+A, SerHMT); glycine A auxotroph
0X	SIdS	31 6--	30990	C	Sulfoiduronate sulfatase (Hunter's, Hurler's, MPS II syndrome)
21q221	SOD-1	1e 1 1	14745	P	Superoxide dismutase-1, sol., dimeric
				P	Indophenol oxidase A (IPO-A)
06q	SOD-2	1e 1 1	14746	P	Superoxide dismutase-2 (mtch.) (IPO-B)
0Yq11d-qter	Sp-3		18290	T	Azoospermia 3rd factor
08 or 12	Sph-1		11131	C	Spherocytosis, Denver type
LGj	Ss		18680	P	Blood group
07 and 17 and 8	SV40T			P	SV40 T-antigen (rarely non-7 chm.)
07	SV40V			P	SV40 V-antigen
07	SV40t		19905	P	Tr (SV40-transforming factor(s))
07 and 17	SV40m		19118	P	SV40 genome tumorigenic factors
07 and 8	SV0g			P	SV40 genome (DNA)
0Xq	TATr	26 1 5	31435	P	Tyrosine aminotransferase regulator
0X	TBG		31420	T	Thyroxin-binding globulin, serum
0X	TEH		30040	C	Agammaglobulinemia, Swiss type (thymic epithelial hypoplasia)
LGd or 01(?)	Tf		19000	T	Transferrin
0X	TF		31370	P	Testicular feminization syndrome; androgen binder deficiency
17q210-q220	TK-1	27 121	18830	P	Thymidine kinase, sol. (TK-S)
16	TK-2	27 121	18829	P	Mtch. thymidine kinase (TK-M)
12	TPI-1	53 1 1	19045	P	Triosephosphate isomerase

81

(Continued)

TABLE I (*Continued*)

HUMAN GENE ASSIGNMENTS

Chromosome[a]	Gene symbol	EC number	McKusick number	Status[b]	Gene name
12	TPI-2	53 1 1		P	Triosephosphate isomerase (in TPI-E)
14	TrpRS	61 1 2	19105	P	Trp-tRNA synthetase
0X	tsBHK			P	Replace BHK hamster ts function
0X	TSDes		30915	T	Testicular steroid 17,20-desmolase
0X	tsDNA			P	Replace hrClAG mouse ts DNA ligation (male pseudohermaphroditism)
02 or LGj	Tys		18160	T	Sclerotylosis
01q21–q23	UGPP-1	27 7 9	19175	P	Glucose-1-phosphate uridylyltransferase (UDPglucose pyrophosphorylase-1)
02	UGPP-2	27 7 9	19176	P	Cathodal, major UGPP
01	UMPK	27 4 4	19173	I	Uridine monophosphate kinase
07	UPy	24 2 3	19174	P	Uridine phosphorylase (UP)
0X	W-A		30100	C	Agammaglobulinemia, Wiskott–Aldrich syndrome
09	WS-1		19350	T	Waardenberg's syndrome, type 1
0Xp	Xg		31470	T	Blood group
0X	Xk			P	Blood group antigen, Kell precursor, acanthocytosis, chronic granulomatous disease
0X	X-LC			P	Duncan's disease (immunodeficiency, progressive combined variable) (lymphoma, etc.) (XLRLS)
09	XP-E		27870	T	Xeroderma pigmentosum, Egyptian
13q	X-ray		18020	C	Retinoblastoma-1 (Rb-1); X-ray sens.

[a] The chromosomal assignment of each gene is shown, together with the particular arm (p or q) and band with which the gene is associated when these data are known.

[b] P, provisional; C, confirmed; I, inconsistent; T, tentative; S, smallest region of overlap.

[c] More detailed information and references to the original research can be found in McKusick and Ruddle (1977) and in Bergsma (1978).

introduction of only a little cytoplasmic substance from the donor, thus reducing the possibility of perturbing the epigenetic program of the recipient cell; and (c) control over the direction of chromosome elimination by the selection of the microcell parent. Nevertheless, the donor chromosomes enter the recipient cell intact, and by essentially the same mechanism as cell hybridization. There is little or no breakage or rearrangement of the donor chromosomes. The microcell scheme in contrast to whole cell hybridization effects chromosome segregation prior to fusion.

Chromosome-mediated gene transfer was first described by McBride and Ozer (1973). Donor cells subjected to mitotic arrest are physically broken, releasing metaphase chromosomes. The chromosomes are mixed with recipient cells, usually in multiplicities of 0.5 to 2 genome equivalents per cell. When conditionally auxotrophic recipient cells (e.g., HPRT$^-$) are treated with chromosomes from a prototrophic donor, cells of the recipient type that express the donor marker can be recovered at a low frequency. Two recent technical improvements, coprecipitation of the chromosomes with calcium phosphate, and post-treatment of the recipient cells with dimethyl sulfoxide, have allowed this frequency to be raised as high as 2×10^{-5} (Miller and Ruddle, 1978). In this system, subchromosomal fragments are transferred to the recipient cell. The fragments range in size from large pieces readily detected by light microscopy (Miller and Ruddle, 1978; Klobutcher and Ruddle, 1979) to pieces carrying no detectable genetic information beyond the selected prototrophic marker itself. We have coined the term "transgenome" to describe these fragments (Ruddle and Fournier, 1977).

The transgenome is typically expressed in an unstable fashion in the recipient cells. That is, in an unstably transformed cell population, between 1 and 10% of the cells lose the ability to express the prototrophic marker in each generation. Loss appears to be an all-or-none phenomenon, in that donor markers that were linked to the prototrophic marker are lost in a concordant fashion (McBride et al., 1978; Miller and Ruddle, 1978). Stable sublines can arise in these cell populations that no longer lose the prototrophic marker at a detectable rate (Degnen et al., 1976; Willecke et al., 1976). The transgenome appears to become closely associated with a recipient chromosome in these stable cell lines (Fournier and Ruddle, 1977b; Willecke et al., 1978). Indeed, in those cases where a large fragment undergoes stabilization, it can subsequently be detected as a morphologically distinct region of a recipient cell chromosome (Miller and Ruddle, 1978; Klobutcher and Ruddle, 1979). In this way, the transgenome appears to acquire a centromere function, facilitating its orderly transmission to daughter cells at each mitosis.

The key questions that now arise concerning the transgenome are structural ones; how is it organized in the "unstable" and in the "stable" states; and what is the molecular basis of stabilization? The recent development of DNA-mediated gene transfer and its application to genes coding for thymidine kinase (TK) provide a promising means of approaching these questions. Murine cell populations deficient in cytosol TK activity, when treated with UV-irradiated herpes simplex virus-1 (HSV-1), give rise to clones of cells expressing high levels of TK activity (Munyon *et al.*, 1971). The TK enzyme expressed by these cells is clearly that encoded by HSV-1 and not the murine enzyme, as judged by its isoelectric point, electrophoretic mobility, immunochemical properties, and ability to phosphorylate iododeoxycytidine (Smiley *et al.*, 1978). Recent studies in our own laboratory have shown that one such stable transformant has a particular mouse chromosome with which the HSV-1 TK phenotype can be correlated (Smiley *et al.*, 1978). This study thereby provides somatic cell genetic evidence for the integration of *HSV-1 TK* gene at a particular chromosome site.

Recently Wigler *et al.* (1977) have reported the efficient transfection of murine TK-deficient cells with purified HSV-1 DNA. Viral DNA pretreated with restriction endonucleases known to cleave the *TK* gene (e.g., *Eco*RI) lost its transforming activity. Endonucleases such as Bam, that did not cleave the gene, did not affect activity. Furthermore, a purified 3.4-kb Bam fragment possessed TK transforming activity, and transfected cells at a frequency of 1 colony per 10^6 cells per 40 pg DNA. The same group has reported biochemical evidence for physical integration of the 3.4-kb Bam fragment into host DNA sequences in transformed mouse thymidine kinase-deficient host cells (Pellicer *et al.*, 1978) and have further shown that integrated single copies of the 3.4-kb HSV TK fragment diluted in recipient mammalian genomes can secondarily transform TK-deficient mouse cells. The transformation frequency for secondary transformation ranges from 1 colony per 10^5 to 1 colony per 5×10^6 cells per 20 μg cellular DNA. Thus, a specific fragment of the HSV-1 genome can be used for the efficient transformation of mammalian cells, and the fate of this fragment can be analyzed biochemically (Scangos et al., 1979).

In related experiments, Wigler *et al.* (1978) have reported successful transformation experiments involving the endogenous *TK* gene from a number of vertebrate species, namely, chicken, calf, Chinese hamster, mouse, and human. Only in the case of human donor TK were experiments described which demonstrated donor-specific biochemical properties of the transferred TK. Clearly, an independent confirmation would be highly desirable. The transformation rates extended over a range of 10-fold, but all were impressively high. The lowest was recorded for human DNA which had a value of 1 colony per 10^6 cells per 20 μg/DNA.

The availability of an efficient transformation system for mammalian cells *in vitro* opens up a number of important possibilities. For example, it should now be possible to transfer very small and well-defined regions of donor chromosome segments into recipient cells. Thus, one could analyze the genetic composition of segments containing selectable markers at a very high level of resolution. A second possibility involves the use of DNA-mediated transformation as a bioassay for specific genetic segments of complex genomes. In this case, the donor DNA could be fractionated by various biochemical means and the fractions tested for biological activity. The DNA could be purified sequentially through multiple dimensions of separation, as, for example, reverse phase chromatography, agar gel electrophoresis, and recombinant DNA cloning. A third possibility lies in the ability to form transgenotes which possess small and highly specified donor transgenomes, either as integrated or independent, episome-like entities. In sum, the advent of DNA-mediated transformation provides a means of performing high-resolution gene mapping in higher eukaryotes, purification of genes from complex mammalian genomes, and the specific genetic modification of mammalian cells. All of these new capabilities should prove invaluable to the analysis of the genetic regulation of differentiated cells in mammalian species.

III. Applications of Somatic Cell Genetics to the Analysis of the Immune System

The most straightforward approach to the genetic analysis of lymphocyte development and lymphocyte-specific markers is to generate hybrid cells that retain the phenotypic properties of lymphocytes and then to analyze them as described in Section II. The application of this approach to lymphoid cells, and indeed to specialized cell types generally is difficult. Analysis of a variety of hybrids between differentiated and "nondifferentiated" cells (e.g., hepatoma or neuroblastoma cells, and fibroblasts), suggests that expression of markers specific to the differentiated cell is blocked in such hybrids. Hybrids between two cells expressing the same differentiated phenotype, however, typically continue to express the markers characteristic of the phenotype (Ringertz and Savage, 1976, especially ch. 11). Consistent with these generalizations, it has been observed that when Ig-producing cells are fused with nonlymphoid cells, Ig production ceases in the resulting hybrids (Zeuthen *et al.*, 1976). Our own preliminary data confirm this observation, and indicate further that the PC-1 antigen normally present on Ig-secreting cells is lost from such hybrids. Hybrids between different B-cell populations, on the other hand, typically remain lymphoid in appearance and continue to produce both parental types of Ig (Schwaber and Cohen, 1974; Köhler and Milstein, 1975). Recent improvements in the methods available for growing and fusing lymphoid cells make the routine production of such hybrids feasible, and in the second part of this section we will discuss the properties of these hybrids.

An alternative, although more limited, solution is to take advantage of available nucleic acid hybridization technology to characterize somatic cell hybrids. Because these techniques allow direct analysis of the cell's genome, they are not affected by the cell's phenotype and can therefore be used to characterize existing panels of somatic cell hybrids irrespective of epigenetic type. In the first part of this section, we will discuss experiments to determine the chromosomal location of Ig genes in mouse–hamster somatic cell hybrids using nucleic acid hybridization.

A. MAPPING Ig κ CHAIN GENES IN THE MOUSE

This analysis is simple in principle: DNA from somatic cell hybrids is tested for its ability to form duplexes with a DNA probe molecule corresponding to the gene of interest. By correlating the presence or absence of duplex formation with the presence or absence of particular "donor" chromosomes in the somatic cell hybrid (Section II), the gene can be assigned directly to a chromosome. Thus, using human–mouse somatic cell hybrids, and conventional liquid hybridization techniques (Britten and Kohne, 1968) the gene coding for human α-globin has been assigned to chromosome 16, and the gene for human β-globin to chromosome 11 (Deisseroth *et al.*, 1977, 1978).

A variety of DNA probes have been prepared that react specifically with the V and C regions of mouse κ chains (e.g., Honjo *et al.*, 1974; Seidman *et al.*, 1978a,b). These probes react also with related sequences in hamster DNA (D. Swan, unpublished). This cross-reaction makes analysis of somatic cell hybrids using conventional liquid hybridization techniques difficult. A DNA fractionation method recently developed by Seidman *et al.* (1978b) allows the separation of hamster and mouse κ chain DNAs, so that the mouse κ chain structural genes can be mapped unambiguously.

The procedure used in these experiments is outlined in Fig. 3.

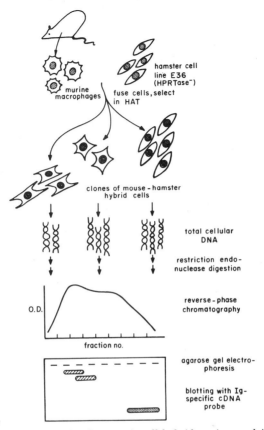

FIG. 3. Scheme for gene mapping in somatic cell hybrids, using nucleic acid probes.

High-molecular-weight DNA is extracted from mouse–hamster hybrid cells that contain the complete genetic material of the hamster parent, and various combinations of mouse chromosomes (Kozak *et al.*, 1974; Leinwand *et al.*, 1978; Ruddle *et al.*, 1978). The DNAs are digested with bacterial restriction endonucleases, producing defined fragments. These are fractionated by reverse-phase chromatography and agarose gel electrophoresis to yield a two-dimensional "map" (Seidman *et al.*, 1978b), and DNA fragments in the map containing Ig-specific sequences are identified by hybridization to a DNA probe using the blotting technique of Southern (1975).

These maps can resolve even closely related DNA fragments because the endonuclease cleaves the DNA reproducibly at well-defined specific sites. These DNA maps can be used to test material from a panel of cell lines for the presence of particular DNA sequences. The "map" obtained for a typical positive mouse hamster hybrid cell line is shown diagrammatically in Fig. 4. Hamster DNA coding for κ chains can be distinguished from mouse DNA coding for κ chains, and within each species, V and C region-specific sequences can be distinguished. Hybrids give either a "positive" pattern that is the sum of the two parental ones or a "negative" pattern indistinguishable from that of the hamster parent. Eleven hybrid lines have been screened in this way. In every case, presence or absence of mouse-specific κ chain DNA was correlated with the presence or absence of mouse chromosome 6 in the hybrid. We have therefore assigned the mouse κ chain gene cluster to this chromosome (Swan *et al.*, 1979). Analogous experiments with heavy-chain-specific probes indicate that this gene cluster is on mouse chromosome 12 (P. D'Eustachio, D. Pravtcheva, K. Marcu, and F. H. Ruddle, unpublished). As the probe molecules become available, experiments to map the λ light chain in the mouse should be possible, as should experiments in other species.

A satisfactory understanding of Ig production and of its relationship to lymphoid function generally requires information not only concerning the physical location of these genes, but also concerning their interactions with each other and with other genes involved in immune

ANALYSIS OF CLONE 7AI3-4A

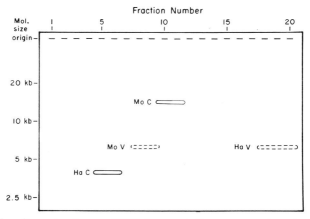

FIG. 4. Two-dimensional map of DNA fragments from a mouse–hamster somatic cell hybrid. DNA from the hybrid line 7A13-4A was digested with *Eco*RI restriction enzyme, fractionated as described in the text, and hybridized with a probe complementary to the V and C regions of a mouse κ chain. Mouse- and hamster-specific bands were identified by comparison with the patterns yielded by mouse and hamster liver DNA. V and C region-specific bands were identified by comparison with a parallel map, developed using a probe complementary only to the C region of mouse κ chain.

function. These more general problems cannot be approached except by analyzing cells that retain the phenotypic properties of lymphocytes. The second part of this section is therefore concerned with experiments designed to generate such hybrid cells and to use these cells to define and characterize additional genes affecting lymphoid function.

B. SOMATIC CELL HYBRIDS WITH LYMPHOID PHENOTYPES

Early attempts to produce somatic cell hybrids with the properties of lymphoid cells used various combinations of murine myeloma, lymphoma, and spleen cells, murine fibroblasts, and human peripheral blood lymphocytes (Periman, 1970; Mohit, 1971; Schwaber, 1975). While in most cases it was possible to demonstrate production of Ig's of both parental types, and sometimes the expression of histocompatibility antigens of both types, these early experiments were hampered by three factors. The efficiency with which hybrids were recovered was very low; Ig production was often at a low level; and the hybrid cell populations lost genetic material very rapidly, making their analysis extremely difficult.

More recent work has allowed at least partial solution of these problems. We will review this work and then will turn to the work of several groups that have begun to use such hybrids to analyze lymphocyte function and its genetic control.

1. Choice of Parental Cell Types

The early experiments tended to involve the fusion of cell populations at least one of which was fully transformed, tissue culture-adapted, and somewhat dedifferentiated. More recent work has emphasized the fusion of a normal lymphoid cell with a tumor cell that retains many of the phenotypic markers of normal lymphoid cells (Köhler and Milstein, 1975; Goldsby *et al.*, 1977). A variety of B-cell- and T-cell-derived tumors adapted for growth in culture have been used. Many of these in addition express drug markers that allow for selection against the unfused parental cells following hybridization (Section II). There is considerable variation in the efficiency with which these cells can be induced to form hybrids, however. For example, three T-cell-derived lines, EL4.Bu, S49, and BW5147, have been used extensively in fusion experiments with normal T cells. BW5147 has consistently yielded viable hybrid cells at a frequency significantly greater than that observed for the other two lines.

A more subtle problem concerns the selective expression of phenotypic markers in the hybrids. Thus, Yelton *et al.* (1978) found that all mouse myeloma cells tested for ability to form hybrids with normal mouse spleen cells did so, but at least one myeloma tested gave rise exclusively to hybrids that had ceased to produce Ig chains specified by the normal parent, and produced only those specified by the myeloma parent. The genetic and epigenetic basis of this phenomenon is not understood. Clearly, at least part of the problem is that the transformed cell lines now available do not correspond to the entire range of phenotypes expressed by normal lymphoid cells. Analysis of some of these phenotypes may therefore have to await the development of the corresponding transformed cell line.

The properties of the "normal" lymphoid parent in these fusions are more difficult to determine. Normal lymphoid cell populations are heterogeneous and the fraction of cells that gives rise to viable hybrids is very small—less than one cell in 10,000 in all the experiments reported so far. Nevertheless, by comparing the properties of hybrid cells with those of the normal parental population, it is possible to deduce some of the properties of the particular normal cells that gave rise to the hybrids.

This analysis has been most extensive in the case of the fusion of murine spleen cells and myeloma cells to form antibody-producing hybrids. The spleen of a normal mouse contains on the order of one B cell in 10,000 capable of binding an antigen strongly enough to be stimulated by it (Rutishauser et al., 1972; Klinman and Press, 1975). Even following extensive immunization, the frequency of such cells does not rise above 1 cell in 100. Nevertheless, when spleen cells from an immunized mouse are used to form hybrids, as many as 10–20% of the hybrids produce antibodies that react with the immunizing antigen (Köhler and Milstein, 1975; Köhler and Shulman, 1978). The overall efficiency of hybridization, furthermore, is time-dependent: the maximum frequency of hybridization occurs with spleen cells taken from the mouse 60 to 90 hours after the last immunization. This time corresponds to the period when maximal cell division and differentiation are occurring in response to the antigenic stimulation (Köhler and Milstein, 1976). In addition, when cells from the spleen of an unimmunized mouse are separated into a pool of small resting lymphocytes and a pool of Ig-producing blast cells, only the latter gives rise to viable hybrids following fusion with myeloma cells (Andersson and Melchers, 1978). When the ability of spleen cells to form hybrids following stimulation in vitro with specific antigen or with nonspecific B-cell mitogens, such as bacterial lipopolysaccharide, was tested, peak recovery of hybrid cells occurred when spleen cells cultured for 4 days were fused with myeloma cells. The distributions both of Ig heavy chain classes and of antigen-binding specificities shown by these hybrid cell populations were indistinguishable from those shown by the mitogen-stimulated parental spleen cell populations (Andersson and Melchers, 1978). All of these data are consistent with the hypothesis that of all the cells in the spleen, only actively dividing B-cell blasts fuse with myeloma cells to give rise to viable hybrids.

Even if this model is correct, however, the hybridization process appears inefficient: in the spleen of an immunized mouse, one cell in a hundred may be a B-cell blast, but only one cell in 10,000 forms a viable hybrid. Whether the remaining cells represent functionally distinct subpopulations incapable of forming hybrids, or whether the "successful" cells are a genuinely random sample of the total population remains unclear. As a consequence, any attempt to extrapolate from the properties of lymphoid hybrids to those of the normal lymphoid population from which they were derived is risky. At the same time, in those cases in which a marker or function is well defined, the formation of hybrids allows, for the first time, the isolation and characterization of a nearly homogeneous cell population expressing the trait of interest. Particularly striking results have been obtained from the analysis of T-cell hybrids.

2. Properties of T-Cell Hybrids

The normal cell parent for these hybrids is obtained by injecting mice with antigen or exposing spleen cells to antigen *in vitro*, under conditions that cause the preferential stimulation and maturation of antigen-specific suppressor cells. The entire cell mixture can be used for fusion, or a population enriched in rapidly dividing T cells can be prepared by fractionation on nylon wool columns (Julius *et al.*, 1973) and unit gravity sedimentation (Hecht *et al.*, 1976).

To date, three groups have obtained hybrids between such stimulated T cells and T-cell lymphomas (Table II). The hybrid nature of the cells was shown by their expression of markers of both parental types. Most of the hybrids tested appeared to lose genetic information derived from the normal parent at an appreciable rate, as shown by the loss of the corresponding markers. Nevertheless, in all three cases, it was possible to obtain lines that expressed the antigen-specific function of the normal parent in a stable fashion. The degree to which the function is expressed, however, is low, when measured as the fraction of cells forming rosettes, or the amount of suppressor factor produced per cell. The possibility that these cell populations are mixtures and that the T-cell-specific function is expressed by a subpopulation of cells can be excluded by subcloning experiments. An alternative explanation is that this low level of function reflects epigenetic variation within the

TABLE II

SOMATIC CELL HYBRIDS THAT EXPRESS T-CELL FUNCTIONS

Cell type	Expression of markers derived from non-tumor parent[a]							Expression of immune function	Reference
	H-2	Ig	Thy-1	I-J	Lyt-2,3	Lyt-1	Iso-zymes		
A. Parental cells[a]									
EL4.Bu lymphoma	+	−	+	?	−	−		None known	
BW5147 lymphoma	+	−	+	−	−	−		None known	
Splenic suppressor cells	+	−	+	+	+[b]	−		+ (Suppressor factor, rosette formation)[b]	
B. Hybrid cell lines									
EL4.Bu × CBA/J splenocytes	±	−	+[c]	±	ND	ND	ND	+ (Suppressor factor)	Taniguchi and Miller (1978b)
BW5147 × C57B1/6 splenocytes	+	−	+	ND	ND	ND	+[d]	+ (Rosette formation)	Ruddle (1978)
BW5147 × CBA/Ca splenocytes	+	ND	+	+[b]	−	+	ND	+ (Suppressor factor)	Kontiainen et al. (1978)

[a] All hybrids continued to express the markers of the lymphoma parent; those of the splenocyte parent were variably expressed, as shown.

[b] A cell line is noted as positive if the material was secreted or found on the cell surface or both.

[c] The lymphoma and splenic parental forms of Thy-1 are indistinguishable in this case.

[d] HPRTase (X chromosome); glucose phosphate isomerase (mouse chromosome 7).

hybrid cell population. In particular N. Ruddle, B. Beezly, and D. Eardley (unpublished) have found that the frequency of rosette-forming cells in a monoclonal hybrid cell population varies systematically through the growth cycle of the cells. An intriguing possibility is that this variation may not reflect any "defect" in the hybrid cells, but may rather be a physiological variation involved in the normal regulation of T-cell function.

IV. Concluding Remarks

Obviously, the present understanding of these hybrid cells, their phenotypic properties, and their genetic regulation is incomplete. Nevertheless, using the techniques of somatic cell hybridization and genetic analysis, clonal populations of functioning antigen-specific cells can be obtained and manipulated in culture. Preliminary evidence indicates that these cell populations are an excellent source of relatively homogeneous T-cell factors, and potentially also of the T-cell antigen-binding receptor, so that the chemical characterization of these molecules may be possible, together with systematic functional and genetic analyses of their production. Many functions characteristic of T cells, B cells, and their immature precursors have not yet been fixed in any somatic cell hybrid. Other markers, such as the Ig structural genes, can only be analyzed at present by relatively indirect and laborious procedures. Nevertheless, these studies are yielding valuable information. Applying the techniques of somatic cell genetics to these hybrid cells should allow us for the first time to distinguish structural genes coding for lymphocyte-specific molecules from genes that regulate their expression. It should likewise be possible to dissect the genetic mechanisms by which panels of surface markers and functional properties are turned on in a coordinated fashion in the differentiation of, for example, a T suppressor cell. With the enumeration and analysis of genetic markers that these studies will allow, it should become possible to apply more sophisticated and finely tuned forms of genetic manipulation, such as gene transfer and DNA transfer, to lymphoid cells.

REFERENCES

Andersson, J., and Melchers, F. (1978). *In* "Lymphocyte Hybridomas" (F. Melchers, M. Potter, and N. Warner, eds.), pp. 130–139. Springer-Verlag, Berlin and New York.

Baker, R., Brunette, D., Mankowitz, R., Thompson, L., Whitmore, G., Siminovitch, L., and Till, J. (1974). *Cell* **1**, 9–21.

Basten, A., Miller, J., Warner, N., and Pye, J. (1971). *Nature (London), New Biol.* **231**, 104–106.

Basten, A., Miller, J., Sprent, J., and Pye, J. (1972). *J. Exp. Med.* **135**, 610–626.

Bergsma, D., ed. (1978). "Human Gene Mapping IV," Orig. Artic. Ser. Nat. Found.— March of Dimes, S. Karger, Basel and New York.

Bianco, C., Patrick, R., and Nussenzweig, V. (1970). *J. Exp. Med.* **132**, 702–720.
Binz, H., and Wigzell, H. (1976). *Cold Spring Harbor Symp. Quant. Biol.* **41**, 275–284.
Boyse, E., Old, L., and Luell, S. (1964). *Nature (London)* **201**, 779.
Boyse, E., Miyazawa, M., Aoki, T., and Old, L. (1968). *Proc. R. Soc. London, Ser. B* **170**, 175–193.
Britten, R., and Kohne, D. (1968). *Science* **161**, 529–540.
Cantor, H., and Boyse, E. (1976). *Cold Spring Harbor Symp. Quant. Biol.* **41**, 23–32.
Capra, J., and Kehoe, M. (1975). *Adv. Immunol.* **20**, 1–40.
Cone, R., Gershon, R., and Askenase, P. (1977). *J. Exp. Med.* **146**, 1390–1404.
Creagan, R., and Ruddle, F. (1977). *In* "Molecular Structure of Human Chromosomes" (J. Yunis, ed.), pp. 89–142. Academic Press, New York.
Degnen, G., Miller, I., Eisenstadt, J., and Adelberg, E. (1976). *Proc. Natl. Acad. Sci. U.S.A.* **73**, 2838–2842.
Deisseroth, A., Nienhuis, A., Turner, P., Velez, R., Anderson, F., Ruddle, F., Creagan, R., and Kucherlapati, R. (1977). *Cell* **12**, 205–218.
Deisseroth, A., Nienhuis, A., Lawrence, J., Giles, R., Turner, P., and Ruddle, F. (1978). *Proc. Natl. Acad. Sci. U.S.A.* **75**, 1456–1460.
DeMars, R. (1974). *Mutat. Res.* **24**, 335–364.
D'Eustachio, P., Rutishauser, U., and Edelman, G. (1977). *Int. Rev. Cytol., Suppl.* **5**, 1–60.
D'Eustachio, P., Cohen, J., and Edelman, G. (1979). *In* "Developmental Immunobiology" (G. W. Siskind, S. D. Litwin, and M. E. Weksler, eds.), pp. 133–158. Grune & Stratton, New York.
Edelman, G. (1976). *Cold Spring Harbor Symp. Quant. Biol.* **41**, 891–902.
Edelman, G., and Gall, W. (1969). *Annu. Rev. Biochem.* **38**, 415–466.
Fournier, R., and Ruddle, F. (1977a). *Proc. Natl. Acad. Sci. U.S.A.* **74**, 319–323.
Fournier, R., and Ruddle, F. (1977b). *Proc. Natl. Acad. Sci. U.S.A.* **74**, 3937–3941.
Gally, J., and Edelman, G. (1972). *Annu. Rev. Genet.* **6**, 1–46.
Gathings, W., Lawton, A., and Cooper, M. (1977). *Eur. J. Immunol.* **7**, 804–810.
Goldsby, R., Osborne, B., Simpson, E., and Herzenberg, L. (1977). *Nature (London)* **267**, 707–708.
Gottlieb, P., and Durda, P. (1976). *Cold Spring Harbor Symp. Quant. Biol.* **41**, 805–815.
Gowans, J., and McGregor, D. (1965). *Prog. Allergy* **9**, 1.
Greaves, M., Owen, J., and Raff, M. (1973). "T and B Lymphocytes: Origins, Properties and Roles in Immune Responses." Am. Elsevier, New York.
Harris, H., and Watkins, J. (1965). *Nature (London)* **205**, 640–646.
Hecht, T., Ruddle, N., and Ruddle, F. (1976). *Cell. Immunol.* **2**, 193–210.
Honjo, T., Packman, S., Swan, D., Nau, M., and Leder, P. (1974). *Proc. Natl. Acad. Sci. U.S.A.* **71**, 3659–3663.
Itakura, K., Hutton, J., Boyse, E., and Old, L. (1971). *Nature (London), New Biol.* **230**, 126.
Itakura, K., Hutton, J., Boyse, E., and Old, L. (1972). *Transplantation* **13**, 239–243.
Julius, M., Simpson, E., and Herzenberg, L. (1973). *Eur. J. Immunol.* **3**, 645–649.
Kabat, E., Wu, T., and Bilofsky, H. (1976). "Variable Regions of Immunoglobulin Genes." Bolt, Beranek & Newman, Cambridge, Massachusetts.
Katz, D. H. (1977). "Lymphocyte Differentiation, Recognition and Regulation." Academic Press, New York.
Kindt, T. (1975). *Adv. Immunol.* **21**, 35–86.
Klobutcher, L., and Ruddle, F. (1979). *Nature (London)* **280**, 657–660.
Klinman, N., and Press, J. (1975). *Transplant. Rev.* **24**, 49–83.
Köhler, G., and Milstein, C. (1975). *Nature (London)* **256**, 495–497.

Köhler, G., and Milstein, C. (1976). *Eur. J. Immunol.* **6,** 511–519.

Köhler, G., and Shulman, M. (1978). *In* "Lymphocyte Hybridomas" (F. Melchers, M. Potter, and N. Warner, eds.), pp. 143–148. Springer-Verlag, Berlin and New York.

Kontiainen, S., Simpson, E., Bohrer, E., Beverley, P., Herzenberg, L. A., Fitzpatrick, W., Vogt, P., Torano, A., McKenzie, I., and Feldman, M. (1978). *Nature (London)* **274,** 477–480.

Kozak, C., Nichols, E., and Ruddle, F. (1974). *J. Exp. Zool.* **187,** 303–308.

Krawinkel, U., Cramer, M., Berek, C., Hämmerling, G., Black, S., Rajewsky, K., and Eichmann, K. (1976). *Cold Spring Harber Symp. Quant. Biol.* **41,** 285–294.

Laskin, J., Gray, A., Nisonoff, A., Klinman, N., and Gottlieb, P. (1977). *Proc. Natl. Acad. Sci. U.S.A.* **74,** 4600–4604.

Leinwand, L., Fournier, R., Nichols, E., and Ruddle, F. (1978). *Cytogenet. Cell Genet.* **21,** 77–85.

Littlefield, J. (1964). *Science* **145,** 709–710.

McBride, O., and Ozer, H. (1973). *Proc. Natl. Acad. Sci. U.S.A.* **70,** 1258–1262.

McBride, O., Burch, J., and Ruddle, F. (1978). *Proc. Natl. Acad. Sci. U.S.A.* **75,** 914–918.

McKean, D., Bell, M., and Potter, M. (1978). *Proc. Natl. Acad. Sci. U.S.A.* **75,** 3913–3917.

McKusick, V., and Ruddle, F. (1977). *Science* **196,** 390–405.

Marchalonis, J., Decker, J., DeLuca, D., Moseley, J., Smith, P., and Warr, G. (1976). *Cold Spring Harbor Symp. Quant. Biol.* **41,** 261–273.

Miller, C., and Ruddle, F. (1978). *Proc. Natl. Acad. Sci. U.S.A.* **75,** 3346–3350.

Mohit, B. (1971). *Proc. Natl. Acad. Sci. U.S.A.* **68,** 3045–3048.

Munyon, W., Kraiselburd, E., Davis, S., and Mann, J. (1971). *J. Virol.* **7,** 813–820.

Murphy, D., Herzenberg, L., Okamura, K., Herzenberg, L., and McDevitt, H. (1976). *J. Exp. Med.* **144,** 699–712.

Natvig, J., and Kunkel, H. (1973). *Adv. Immunol.* **16,** 1–60.

Obata, Y., Ikeda, H., Stockert, E., and Boyse, E. (1975). *J. Exp. Med.* **141,** 188–197.

Old, L., and Stockert, E. (1977). *Annu. Rev. Genet.* **11,** 127–160.

Pellicer, A., Wigler, M., Axel, R., and Silverstein, S. (1978). *Cell* **14,** 133–141.

Periman, P. (1970). *Nature (London)* **228,** 1086–1087.

Pontecorvo, G. (1976). *Somat. Cell Genet.* **1,** 397–400.

Raff, M. (1970). *Immunology* **19,** 637–650.

Reif, A., and Allen, J. (1964). *J. Exp. Med.* **120,** 413–433.

Ringertz, N. R., and Savage, R. E. (1976). "Cell Hybrids." Academic Press, New York.

Ruddle, F., and Creagan, R. (1975). *Annu. Rev. Genet.* **9,** 407–486.

Ruddle, F., and Fournier, R. (1977). *Brookhaven Symp. Biol.* **29,** 96–105.

Ruddle, N. (1978). *In* "Lymphocyte Hybridomas" (F. Melchers, M. Potter, and N. Warner, eds.), pp. 203–211. Springer-Verlag, Berlin and New York.

Ruddle, N., Conta, B., Leinwand, L., Kozak, C., Ruddle, F., Besmer, P., and Baltimore, D. (1978). *J. Exp. Med.* **148,** 451–465.

Rutishauser, U., and Edelman, G. (1972). *Proc. Natl. Acad. Sci. U.S.A.* **69,** 3774–3778.

Rutishauser, U., Millette, C., and Edelman, G. (1972). *Proc. Natl. Acad. Sci. U.S.A.* **69,** 1596–1600.

Scangos, G., Huttner, K., Silverstein, S., and Ruddle, F. (1979) *Proc. Natl. Acad. Sci. U.S.A.* **76,** 3987–3990.

Schwaber, J. (1975). *Exp. Cell Res.* **93,** 343–354.

Schwaber, J., and Cohen, E. (1974). *Proc. Natl. Acad. Sci. U.S.A.* **71,** 2203–2207.

Seidman, J., Edgell, M., and Leder, P. (1978a). *Nature (London)* **271,** 582–585.

Seidman, J., Leder, A., Nau, M., Norman, B., and Leder, P. (1978b). *Science* **202,** 11–17.

Siminovitch, L. (1976). *Cell* **7,** 1–11.

Smiley, J., Steege, D., Juricek, D., Summers, W., and Ruddle, R. (1978). *Cell* **15**, 455–468.

Southern, E. (1975). *J. Mol. Biol.* **98**, 503–517.

Stockert, E., Old, L., and Boyse, E. (1971). *J. Exp. Med.* **133**, 1334–1355.

Swan, D., D'Eustachio, P., Leinwand, L., Seidman, J., Keithley, D., and Ruddle, F. (1979). *Proc. Natl. Acad. Sci. U.S.A.* **76**, 2735–2739.

Takahashi, T., Old, L., and Boyse, E. (1970). *J. Exp. Med.* **131**, 1325–1341.

Taniguchi, M., and Miller, J. (1978a). *J. Immunol.* **120**, 21–26.

Taniguchi, M., and Miller, J. (1978b). *In* "Lymphocyte Hybridomas" (F. Melchers, M. Potter, and N. Warner, eds.), pp. 212–220. Springer-Verlag, Berlin and New York.

Taylor, B., Bailey, D., Cherry, M., Riblet, R., and Weigert, M. (1975). *Nature (London)* **256**, 644–646.

Tung, J., Vitetta, E., Fleissner, E., and Boyse, E. (1975). *J. Exp. Med.* **141**, 198–205.

Wigler, M., Silverstein, S., Lee, L., Pellicer, A., Cheng, Y., and Axel, R. (1977). *Cell* **11**, 223–232.

Wigler, M., Pellicer, A., Silverstein, S., and Axel, R. (1978). *Cell* **14**, 725–731.

Willecke, K., Lange, R., Krüger, A., and Reber, T. (1976). *Proc. Natl. Acad. Sci. U.S.A.* **73**, 1274–1278.

Willecke, K., Mierau, R., Krüger, A., and Lange, R. (1978). *Mol. Gen. Genet.* **161**, 49–57.

Yelton, D., Diamond, B., Kwan, S., and Scharff, M. (1978). *In* "Lymphocyte Hybridomas" (F. Melchers, M. Potter, and N. Warner, eds.), pp. 1–7. Springer-Verlag, Berlin and New York.

Zeuthen, J., Stenman, S., Fabricius, H., and Nilsson, K. (1976). *Cell Differ.* **4**, 369–383.

CHAPTER 4

COMPLETE PRIMARY STRUCTURE OF HUMAN HISTOCOMPATIBILITY ANTIGEN HLA-B7: EVOLUTIONARY AND FUNCTIONAL IMPLICATIONS

Jack L. Strominger, Victor H. Engelhard,[1] Braydon C. Guild, Thomas G. Kostyk, Doron Lancet, Jose A. Lopez de Castro, Harry T. Orr, Peter Parham, Hidde L. Ploegh, and Jordan S. Pober

BIOLOGICAL LABORATORIES
HARVARD UNIVERSITY
CAMBRIDGE, MASSACHUSETTS

I. Introduction

Individuals in outbred populations are unable to exchange tissue grafts. The genetic loci responsible for this phenomenom, called histocompatibility loci, were identified originally as a consequence of mouse breeding studies carried out principally by Peter Gorer in England and George Snell in the United States. More than 15 loci were identified, differences at which led to rejection of tissue allografts. These loci differed in their "strength," i.e., speed at which an allograft was rejected as a consequence of this genetic difference. The strongest barrier to transplantation in mice is called *H-2*. Differences in *H-2* lead to graft rejection within a week accompanied by the formation of antibodies as well as cytotoxic lymphocytes which destroy the grafted tissue. Further studies led to the realization there were two loci in the

[1] Present address: Department of Microbiology, University of Virginia School of Medicine, Charlottesville, Virginia.

97

CURRENT TOPICS IN
DEVELOPMENTAL BIOLOGY, VOL. 14

H-2 region called *H-2D* and *H-2K*. The products of these loci are called the major histocompatibility antigens. They are expressed on the surfaces of almost all nucleated cells.

An enormous impetus to the development of this field has been provided by the development of surgical techniques for kidney grafts in man and subsequently of other organs accompanied by the realization that the success of organ grafts is limited by the histocompatibility antigen system. The alloantibodies which form as the consequence of such grafts were in fact first recognized in patients who had received multiple blood transfusions. The white blood cells of transfused blood, of course, contained histocompatibility antigens different from the ABO antigens of the red blood cells for which the recipient and donor were matched. Not long after, the occurrence of alloantibodies in the serum of multiparous females was recognized. These antibodies result from the immunization of the pregnant female by paternal antigens present on the hemiallogeneic fetus. Serological analysis also led to the discovery that these antigens were the products of two histocompatibility loci, now called HLA-A and HLA-B. Similar loci have been found in all mammalian species which have been studied. They are encoded in a region on the seventeenth mouse chromosome or sixth human chromosome called the major histocompatibility complex. It is a region several centimorgans in size (and therefore having the potential for encoding several thousand genes). A number of genes have been located in this region. It is striking that all of those which have been identified encode cell surface proteins and/or are involved in immune functions of the organism. These include a number of components of the complement system and the immune response genes. The immune response genes which determine the ability of the organism to respond immunologically to a foreign protein were located in the *I* region of the mouse between the *H-2D* and *H-2K* loci. Their products are probably the Ia antigens which are also cell surface proteins probably involved in the phenomenom of allograft rejection. The human analogs of the murine Ia antigens are the HLA-DR antigens.

A most unusual feature of the loci encoding these cell surface proteins is their extraordinary polymorphism. In feral mouse populations over 100 antigens of the *H-2K* and *H-2D* loci are known and in man at least 25 alleles of each of the *HLA-A* and *HLA-B* loci have been identified. The products of these genes are expressed codominantly. Therefore, every nucleated cell in the organism expresses on its surface four proteins selected from 100 alleles at each of the two loci in the mouse and at least 25 alleles at each of the two loci in man. In addition, the products of other loci in the major histocompatibility complex contribute to this extraordinary diversity of cell surface proteins. The potential for biological variability in outbred populations is extreme. Although transplantation phenomena led to the discovery of this system and have provoked the most interest in it, it is clear that the exchange of surgical grafts was not the evolutionary pressure which led to the polymorphism and resulted in its survival during evolution of the species. It must play a role in some phenomena of great importance to the species. The purification and characterization of these molecules was undertaken, in part, with the hope that knowledge of their structure would contribute to an understanding of their function.

The alloantisera which are produced as the consequence of immunization by allografts or in some cases by intentional appropriate immunizations with foreign cells are the tools that are used to identify and purify histocompatibility antigens (as well as to type individuals for organ transplantation). In the presence of complement, these antibodies bring about lysis of cells bearing the appropriate antigens. In the case of tissue typing, the lysis is measured by the penetration of cells by a dye, usually trypan blue, or eosin. For more quantitative measurements, the release of [^{51}Cr]chromate from labeled cells is employed. Both particulate and soluble alloantigens can be measured quantitatively by their ability to combine with alloantibody and inhibit lysis, i.e., inhibit the release of [^{51}Cr]chromate. This assay has been employed in the studies described in the following.

What is the function of the histocompatibility antigens and how did their polymorphism evolve? One can imagine several possible functions for cell surface proteins in primitive organisms. One possibility is that molecules of this type are required for cell recognition in mating reactions. In addition, in marine metazoans there may have been a need to preserve colonial individuality on the sea floor, and molecules of this type may have served to prevent, in some manner, the invasion of one colony by a neighboring colony of closely related organisms. Presumably, at this stage of evolution, only one genetic locus and its product were sufficient to serve this function. As animals become more complex, however, additional evolutionary pressures occurred. One of these may have been the evolution of viruses and the need to protect animals from uncontrolled proliferation of viruses in infected cells. There is abundant evidence now that virus-infected cells are killed by a system in which the histocompatibility antigens, modified by or associated with viral antigens, are recognized as foreign by cytotoxic T lymphocytes. Thus, the histocompatibility antigens are involved in at least one cell interaction phenomenon, the interaction of the cytotoxic T cells with the virally infected syngeneic cells. Other examples of histocompatibility antigens in cell interactions are known, as, for example, the interactions of various cells in antibody formation (B cell, helper T cell, and macrophages) where some histocompatibility determinants must be shared for a productive interaction to occur. There is also some evidence that syngeneic tumor cells may be rejected in reactions in which histocompatibility antigens play a role.

Finally, there is one other phenomenon that deserves consideration: the role of histocompatibility antigens in protecting the pregnant female from invasion by foreign hemiallogeneic cells. With the evolution of placentation as a reproductive system, this need developed. The trophoblast is the highly invasive portion of the placenta which invades the uterine wall, and bits of it may break off and circulate in the maternal circulation during pregnancy. This phenomenon must surely place an additional stress on the organism in the need for rejection of foreign cells during evolution. Both in man and in the mouse, a third histocompatibility locus has been identified (called HLA-C in man, or *H-2L* in the mouse), which encodes molecules closely related in structure to the HLA-A and -B, or H-2K and -D antigens. Moreover, these HLA-C and H-2L antigens are in strong linkage disequilibrium with and exhibit a much lower degree of polymorphism than the classical antigens. It is possible that they arose as a consequence of a relatively recent gene duplication and have survived in response to the relatively recent evolutionary needs of placental mammals. It would be indeed interesting to compare the histocompatibility systems of marsupial mammals with those of placental mammals. The large variety of phenomena involving these interesting molecules remains to be explored.

II. Purification of HLA-A and -B Antigens after Papain Solubilization

Efforts to isolate these molecules and elucidate their structure were initiated in our laboratory in the belief that this knowledge might lead to information about their evolution and function. It was initially discovered that the murine H-2 antigens can be solubilized by papain. Correspondingly, the first step in solubilizing the HLA-A, -B, and -C antigens from cell membranes is treatment with papain. After this solubilization, the purification of HLA-A and -B antigens is a relatively straightforward biochemical procedure, requiring only three additional steps to obtain pure antigens from the membranes of cultured human B-lymphoblast cell lines (Turner *et al.*, 1975; Parham *et al.*, 1977). This procedure requires only about 100-fold purification of the HLA-A and -B antigens, i.e., they represent about 1% of the total membrane protein. Their density on the cultured cells is about 20 times that on normal peripheral blood (or spleen) lymphocytes. About 30 mg each of HLA-A and -B antigens can be obtained from 1 kg of cultured cells. The use of a doubly homozygous cell line (HLA-A2,2; -B7,7) established from an individual, JY, from the highly inbred Indiana Amish Community, has greatly simplified the problem of separation of specificities.

The first interesting discovery was that the purified material contains two polypeptide chains (Cresswell et al., 1973). One of these is a glycoprotein with a MW of about 34,000 and the other is a small protein with a MW of 12,000. The small subunit was identical to a small urinary protein called β_2-microglobulin, first isolated from nephrotic human urine. It was subsequently sequenced in several laboratories and found to have sequence homology to immunoglobulin domains, particulary to the C_3H domain of Ig (Möller, 1974). Therefore, early in these studies, there were several striking similarities of the cell bound histocompatibility antigens to the circulating immunoglobulins. They included the limited proteolysis by papain, the two chain structure, and the sequence homology of the small chain to immunoglobulins. In addition, the heavy chain of HLA, which is about three times the size of an immunoglobulin domain, contained four cysteine residues in two intrachain disulfide bridges (Strominger et al., 1974). Later it was shown that these two intrachain disulfide linkages are linearly arranged as they are in immunoglobulins and have about the same size as immunoglobulin loops (Terhorst et al., 1977; Ferguson et al., 1979).

III. Dissection of the Papain-Solubilized Heavy Chain into Three Regions by Chemical Cleavages

For further structural work on the large extracellular portion of the molecule released by papain, the heavy chains (p34) of papain-solubilized HLA-A and -B antigens were cleaved further. Most of these antigens (including HLA-B7, but not HLA-A2) have a single acid cleavable linkage, fortuitously located between the two disulfide bridges (Terhorst et al., 1977). After cleavage with acid, two large fragments (ac-1 and ac-2) were separated from HLA-B7. They each contained an intrachain disulfide. Therefore, the disulfide bridges in histocompatibility antigens are linearly arranged. HLA-B7 also has two methionine residues which can be cleaved with CNBr (Terhorst et al., 1977). That cleavage results in formation of two equal sized fragments from ac-1, together with the unimportant loss of the N-terminal pentapeptide. The large N-terminal region carries the single asparagine-linked glycan of the whole molecule and contains no cysteine residues (Parham et al., 1977; Terhorst et al., 1977). Thus acid and CNBr cleavages together dissect the molecule into three fragments of approximately equal size, the N-terminal glycosylated region, the first disulfide loop region, and the second disulfide loop region. With the reagent NTCB, which cleaves at Cys residues, it was further established that the size of the two disulfide loops was similar to the size of disulfide loops in immunoglobulins (Ferguson *et al.*, 1979). Further tryptic and chymotryptic cleavages of the three fragments gave all the peptides required for sequencing (Lopez de Castro *et al.*, 1979; Orr *et al.*, 1979a).

IV. Complete Primary Sequence of Papain-Solubilized HLA-B7

The complete primary sequence of a human histocompatibility antigen, HLA-B7, is shown in Fig. 1 (Orr *et al.*, 1979a,b). About 70% of the HLA-A2 sequence has also been obtained (Orr *et al.*, 1979b). Although these two antigens are encoded by genes which are about 1 cM apart on the sixth human chromosome, their sequence homology is 81%. One of the most interesting questions about the structure is the location of the alloantigenic site(s). In the HLA-A and -B antigens, these structures are determined by the polypeptide, and not by the carbohydrate as in the red cell ABO system (Parham *et al.*, 1977). A clustering of amino acid differences between HLA-A2 and -B7 occurs in the region of residues 65 to 80 (9 out of 15 residues different). A second cluster is found between residues 105 and 114 (5 out of 10 residues different). Therefore, in comparing HLA-B7 and HLA-A2, a pattern of highly conserved regions separating two clusters of variability is seen. How

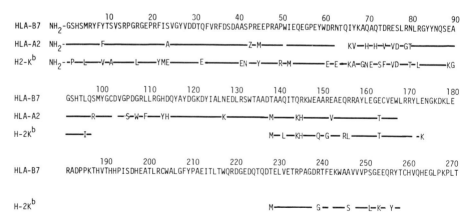

Fig. 1. The complete amino acid sequence of HLA-B7$_{\text{pap}}$ aligned with the known sequences of HLA-A2 (Orr *et al.*, 1979b) and H2-K^b (Coligan *et al.*, 1979). From Orr *et al.* (1979b).

these clusters relate to a given alloantigenic specificity awaits additional evidence.

The structure of H-2K^b antigen is also being elucidated (Coligan *et al.*, 1979). There is 72 or 74% homology between human HLA-A2 or -B7 antigens and the sequences presently available for H-2K^b. Clearly, the structure of these histocompatibility antigens has been greatly conserved during the evolution of mammals. A clustering of differences between HLA-A2 or -B7 and H-2K^b also occurs at residues 60–80 (10 or 11 out of 20 residues different). Thus, this same region stands out as one which is highly variable both within and between species.

V. Sequence Homology to Immunoglobulin Sequences

A structural relationship between histocompatibility antigens and Ig has been postulated for some time. Only recently have enough sequence data for HLA been obtained so that meaningful comparisons can be made. The ac-2 fragment containing the last 88 residues of the papain-solubilized molecules was the first sequence available of sufficient size to compare to immunoglobulin sequences in a critical way (Orr *et al.*, 1979c; Strominger *et al.*, 1980b). This region also appears to be highly conserved between human and mouse; there is about 80% homology with sequences presently available for the corresponding H-2K^b region (Coligan *et al.*, 1979). Without question the ac-2 fragment (α_3), a region which is the size of an immunoglobulin domain and which contains the second disulfide loop of HLA-B7, is highly homologous in sequence to immunoglobulin constant domains. Using the PROPHET computer system, alignments based only on identities were obtained. A maximum of 35% sequence homology with a number of immunoglobulin domain sequences was found (Strominger *et al.*, 1980b). These alignments also included the important features of matches at the rare amino acids, 2 Cys, 1 His, and 1 Trp. (For a discussion of the critical importance both of matches at rare amino acids and of statistical evaluation of homology data, see Strominger *et al.*, 1980b.)

Identities are not the only way to compare sequences. Beale and Feinstein (1976), in their analysis of the structure of immunoglobulins based on crystallographic data, identified a number of residues which are very important in chain folding of immunoglobulin domains and which were conserved in the sense that substitutions were permitted only within a closely related group of hydrophobic amino acids, Phe, Pro, Met, Val, Leu, Ile, and to some extent Ala and Gly. A second series of alignments were obtained by computer in which the number of gaps and residues in gaps were minimized and in which consideration was given to conservative substitutions (Orr *et al.*, 1979c). In this align-

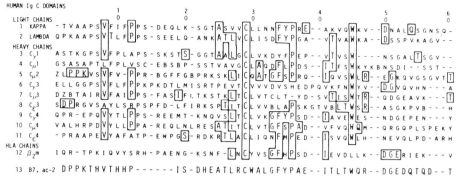

FIG. 2. The alignment of the ac-2 fragment of HLA-B7 with the human-derived sequences of the superfamily of Ig constant domains and related proteins. From Orr et al. (1979c).

ment (Fig. 2), six of the seven highly conserved immunoglobulin residues are conserved in the ac-2 fragment. The clustering and location of these residues also points to the fact that most probably the ac-2 region of HLA-B7 folds in the β-pleated sheet structure, as do immunoglobulin domains (Fig. 3). Circular dichroism spectra had already been carried out and revealed the high content of β-pleated sheet structure in HLA-A2 and -B7 (Lancet and Strominger, 1979; Lancet et al., 1979).

Z scores were calculated by the methods of Barker and Dayhoff (1976), comparing immunoglobulin domain sequences with the various regions of HLA-B7 (Table I). To a first approximation, the Z score is a measure of the probability that the homology observed is statistically significant. A Z score of 3 or larger is considered as indicative of significant homology. The α_3 or ac-2 fragment sequence was compared with different immunoglobulin domain sequences and with the β_2-microglobulin sequence. When compared with the sequences of Ig constant region domains, Z scores as high as 11 were obtained (Orr et al., 1979c). Similarly, a comparison of α_3 region with β_2-microglobulin gave a Z score of 8.4. These values and the other features of the homology leave no doubt that the α_3 region of HLA-B7, β_2-microglobulin, and the constant region domains of immunoglobulins belong to the same superfamily of polypeptides. No homology of α_3 to immunoglobulin variable regions occurs (Z score 0.8).

Interestingly, the α_1 region (the N-terminal fragment) has no sequence homology to immunoglobulin V or C region sequences and has homology of borderline significance to the α_3 fragment (Z score 2.7). The α_2 fragment (containing the first disulfide loop) also has no sequence homology to immunoglobulin C or V region domain sequences,

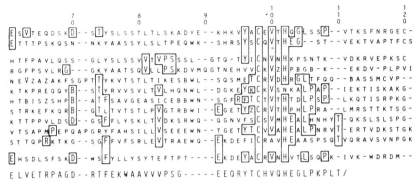

FIG. 2 (Continued)

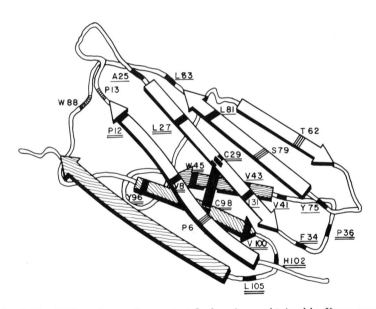

FIG. 3. The folding scheme of a constant Ig domain, as obtained by X-ray crystallographic studies of the Mcg λ human light chain dimer. Arrows denote the location and direction of strands in the β-pleated sheet structure (open, the four-stranded sheet; hatched, the three-stranded sheet). The dark bar between positions 29 and 98 represents the intradomain disulfide bond. Numbering is according to Fig. 2. Solid bars denote residues that are invariable in all or most Ig constant domains and appear in the second disulfide region of HLA-B7 (double underline) or restricted to a group of hydrophobic residues in all of the above (single underline). Residues which are highly conserved in Ig constant domains, but different in the second disulfide region, are indicated by the hatched bars. From Orr et al. (1979c).

TABLE I[a]

Statistical Scores (Z Factors) for HLA-B7 and Human Ig Regions[b]

	α_1	α_2	α_3	β_2m	C	V
α_1	—	5.2[c]	2.7	1.1	1.5	0.0
α_2	5.2[c]	—	0.1	0.9	1.1	0.6
α_3	2.7	0.1	—	8.4	8.7	0.8
β_2m	1.1	0.9	8.4	—	5.5	1.0
C	1.5	1.1	8.7	5.5	11.8	1.6
V	0.0	0.6	0.8	1.0	1.6	10.5

[a] From Orr et al. (1979a).

[b] α_1, α_2, and α_3 are, respectively, the amino-terminal, first, and second disulfide loop regions of the HLA-B7 heavy chain. V, human Ig variable regions; sequences used are V_κI (AG) and V_λIII (SH); C, human Ig constant regions; sequences used are C_κ(EU), C_λ (SH)m C_λ1, C_λ2, C_λ3 (EH), C_μ3, C_μ4 (GAL), all taken from Barker and Dayhoff (1976). Values involving Ig regions are averages. Z factors are calculated as described in Section V. Values of $Z > 3.0$ are in italics to indicate statistical significance. The table is symmetric, each value appearing for facile reference. All Z values are obtained with a gap penalty of 2 and a bias parameter of 2.

[c] Under stricter gap control parameters, a value of 2.9 is obtained for this pair. In all cases 50 randomizations were performed except for internal HLA-B7 comparisons in which 150 randomizations were performed.

despite the fact that the size of its disulfide loop, 63 residues, is in the range of V region loop sizes. α_2 has no sequence homology to α_3, but α_1 and α_2 have a statistically significant homology to each other (Z score 2.9 or 5.2, the higher score being obtained by placing a single gap in α_2). These data are highly suggestive of internal homology of α_1 and α_2 and perhaps α_1 and α_3. Computer analysis also indicated that homology was maximized when α_1, α_2, and α_3 were divided at residues 1–90, 91–180, and 181–270, respectively.

Thus, HLA-A and -B antigens appear to be made up of regions which have either evolved from different genes or in which α_1 and α_2 have undergone considerably more evolution than α_3. These data lead to the speculation that, like the immunoglobulins, the heavy chains of HLA antigens may be synthesized from a spliced gene product.

One other very interesting and speculative point relates to the role of the β_2-microglobulin chain. When β_2-microglobulin is released by denaturation of the molecules, the heavy chain irreversibly unfolds (Lancet et al., 1979). The circular dichroism spectrum is only partially restored in efforts to renature the molecule and it has so far been impossible to reassociate the two chains and restore alloantigenic reactivity. β_2-Microglobulin may function to hold the HLA heavy chain in its alloantigenic conformation.

VI. Purification of HLA-A and -B Antigens after Detergent Solubilization

A second way of solubilizing membrane proteins makes use of detergent rather than proteolysis. Two different methods for purification after detergent solubilization were developed (Springer *et al.*, 1974; Robb *et al.*, 1976). One employed ordinary chromatographic methods (Springer *et al.*, 1974) and the other used immunoaffinity chromatography on an anti-β_2-microglobulin column (Robb *et al.*, 1976). Again, two chains were obtained in the purified HLA antigen preparation, one of MW about 44,000 and the other MW 12,000. The light chain was identical to that obtained after papain solubilization. The heavy chain was 10,000 daltons larger than the chain obtained after papain solubilization. Most importantly, the occurrence of a two chain structure for HLA-A and -B antigens after detergent solubilization showed that this structure was not an artifact of papain proteolysis.

Recently, more elegant methods for separating the detergent-soluble antigens from the JY cell line have been developed (Parham, 1979). Monoclonal antibodies, specifically recognizing HLA-A2 and HLA-B7, were obtained (Parham and Bodmer, 1978; Brodsky *et al.*, 1979) using the technique described by Milstein and his collaborators (Kohler and Milstein, 1975). When mice were hyperimmunized with the papain-solubilized purified HLA-A and -B antigens obtained as previously described before carrying out the cell fusion, the identification of the appropriate clones synthesizing monoclonal HLA-A2 and HLA-B7 antibodies was greatly facilitated. For the purification cells are lysed in detergent and the extract applied to a monoclonal anti-HLA-A2 immunoaffinity column. Pure HLA-A2 was eluted by raising the pH of the column. The effluent was applied to an immunoaffinity column to which the monoclonal anti-HLA-B7 was bound and that effluent was then applied to a column containing the W6/32 monoclonal antibody (Barnstable *et al.*, 1978) which recognizes all HLA-A, -B, and -C specificities. The small amount of eluate from the last column could be an HLA-C locus antigen.

The heavy chain of the detergent-soluble isolated histocompatibility antigens is cleaved by papain to the 34,000-MW species; an intermediate of 39,000 MW is formed in the process (Springer *et al.*, 1974). The native molecule (p44), the intermediate (p39), and the final product (p34) were isolated. From their amino acid compositions it was deduced that the peptide removed by the first papain cleavage was a highly hydrophilic peptide, containing a large number of Asp, Glu, Ser, Lys, and Arg residues and virtually no hydrophobic amino acids. The second peptide removed, by contrast, had a very large amount of hydrophobic residues and virtually no charged residues. In fact, the molecule spans the membrane with a comparatively large N-terminal extracellular portion (p. 34) and a small C-terminal hydrophilic peptide inside the cell (Fig. 4).

VII. Structure of the Penultimate Hydrophobic and C-Terminal Hydrophilic Peptides

A tentative sequence of the hydrophobic region is available (Robb, 1977). It is 25 residues long and contains only hydrophobic residues, essentially Val, Ile, Leu, and Ala. The sequence of the intracellular hydrophilic region has a number of interesting structural features (Robb *et al.*, 1978). One of them is the clustering of positively charged amino acids near the membrane interface, similar to that found in the red cell membrane protein glycophorin, which also spans the membrane. One other structural feature of the internal piece which is extremely interesting is its unusually high content of serine residues. The occurrence of these residues led to the discovery that one of these serine residues is phosphorylated *in vivo* (Pober *et al.*, 1978). Similarly, membranes of the JY cell line contain an enzyme which phosphorylates the C-terminal region in the endogenous histocompatibility antigens using $[\gamma\text{-}^{32}\text{P}]$ATP as the phosphate donor. Microphosphate analyses of isolated HLA-B7 antigen (kindly carried out by Dr. O. H. Lowry) revealed that there was 0.68 nmole of organic phosphate per nanomole of HLA-B7 in the steady state. The location of this phosphate residue may point to some function of these molecules. They are oriented in the membrane so that they have the potential for signaling from outside the cell to inside. Such signaling could be reflected by turnover of the phosphate residue at the inside of the cell. It has been suggested that H-2K and H-2D antigens are associated with intracellular actin (Koch and Smith, 1978), and if HLA-A and -B antigens similarly interact with actin, then the phosphorylation may be crucial for this association.

VIII. Use of HLA-A and -B Antigens Reconstituted in Liposomes to Study Function

If purified HLA-A and -B antigen are isolated in or exchanged into a dialyzable detergent, such as octyl glucoside or deoxycholate, removal of detergent by dialysis in the presence of phospholipid results in the formation of phospholipid vesicles containing HLA-A and -B antigens (Engelhard *et al.*, 1978a). In these liposomes, the protein molecules appear to orient with the hydrophobic region in the lipid bilayer and the bulk of the molecule outside of the liposome, just as they are oriented in the cell membrane.

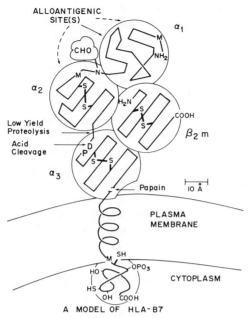

FIG. 4. A model of detergent-solubilized HLA-B7. The heavy (α) and light (β_2M) chains are delineated by their amino (NH$_2$) carboxyl (COOH) termini. Primary structural features of the heavy chain are: M, Cyanogen bromide cleavage points at methionine residues (positions 5, 98, and tentative position 307); DP, the acid cleavage point between aspartic acid 183 and proline 184; N, asparagine 86 at which the single complex type carbohydrate moiety is attached. Papain cleavage point(s) occur at positions 270 and 271. Other proteolytic cleavage points (papain, trypsin) occur around position 310 (not shown), and low yield proteolysis has been reported to occur slightly amino-terminal to the acid cleavage point. S—S denotes a disulfide bond. The light chain is drawn as a single domain. The heavy chain has three putative domains in its extracellular portion (residues 1–281) which are denoted α_1, α_2, and α_3. α_2 and α_3 have internal disulfide bonds, as does β_2M. The hydrophobic region (tentative positions 282–306) is believed to span the plasma membrane and is drawn here in an α-helical conformation. The carboxyl-terminal region (tentative positions 307–337) is believed to protrude into the cytoplasm. It has two sulfydryl groups (SH), presumably in the reduced state, and at least one of eight serines (some of which are depicted as OH) may be phosphorylated (denoted OPO$_3$). The model is roughly drawn to scale based on molecular weights and measured Stokes radii. The schematic folding depicted here for the extracellular putative domains is based on the following findings: both β_2M and α_3 bear sequence homology to Ig constant domains and to each other; α_1 and α_2 have no Ig homology but are homologous to each other; papain-solubilized HLA-B7 has a high percentage of β-pleated sheet secondary structure. The positions marked as alloantigenic sites are where higher variability occurs when HLA-B7 and HLA-A2 are compared.

These liposomes can be used to generate secondary cytotoxic lymphocytes (CTL) *in vitro* after appropriate primary immunization of mice (Engelhard *et al.*, 1978b). These secondary CTL, when assayed on different target cells carrying a number of HLA allospecificities, are highly specific for the alloantigens which were inserted in the liposomes during the stimulation. The ability to generate CTL by HLA-containing liposomes is nearly equivalent to the ability to generate them using membranes which have been solubilized and then reconstituted. Similarly, HLA-DR locus antigens can be inserted in liposomes and used to generate specific secondary CTL *in vitro* (Burakoff *et al.*, 1980).

When membranes or cells are used for stimulation, CTL are generated which recognize both the HLA-A and -B antigens and the structurally different HLA-DR antigens (Burakoff *et al.*, 1980). The CTL generated by the HLA-A2 and -B7 antigens in liposomes are directed against HLA-A and -B determinants on the target cells since cytotoxicity is blocked by antiserum to these molecules (the monoclonal W6/32 antibody), but not by antisera against HLA-DR (anti-p29,34 serum). In contrast, the second class of CTL which are generated, those which are stimulated by HLA-DR liposomes, are blocked by anti-p29,34 serum (the anti-HLA-DR serum) and not by W6/32. The specificity of the CTL argues that they are being stimulated directly by the antigen-containing liposome, rather than by nonspecific helper factors, as has been suggested. Since the CTL are capable of distinguishing among different -A, -B, and -DR alloantigens, they should be useful tools for probing the location of the alloantigenic site(s) on these molecules. Correspondingly, the purified antigens are very useful tools with which to carry out functional studies.

HLA-A and -B antigens in vesicles have also been used as a tool to examine the interaction of Semliki Forest virus (SFV) glycoprotein with its cell surface receptor (Helenius *et al.*, 1978). Because antisera against HLA and H-2 inhibited the binding of the isolated glycoprotein to cells, it was thought that histocompatibility antigens might be the receptors on the cell surface for the virus. Direct interaction between HLA and the SFV glycoprotein can be shown in a number of ways and this interaction is particularly strong if one or both proteins have been reconstituted into phospholipid vesicles. This suggests that the interaction between the virus and HLA or the cell surface involves multiple attachments to a single viral particle. These results are very intriguing and suggest that HLA may in fact be the surface receptor for Semliki Forest virus. However, it has yet to be demonstrated that blocking the HLA on the cell surface will block viral infection, showing that this interaction is physiologically significant.

IX. Concluding Remarks

The histocompatibility antigens and immunoglobulins are both probably descendants of some common ancestral gene which may have originally coded for a cell-bound defense molecule. The development of animals with circulatory systems and duplication of that gene resulted later in evolution in the secretion of the product of some of these genes into the circulation, i.e., the immunoglobulins. The product of the other genes remained membrane bound and probably went on to evolve to become the histocompatibility antigens. Presumably, like their cousins, the immunoglobulins, the histocompatibility antigens also serve a defense function for the organism. In this case, the cell-bound defense mechanism may serve to protect the organism from invasion by closely related cells, perhaps serving in primitive organisms to maintain colonial identity on the sea floor. In higher evolutionary forms there is increasing evidence that a major function of this system is to participate in the control of proliferation of modified syngeneic cells, in particular virus-infected and/or tumor cells. Still later in evolution, the Placentalia emerged as a subspecies of Mammalia. With this development came another need for rejecting foreign cells, i.e., the need to prevent the invasion of the maternal organism by foreign tissue containing paternal antigens derived from the highly invasive trophoblast. Thus, a variety of situations in which the organism needs to protect itself from closely related invading foreign cells occurs. It seems likely that the substances called histocompatibility antigens have evolved to serve that need.

The past decade has seen tremendous progress in the analysis of the MHC from the viewpoints of both structure and function, although a solid bridge between the two has yet to be made. A relatively rapid accumulation of amino acid sequences in the near future should give insight into the extent and distribution of structural polymorphism within the molecule. Further comparisons among MHC products of different species may elucidate the evolution of histocompatibility antigens. The availability of tens of milligram quantities of papain-solubilized HLA will allow spectroscopic studies of the conformation of the molecule as well as X-ray crystallographic determination of its three-dimensional structure in atomic detail. These data may provide an assessment of the structural significance of the polymorphism.

Functional correlations can be made by studies on the interaction of MHC products with other molecules, i.e., foreign cell surface antigens and T-cell receptors. An important means to approach this area may be provided by liposomes containing the purified antigens, or by antigens immobilized to solid supports.

Spectroscopic and protein chemical approaches to the structure of the carboxyl-terminal regions may suggest general features for the structure of the membrane-binding regions of eukaryotic membrane proteins. The elucidation of the conformation of the hydrophilic carboxyl terminus may also be important for an understanding of the physiological role of the phosphorylation and the potential ability of this region to interact with components of the cytoskeleton. Liposomes may provide a convenient approach to studies of this kind.

At a different level, the organization of information within the genome can be approached via the cloning of MHC genes by recombinant DNA techniques. The probes produced will enable the counting and mapping of genes within the MHC, as well as providing a rapid method for determining the primary structure of many different allospecificities. With this approach, MHC structure of species for which no biochemical or serological tools are available may also be studied. The question of whether all HLA and H-2 antigens are true alleles or if polymorphism is a result of regulation of a tandem array of structural genes present in the genome of all individuals may be answered. Since MHC products are also differentiation antigens, the regulation of their expression during development can also be examined by molecular genetics.

Thus, the study of histocompatibility antigens should prove illuminating in many areas: membrane biochemistry, control of immune responsiveness and cell–cell interactions, eukaryotic gene organization and expression, and cellular differentiation.

REFERENCES[2]

Barker, W. C., and Dayhoff, M. O. (1972). In "Atlas of Protein Sequence and Structure" (M. O. Dayhoff, ed.), Vol. 5, pp. 101–110. Nat. Biomed. Res. Found., Washington, D. C.

Barker, W. C., and Dayhoff, M. O. (1976). In "Atlas of Protein Sequence and Structure" (M. O. Dayhoff, ed.), Vol. 5, Suppl. 2, pp. 165–190. Nat. Biomed. Res. Found., Washington, D. C.

Barnstable, C. J., Bodmer, W. F., Brown, G. Galfrè, G., Milstein, C., Williams, A. F., and Ziegler, A. (1978). Cell 14, 9–20.

Beale, D., and Feinstein, A. (1976). Q. Rev. Biophys. 9, 135–180.

Bodmer, W. F., ed. (1978). Br. Med. Bull. 34, 213–309.

Brodsky, F. M., Parham, P., Barnstable, C. J., Crumpton, M. J., and Bodmer, W. F. (1979). Immunol. Rev. 47, 3–61.

Burakoff, S., Engelhard, V. H., Kaufman, J. F., and Strominger, J. L. (1980). Nature (London) 283, 495–497.

Coligan, J. E., Kindt, T. J., Ewenstein, B. M., Uehara, H., Martinko, J. M., and Nathenson, S. G. (1979). Mol. Immunol. 16, 3–8.

---

[2] Only a limited number of references have been provided, mainly from the author's laboratory. A more complete documentation and reference list can be found in Strominger et al. (1980a).

Cresswell, P., Turner, M. J., and Strominger, J. L. (1973). *Proc. Natl. Acad. Sci. U.S.A.* **70,** 1503–1607.
Engelhard, V. H., Guild, B. C., Helenius, A., Terhorst, C., and Strominger, J. L. (1978a). *Proc. Natl. Acad. Sci. U.S.A.* **75,** 3230–3234.
Engelhard, V. H., Strominger, J. L., Mescher, M., and Burakoff, S. (1978b). *Proc. Natl. Acad. Sci. U.S.A.* **75,** 5688–5691.
Ferguson, W. S., Terhorst, C. T., Robb, R. J., and Strominger, J. L. (1979). *Mol. Immunol.* **16,** 23–28.
Helenius, A., Morein, B., Fries, E., Simons, K., Robinson, P., Schirrmacher, V., Terhorst, C., and Strominger, J. L. (1978). *Proc. Natl. Acad. Sci. U.S.A.* **75,** 3846–3850.
Koch, G. L. E., and Smith, M. J. (1978). *Nature (London)* **273,** 274.
Kohler, G., and Milstein, C. (1975). *Nature (London)* **256,** 495–497.
Lancet, D., and Strominger, J. L. (1979). In "Molecular Mechanisms of Biological Recognition" (M. Balaban, ed.), pp. 289–298. Elsevier/North Holland Medical, Amsterdam.
Lancet, D., Parham, P., and Strominger, J. L. (1979). *Proc. Natl. Acad. Sci. U.S.A.* **76,** 3844–3848.
Lopez de Castro, J. A., Orr, H. T., Kostyk, T., Robb, R. J., Mann, D. C., and Strominger, J. L. (1979). *Biochemistry* **18,** 5704–5711.
Möller, G., ed. (1974). *Transplant. Rev.* **21.**
Orr, H. T., Lopez de Castro, J. A., Lancet, D., Mann, D. L., and Strominger, J. L. (1979a). *Biochemistry* **18,** 5711–5720.
Orr, H. T., Lopez de Castro, J. A., Parham, P., Ploegh, H. L., and Strominger, J. L. (1979b). *Proc. Natl. Acad. Sci. U.S.A.* **76,** 4395–4399.
Orr, H. T., Lancet, D., Robb, R. J., Lopez de Castro, J. A., and Strominger, J. L. (1979c). *Nature (London)* **282,** 266–270.
Parham, P. (1979). *J. Biol. Chem.* **254,** 8709–8712.
Parham, P., and Bodmer, W. F. (1978). *Nature (London)* **276,** 397–399.
Parham, P., Alpert, B. N., Orr, H. T., and Strominger, J. L. (1977). *J. Biol. Chem.* **252,** 7555–7567.
Pober, J. S., Guild, B. C., and Strominger, J. L. (1978). *Proc. Natl. Acad. Sci. U.S.A.* **75,** 6002.
Robb, R. J. (1977). Ph.D. Thesis, Harvard University, Cambridge, Massachusetts.
Robb, R. J., Strominger, J. L., and Mann, D. L. (1976). *J. Biol. Chem.* **251,** 5427–5428.
Robb, R. J., Terhorst, C., and Strominger, J. L. (1978). *J. Biol. Chem.* **253,** 5319–5324.
Springer, T. A., Strominger, J. L., and Mann, D. (1974). *Proc. Natl. Acad. Sci. U.S.A.* **71,** 1539–1543.
Strominger, J. L., Cresswell, P., Grey, H., Humphreys, R. E., Mann, D., McCune, J., Parham, P., Robb, R., Sanderson, A. L., Springer, T. A., Terhorst, C., and Turner, M. J. (1974). *Transplant Rev.* **21,** 126–143.
Strominger, J. L., Engelhard, V. H., Fuks, A., Guild, B. C., Hyafil, F., Kaufman, J. F., Korman, A. J., Kostyk, T. G., Krangel, M. S., Lancet, D., Lopez de Castro, J. A., Mann, D. L., Orr, H. T., Parham, P., Parker, K. C., Ploegh, H. L., Pober, J. S., Robb, R. J., and Shackelford, D. A. (1980a). In "The Role of the Major Histocompatibility Complex in Immunobiology" (B. Benacerraf and M. E. Dorf, eds.). Garland Press (in press).
Strominger, J. L., Orr, H. T., Robb, R. J., Parham, P., Ploegh, H. L., Mann, D. L., Bilofsky, M., Saroff, M. A., Wu, T. T., and Kabat, E. A. (1980b). *Scand. J. Immunol.* (in press).
Terhorst, C., Robb, R., Jones, G., and Strominger, J. L. (1977). *Proc. Natl. Acad. Sci. U.S.A.* **74,** 4002–4006.
Turner, M. J., Cresswell, P., Parham, P., Strominger, J. L., Mann, D. L., and Sanderson, A. R. (1975). *J. Biol. Chem.* **250,** 4512–4519.

CHAPTER 5

ASPECTS OF SURFACE MEMBRANE DIFFERENTIATION DURING MATURATION OF HUMAN HEMATOPOIETIC AND TUMOR CELLS: THE Ia SYSTEM

R. J. Winchester[1]

HOSPITAL FOR JOINT DISEASES AND
THE ROCKEFELLER UNIVERSITY
NEW YORK, NEW YORK

This chapter is primarily concerned with the evidence for the presence of Ia antigens on normal and malignant hematopoietic cells and their role as a surface marker related to differentiation events. It will also include a brief discussion of the occurrence of Ia antigens on certain solid tumors such as malignant melanoma. The scope of this contribution is limited and will be principally based on data obtained in this laboratory.

I. Demonstration of Ia on Leukemic Granulocyte Membrane

The observation that Ia antigens are a dominant component on the membrane of granulocyte progenitors in the blood of patients with acute myelogenous leukemia was the first direct finding in this area. The Ia molecules were demonstrated by rabbit antisera to isolated human Ia molecules (Billing *et al.*, 1976; Schlossman *et al.*, 1976; Winchester *et al.*, 1976) and by human alloantisera with specificities for DR and related Ia alloantigens (Winchester *et al.*, 1976). Polymorphonuclear cells of normal peripheral blood, however, were found to be nega-

[1] Supported by U.S. Public Health Service grant CA-20107 and Research Career Development award AI-00216.

CURRENT TOPICS IN
DEVELOPMENTAL BIOLOGY, VOL. 14

R. J. WINCHESTER

tive; and one possibility that was considered was that the expression of Ia antigens was an event related to the leukemic transformation. Reports that Ia-bearing leukocytes in patients with chronic myelogenous leukemia are low in number (Billing et al., 1976; Winchester et al., 1976) or absent (Schlossman et al., 1976) and that, in normal bone marrow, only lymphoid cells bear Ia determinants lent further support to this interpretation. The isolation of relatively pure preparations of the Ia-bearing leukemic myeloid cells by either multistep density gradients (Winchester et al., 1977) or fluorescence-activated cell sorting (Janossy et al., 1977) and the recognition that these cells are primarily myeloblasts, however, led to experiments demonstrating that the expression of Ia is a phenomenon related to hematopoietic differentiation.

DENSITY SEPARATION APPROACH

Table I illustrates the use of multistep density gradients, prepared from Ficoll–Hypaque, to obtain enriched preparations of Ia-bearing cells from the blood of a patient with chronic myelogenous leukemia. Parallel study of the morphology revealed that the most immature forms are present only in these low-density fractions. The appearance of the majority of cells bearing the Ia determinants is that of a myeloblast, whereas a small fraction of cells with the cytoplasmic and nuclear morphology of promyelocytes has weaker expression of Ia determinants (Fig. 1).

TABLE I

REPRESENTATIVE SEPARATION OF CML PERIPHERAL BLOOD LEUKOCYTES INTO FRACTIONS OF DIFFERING DENSITY: PARALLEL ENRICHMENT OF EARLY FORMS AND CELLS EXPRESSING Ia ANTIGENS[a]

Density (g/ml)	Total cells (%)	Myelo-blast	Pro-mye-locyte	Mye-locyte	Meta	Band	PMN[b]	Cells in each fraction with Ia antigen (%)
			Wright's stain cell morphology (%)					
1.06	0.26	15	32	24	11	5	0	15.1
1.07	25.0	0	2	30	59	8	1	0.2
1.08	10.8	0	0	15	61	19	5	0.16
1.09	16.6	0	0	3	10	23	64	0
1.105	45.5	0	0	0	7	14	79	0
Unseparated	100	0	0	3	15	13	70	0.18

[a] From Winchester et al. (1977).
[b] PMN, polymorphonuclear neutrophil.

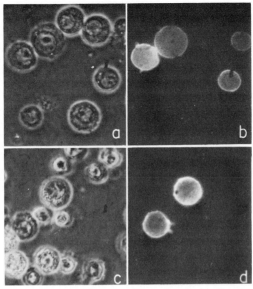

FIG. 1. Leukemic cells isolated in low-density fractions from a patient with chronic myelogenous leukemia. The unseparated cells contained 0.5% myeloblasts and 0.4% cells with Ia antigens. (a) Phase micrograph of < 1.06 g/ml density fraction illustrating the enrichment of myeloblasts. (b) Fluorescence micrograph of the preceding field with positive staining by a fluorescent Ia antiserum on some cells. (c) Phase micrograph of 1.07 g/ml density fraction illustrating a larger proportion of cells with cytoplasmic granules than was found in the lower density fraction. (d) Fluorescence micrograph of the preceding field illustrating only one cell with the appearance of a promyelocyte that bears Ia antigens. A myeloblast is also stained whereas several more mature cells are negative. From Winchester *et al.* (1977).

Chemical and antigenic characterization of the Ia antigen-bearing molecules on leukemic cells was accomplished by isolating enriched preparations of myeloblasts in 1.06 g/ml density fractions. Upon radiolabeling and subsequent immunoprecipitation with anti-Ia sera, the molecular profile characteristic of the molecule containing Ia antigens as it occurs on B cells was found. Figure 2 illustrates the similar profile of molecules bearing Ia determinants on these two cell types. Absorption experiments were performed using preparations that contained over 99% myeloblasts. Since, as will be discussed subsequently, myeloblasts lack complement receptors, the presence of cells bearing complement receptors served as a measure of the contamination of the cell preparations by monocytes or B lymphocytes. The results of the absorption experiments demonstrated that all reactivity of the rabbit Ia antiserum with B-type lymphoblastoid cells and normal B cells is

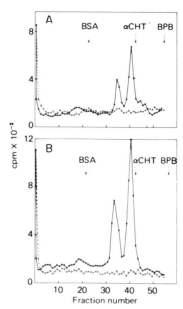

FIG. 2. Similar immunoprecipitation profiles of radiolabeled myeloblasts and B lymphocytes upon SDS/polyacrylamide gel electrophoresis with an Ia antiserum. (A) A myeloblast preparation from a patient with acute myelogenous leukemia. (B) Peripheral blood B lymphocytes depleted of adherent cells. Molecules of 28,000 and 37,000 daltons are detected in both samples. ●; Ia antiserum; ○, control preimmune serum; BSA, bovine serum albumin; αCHT, α-chymotrypsinogen; BPB, bromphenol blue dye front. From Winchester et al. (1977).

abolished by myeloblast absorptions and, reciprocally, reactivity with myeloblasts is abolished by extensive B-cell absorptions (Winchester et al., 1977).

These demonstrations of a similar molecular structure and extensive antigenic commonality argue strongly in favor of the view that similar, if not identical, Ia antigen gene products are expressed on the leukemic granulocyte and the B cell. Additional absorption and surface labeling experiments performed with more mature granulocytes obtained from patients with chronic myelogenous leukemia did not reveal detectable Ia antigens, emphasizing the restriction in expression of Ia to the earlier phases of granulocyte differentiation.

II. Occurrence of Ia Determinants on Myeloid Cells from Normal Bone Marrow

Studies of whole normal bone marrow revealed an average of less than 3% of all cells stained by antisera to Ia antigens. Here the occurrence of lymphocytes and monocytes complicated the findings because of their expression of Ia determinants. This necessitated the use of simultaneous complement rosette assays or staining for surface Ig in a double marker format to permit the exclusion of these cells (Winchester *et al.*, 1977; Janossy *et al.*, 1977).

Density separation experiments were performed on normal marrow in order to attempt enrichment of this minor population of cells for purposes of characterization. The average values from three representative experiments using multistep density gradients to obtain the early forms in high yield are shown in Table II.

As was found in the leukemic peripheral blood, normal bone marrow fractions of low density were shown to contain a significant enrichment of myoblasts; and in the same fractions a parallel enrichment of cells bearing Ia antigens was found. Lymphocytes were excluded from analyses, as were monocytes. Examination by phase microscopy, and using Wright's stained preparations as a supplemental guide, revealed that the vast majority of normal myeloblasts and a minor fraction of promyelocytes have Ia antigens. Furthermore, Ia antigens were demonstrable on cells with the appearance of pronormoblasts and

TABLE II

RELATIONSHIP OF Ia EXPRESSION AND GRANULOCYTE MATURATION IN NORMAL
BONE MARROW SEPARATED BY DENSITY GRADIENT CENTRIFUGATION[a]

Density layer g/ml	Proportion of total cells	Cells in each fraction with myeloid morphology positive for Ia antigen (%)	Cells with myeloid morphology in fractions[b] (Wright–Giemsa)				
			Blast.	Pro.	Myel.-mta.	Band	PMN
1.05	4	44	43	26	30	0	0
1.06	17	31	44	33	21	2	0
1.07	10	5	1	13	69	10	7
1.08	15	3	0	1	47	39	13
1.09	19	1	0	0	28	63	32
1.105	26	0	0	0	9	38	53
1.12	5	0	2	0	3	17	77
>1.12	4	1	6	0	10	16	68
Unseparated	100	2	2	2	30	35	35

[a] From Ross *et al.* (1978).

[b] Blast., myeloblast; pro., promyelocyte; myel.-mta., myelocyte or metamyelocyte; band, band form; PMN, polymorphonuclear neutrophil.

basophilic normoblasts (Winchester *et al.*, 1977). The finding of Ia on normal myeloblasts and promyelocytes closely resembled the situation present in leukemic peripheral blood, a conclusion also reached by Janossy and co-workers (1977). Therefore, the expression of Ia determinants in the granulocytic lineage is primarily a property of the differentiation stage of the myeloblast with a much diminished number of promyelocytes also bearing Ia. The membrane differentiation steps that have occurred by the level of the promyelocyte in either normal or leukemic maturation sequences are associated with the cessation of Ia expression.

III. Expression of Receptors for Complement and IgG Fc

Examination of the expression of Fc, CR_1, and CR_2 on granulocytes in normal bone marrows using the multistep density gradient techniques reveals that strong Fc receptors appear at the level of the promyelocyte and the number of positive cells increases through the myelocyte stage. Complement receptors (Ross *et al.*, 1978) undergo a transition with CR_2, the first receptor to appear. It is the dominant complement receptor of the myelocyte. Receptor CR_1 then appears in large numbers at the level of the metamyelocyte and ultimately becomes the dominant complement receptor on more mature cells, as illustrated by the data in Table III. Therefore, quite in contrast to the lymphoid and monocyte lineages where Ia antigens coexist on many cells with the Fc and complement receptors, in the case of neutrophils, the Ia antigens are found only on functionally immature cells as shown by the lack of membrane specialization. This sequential change in the surface membrane of the granulocyte lineage is summarized in Table IV.

TABLE III

EXPRESSION OF CR_1 AND CR_2 ON NEUTROPHIL
MATURATION STAGES ISOLATED FROM
NORMAL BONE MARROW[a]

Wright–Giemsa morphology	CR_1 (%)	CR_2 (%)
Myeloblast	1	2
Promyelocyte	2	3
Myelocyte	3	18
Metamyelocyte	18	21
Band form	29	23
Polymorphonuclear	54	35

[a] From Ross *et al.* (1978).

TABLE IV

CORRELATION OF SURFACE MARKERS WITH MATURATION STAGE AND CELL DENSITY[a]

CFU-c $\longrightarrow$	Myeloblast $\longrightarrow$	Promyelocyte $\longrightarrow$	Myelocyte $\longrightarrow$
1.05–1.06 g/ml		1.05–1.06 g/ml	1.06 g/ml
Ia^+		$Ia^+CR_1{}^-CR_2{}^-$	$Ia^-CR_1{}^-CR_2{}^+$

Metamyelocyte $\longrightarrow$	Band form $\longrightarrow$	Polymorph $\longrightarrow$	Polymorph
1.07 g/ml	1.08 g/ml	1.09–1.105 g/ml	1.12 g/ml
$Ia^-CR_1{}^+CR_2{}^+$	$Ia^-CR_1{}^+CR_2{}^+$	$Ia^-CR_1{}^+CR_2{}^+$	$Ia^-CR_1{}^+CR_2{}^-$

[a] From Ross et al. (1978).

IV. Presence of Ia on Megakaryocytes

With the development of further improvements in methods for isolation of megakaryocytes from human bone marrow, it has proved possible to characterize these cells for the presence of Ia antigens (Rabellino et al., 1979). From 7 to 23% of megakaryocytes exhibit bright staining for Ia antigens using rabbit anti-Ia reagents. Nearly all megakaryocytes were shown to have Fc receptors, but complement receptors were not detectable. In view of the well-documented absence of Ia antigens from normal platelets in peripheral blood, it is apparent that this illustrates another instance of the loss of this antigen with progression through differentiation. Presumably, the variation among megakaryocytes regarding Ia expression reflects cells at differing stages of maturation although the alternate explanation of two parallel pathways of megakaryocyte differentiation cannot be excluded.

V. Ia Expression on Hematopoietic Progenitor Cells

The finding of Ia molecules on early members of the granulocytic lineage, on pronormoblasts, as well as on certain megakaryocytes would suggest that committed hematopoietic stem cells also possess Ia determinants. Direct evidence for the occurrence of Ia on progenitor cells has been obtained through inhibition of colony forming cells in *in vitro* assays. Both the granulocyte-macrophage committed progenitor cell, CFU-c (Cline et al., 1977; Winchester et al., 1977), and the erythropoietin-dependent colonies and bursts, CFU-e and BFU-e (Winchester et al., 1978b), were eliminated by treatment with Ia antiserum and complement. A representative experiment is illustrated in Table V. This finding provided the first definition of a well-defined antigen present on progenitor cells but absent from cells in the terminal stages of differentiation.

122   R. J. WINCHESTER

TABLE V

COMPLEMENT-DEPENDENT INHIBITION BY ANTISERUM TO Ia DETERMINANTS OF
ERYTHROPOIETIC AND GRANULOCYTIC COLONY FORMATION BY BONE MARROW CELLS[a]

	Colonies per 2×10^5 cells		
Treatment of bone marrow cells	CFU-e (7 days)	BFU-e (13 days)	CFU-c (7 days)
Medium	444 ± 14	113 ± 2	387 ± 9
Complement	400 ± 15	102 ± 10	388 ± 17
Anti-Ia serum 1:40 + complement	41 ± 5	5 ± 2	13 ± 2
Anti-Ia serum 1:160 + complement	49 ± 5	12 ± 2	41 ± 4
Anti-Ia serum 1:640 + complement	69 ± 8	20 ± 3	141 ± 5
Anti-Ia serum 1:2500 + complement	71 ± 7	33 ± 4	238 ± 4
Anti-Ia serum 1:10,000 + complement	105 ± 6	47 ± 3	308 ± 5
Anti-Ia serum 1:40,000 + complement	213 ± 8	63 ± 1	390 ± 8
Anti-Ia serum 1:160,000 + complement	384 ± 12	92 ± 4	380 ± 10
Anti-Ia serum 1:40 absorbed with B cells + complement	367 ± 15	98 ± 12	375 ± 22

[a] From Winchester et al. (1978b).

Not shown in Table V are data on the preferential elimination of CFU-c at dilutions of anti-Ia serum that do not cause complement-dependent killing of myeloblasts. This finding, along with the decrease in intensity of Ia expression on promyelocytes compared with myeloblasts, suggests the possibility that the concentration of Ia molecules is greater on early members of the series such as the committed progenitor cells.

Evidence exists for a degree of variability in the persistence of a small fraction of colony-forming units after treatment with Ia and complement (Table V). Direct evidence for this variation was provided by the finding that Ia-poor progenitors isolated by fluorescence-activated cell sorting also contained significant amounts of colony-forming units (Janossy et al., 1978).

Recently, it has proved possible to culture human marrow cells that are pluripotent in that they are capable of differentiating into progenitor cells committed to the myeloid and erythroid series (Moore et al., 1979). These pluripotent cells are not eliminated by treatment with anti-Ia and complement (Moore et al., 1979).

These findings suggest that Ia antigens are induced to appear on the cell surface as the pluripotent cell enters the progenitor cell stage. The density of Ia antigens reaches a maximum and then decays to undetectable levels at the level of the promyelocyte and normoblast.

VI. Presence of Ia on Certain Cultured Malignant Melanoma Cells

A survey of the occurrence of Ia antigens on various solid tumors maintained in cell culture revealed that only one line, an epidermoid carcinoma of the larynx, expressed Ia antigens (Table VI). In contrast, Ia antigens are well expressed on a number of established melanoma lines (Table VII), as well as on freshly isolated tumors (Winchester *et al.*, 1978a; Wilson *et al.*, 1979). Certain melonoma lines contained Ia antigens at quantities that are equivalent to those on B-cell lymphoblastoid lines. Chemical and absorption studies, as with the myeloblast, demonstrated a close antigenic and molecular relationship of Ia antigens on melanoma cells to those present on B cells (Winchester *et al.*, 1978a). The size of the molecules on malignant melanoma cells has been reported to be smaller than that of B cells (Wilson *et al.*, 1979).

It remains to be established whether the presence of Ia antigens has a role in the host–tumor relationship. It is possible that the presence of Ia serves as an additional stimulus to the immune system, rendering the tumor more immunogenic through the proliferative effect of Ia antigens on T cells. Alternatively, the occurrence of Ia could signify a more primitive cell with a greater proliferative potential. No data are

TABLE VI

CONTRASTING EXPRESSION OF β_2-MICROGLOBULIN AND Ia ON DIFFERENT CULTURED CELL LINES[a]

Culture designation	Tissue type	Intensity and percentage of cell expression[b]	
		$\beta_2\mu$	Ia
Hep 2	Epidermoid carcinoma	(2–4+)100%	(1–2+)100%
U 20S	Sarcoma	(tr–1+)100%	0
Nemeth	Renal carcinoma	(1+)100%	0
J82	Astrocytoma	(1–2+)100%	0
Viola	Renal carcinoma	(4+)100%	0
T24	Bladder carcinoma	(3+)100%	0
Lawson	Lung (carcinoma)	(2+)100%	0
ME 180	Cervical carcinoma	(3+)100%	0
WI 38	Fetal lung	(2+)100%	0
Gm 43	Normal fibroblast	(3+)100%	0
ALAB	Breast cancer	(tr)100%	0
SK-Lu-1	Undifferentiated	(1+)100%	0
SK-Ov-3	Ovarian cancer	(2+)100%	0

[a] From Winchester *et al.* (1978a).
[b] tr, trace.

TABLE VII

VARIABLE EXPRESSION OF Ia DETERMINANTS ON MELANOMA CELL LINES AND
LACK OF RELATION TO β_2-MICROGLOBULIN[a]

Cell line designation	β_2-Microglobulin direct immunofluorescence		Ia direct immunofluorescence		Ia chemical isolation
	Relative intensity[b]	Positive cells (%)	Relative intensity	Positive cells (%)	Total glyco-protein[b] (%)
SK-Mel-13	2–4	100	3–4	100	7.8
SK-Mel-37	3–4	100	3–4	100	16.7
SK-Mel-42	tr–1	100	2–4	100	3.7
SK-Mel-29	2–4	100	tr–3	100	<2
SK-Mel-33	1–3	100	tr–3	100	<1
SK-Mel-41	tr–1	100	tr–3	100	ND
SK-Mel-28	2–4	100	tr–3	35	<1
MeWO	2–3	100	tr–1	24	<2
SK-Mel-19	2–4	100	tr–1	3	<2
SK-Mel-27	1–2	100	tr–1	2	<1

[a] From Winchester et al. (1978a).
[b] tr, trace; ND, not done.

yet available on the significance of the presence or absence of Ia antigens on these tumors in terms of patient survival.

VII. Concluding Remarks

Ia antigens are selectively distributed as dominant glycoproteins on a limited number of cells. They are restricted both to certain cell lineages and, further, only to particular stages of differentiation within the cell series. Yet, at least in the T and B lymphocytes, Ia antigens can be induced with appropriate stimulation and their expression appears to be under flexible control (Halper et al., 1978; Evans et al., 1978; see Winchester and Kunkel, 1979). The period in the differentiation sequence in marrow cells when the Ia antigens are a dominant membrane component is the time when maximal control of proliferation would be anticipated to occur, suggesting a role in this process for the Ia antigens. This raises the question of interesting parallels between aspects of the immune response and events in early stages of hematopoiesis. In the case of the melanoma cell, the absence of knowledge regarding normal melanocytes leaves the question open as to whether the Ia antigens are differentiation antigens or are expressed as a function of derepression related to the malignant transformation.

REFERENCES

Billing, R., Rafizadeh, B., Drew, I., Hartman, G., Gale, R., and Terasaki, P. (1976). *J. Exp. Med.* **144,** 167.

Cline, M. J., and Billing, R. (1977). *J. Exp. Med.* **146,** 1143.

Evans, R. L., Faldetta, T. J., Humphrys, R. E., Pratt, D. M., Yunis, E. J., and Schlossman, S. F. (1978). *J. Exp. Med.* **148,** 1440.

Halper, J., Fu, S. M., Wang, C. Y., Winchester, R., and Kunkel, H. G. (1978). *J. Immunol.* **120,** 1480.

Janossy, G., Goldstone, A. H., Capellaro, D., Greaves, M. F., Kulenkempff, J., Pippard, M., and Welsh, K. (1977). *Br. J. Haematol.* **37,** 391.

Janossy, G., Francis, G. E., Capellaro, D. G., Goldstone, A. H., and Greaves, M. F. (1978). *Nature (London)* **276,** 176.

Moore, M. A. S., Broxmeyer, H. E., Sheridan, A. P. C., Meyers, P. A., Jacobsen, N., and Winchester, R. J. (1980). *Blood* (in press).

Rabellino, E. M., Nachman, R. L., Williams, N., Winchester, R. J., and Ross, G. D. (1979). *J. Exp. Med.* **149,** 1273.

Ross, G. D., Jarowski, C. I., Rabellino, E. M., and Winchester, R. J. (1978). *J. Exp. Med.* **147,** 730.

Schlossman, S. F., Chess, L., Humphreys, R. E., and Strominger, J. L. (1976). *Proc. Natl. Acad. Sci. U.S.A.* **73,** 1288.

Wilson, B. S., Indiveri, F., Pellegrino, M. A., and Ferrone, S. (1979). *J. Exp. Med.* **149,** 658.

Winchester, R. J., and Kunkel, H. G. (1979). *Adv. Immunol.* **27,** 222.

Winchester, R. J., Wang, C. Y., Halper, J., and Hoffman, T. (1976). *Scand. J. Immunol.* **5,** 745.

Winchester, R. J., Ross, G. D., Jarowski, C. I., Wang, C. Y., Halper, J., and Broxmeyer, H. E. (1977). *Proc. Natl. Acad. Sci. U.S.A.* **74,** 4012.

Winchester, R. J., Wang, C. Y., Gibofsky, A., Kunkel, H. G., Lloyd, K. O., and Old, L. J. (1978a). *Proc. Natl. Acad. Sci. U.S.A.* **75,** 6235.

Winchester, R. J., Meyers, P. A., Broxmeyer, H. E., Wang, C. Y., Moore, M. A. S., and Kunkel, H. G. (1978b). *J. Exp. Med.* **147,** 613.

CHAPTER 6

THE ABH BLOOD GROUPS AND DEVELOPMENT[1]

Aron E. Szulman

DEPARTMENT OF PATHOLOGY
MAGEE-WOMENS HOSPITAL
UNIVERSITY OF PITTSBURGH
SCHOOL OF MEDICINE
PITTSBURGH, PENNSYLVANIA

I. Introduction

The ABH antigens are widely distributed in the tissues of the human embryo/fetus from the earliest ascertainable stages of development—fifth week postfertilization. They are not only present on the surfaces of the erythrocytes but also, in large amounts, on the cell surfaces of the endothelium and of the epithelia of most early organs. While their physiologic function remains unknown, it is their early appearance in embryonal life and wide distribution in most epithelial primordia that causes them to be of interest in human reproduction.

[1] The author's work was supported by research grants from the National Institutes of Health, USPHS: RG-5582, AI-3554, AI-6443, and NICHD 1-FO3-HO42, 273-01.

CURRENT TOPICS IN
DEVELOPMENTAL BIOLOGY, VOL. 14

The research and speculation presented here have been motivated by this author's hypothesis that maternal, transplacental IgG antibodies are capable of abrogating normal organogenesis by virtue of their reaction with the surface A/B antigens, thus modifying appropriate cell behavior and leading to early demise of the embryo. While there is accumulating experimental evidence in favor of the above idea—to be presented in Section V—the molecular mechanisms involved remain in the sphere of speculation, be they related to the interference with the cellular physiological function of the antigens themselves or with their putative role in cell-to-cell relationships.

It is generally accepted that there is an increased risk of survival of early conceptuses incompatible with their mothers across an ABO barrier. This chapter is an attempt to explore the subject on the cellular and tissue level with some initial projections onto a molecular level in the light of theory and experiment.

II. The ABH Substances

Of the vast and growing number of known antigenic systems of man the ABH is the best understood in terms of both genetics and biochemistry (Watkins, 1974, 1978). The antigens are well-defined oligosaccharidic structures at the nonreducing ends of simple or branching sugar chains of various lengths (Lloyd et al., 1968; Hakamori et al., 1977). In the erythrocytes they are known to be anchored to lipids (cermide) of the plasma membrane (Watkins, 1978) and to some intrinsic plasma membrane proteins (Marchesi et al., 1972); this probably holds as well for endothelial and epithelial cells although no precise information is available. The other important kind of group substances are found in the mucus where the ABH-specific glycoproteins are found in convenient abundance and serve as the main material of study for the biochemist. The following is a brief outline, more detailed accounts being available elsewhere (Lloyd et al., 1968; Watkins, 1974; Horowitz, 1978).

A. The ABH Antigens of the Glycoproteins of
   the Mucous Secretions

The polypeptide backbone of the specific substance is studded with numerous oligosaccharide chains, the terminal groupings of which constitute the multiple, coexisting specificities A, B, and H (as well as Le[a] and Le[b]). These are built up in a stepwise fashion by a host of highly specific competing glycosyltransferases associated with the A/B/O, H/h, Le/le loci as well as the secretor, Se/se locus, partially controlling the activity of the H gene (see following). The terminal grouping of a saccharide chain that constitutes the A antigen is illustrated in Fig. 1. Its immunodominant amino sugar (N-acetyl galactose) is attached to the nonreducing end of the chain by a transferase specified by gene A. Antigen B is associated with a terminal plain galactose, attached by an enzyme specified by gene B. Group O persons possess no known active transferase associated with the locus and are thus left with an intact H structure, characterized by a terminal fucosyl residue. The latter is integrated into the molecule by an H enzyme associated with a separate H/h locus. The existence of a full H structure is essential for the function of the A and B transferases and in its absence no A or B antigens can be synthesized. While the h allele is an amorph (i.e., it specifies no active enzyme) it is sufficiently rare to leave the H antigen as a virtually universal species marker. In many types of cells secreting the ABH substances, including the glycoproteins of mucus and the glycolipids of the plasma, the H gene is subject to activation by the secretor gene of the Se/se locus. The inhibition of ABH secretion, however, is never complete—since in the so-called nonsecretors (genotype se/se), although there are no ABH-specific substances in the salivary

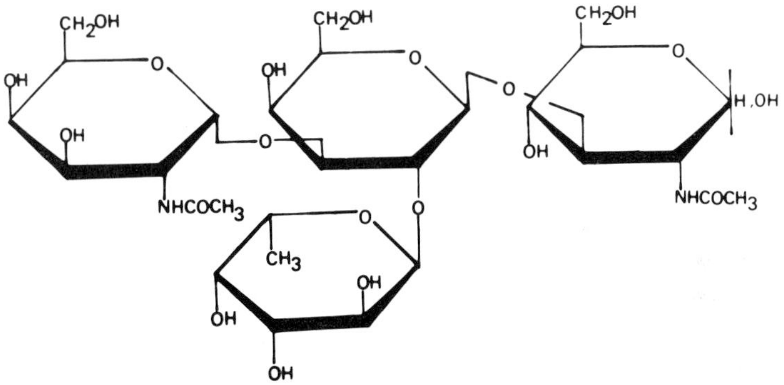

FIG. 1. N-Acetyl-D-galactosaminyl-(1,3)-[O-α-L-fucosyl-(1,2)-]-O-β-D-galactosyl-(1,4 or 1,3)-N-acetyl-D-glucosaminyl-. Formula of blood group antigen A. The terminal N-acetylgalactose is the characteristic sugar for A, while a plain galactose characterizes the B antigen. In the absence of either, the oligosaccharide presents the fucose as an immunodominant sugar, characteristic of blood group O individuals. The attachment of this hexose is governed by the H gene, that is subject to activation in most (but not all) secretions by the secretor gene. The latter has no influence in the production of the H (and hence also of the A/B) antigen found at the cell surfaces. Mucous secretions in the depths of the gastrointestinal mucosa are also exempt, a fact that merits emphasis in considering feto-maternal ABO relationships (see text). Another fucose can be attached to the N-acetylglucosamine by an Le gene specified transferase. The latter operates in secretions only; the Le^a antigen comes to full expression in the absence of the H-directed fucose. The attachment of both H and Le specified fucoses results in the formation of the Le^b antigen, a product of H, Se, and Le genes.

glands and the rest of the mucus-secreting apparatus, there is considerable production in the depths of the mucosa of the gastrointestinal tract (Szulman, 1962, 1977; Szulman and Marcus, 1973). This is connected with the important fact that a considerable amount of the group-specific glycoprotein finds its way into the tissue fluids and the plasma of the fetus irrespective of the individuals' secretor status (Høstrup, 1963) (see Sections III, B and V).

B. THE ABH ANTIGENS OF THE ERYTHROCYTES AND TISSUE CELLS

The biosynthesis of the antigens looks simpler in the red cells and in tissue cells for here the H gene operates irrespective of the secretor gene and no Le^a and Le^b antigens complicate the picture. These antigens are briefly mentioned here (Fig. 1) for the sake of clarity since they reside on the same hexose chain(s) as the ABH antigens both in glycoproteins and in plasma glycolipids. Neither Lewis antigen, however, is produced at the cellular surfaces of erythrocytes or of tissue cells (Szulman and Marcus, 1973; Watkins, 1978). Since no ABH-Lewis glycolipids are present in the plasma during intrauterine life (Lawler and Marshall, 1961), the question of secondary acquisition of the Lewis antigens by embryonal epithelial cells does not arise and no fetal–maternal conflict is to be expected with respect of these antigens.

C. THE ABH SUBSTANCE: THE TOTAL MACROMOLECULE

As presented in Section II, B, the ABH substances of the erythrocytes and of the mucoid secretions have been characterized to a large extent and can be now visualized as belonging to several families of macromolecules either glycoprotein or glycolipid. On the contrary little precise information is available as to the macromolecular background of the ABH antigens of the endothelium and the epithelia whether of primordia or of adult organs, as they have not been—for obvious reasons—extracted and studied systematically by the immunochemist. The presumption is that they may well resemble the ABH substances of the erythrocyte some of which—at least—are intrinsic, transmembrane glycoproteins (Marchesi et al., 1972). Some of the functions of the blood group substances may in fact be referable to such background macromolecules, their chemistry, topography, and cytoplasmic connections.

III. The Distribution of the ABH Antigens in the Body

In the account that follows the ABH antigens are described without reference to the underlying molecular structures. They have been mapped out in the human body—in its intrauterine and extrauterine phases—by this author with the aid of immunofluorescence, a method that offers high-resolution histological visualization (Szulman, 1960). Frozen sections have been used in order to ensure the preservation of the antigens and their background macromolecules in their native state with a minimal risk of denaturation and of topographic disorientation (Feltkamp-Vroom, 1975). Another method, available more recently, is that of horseradish peroxidase-conjugated antibody combined with chromogenic substrate for histologic visualization (Taylor, 1978). This technique has not yet been used extensively in the demonstration of ABH antigens but promises to be worthwhile since it requires no ultraviolet fluorescence apparatus and reportedly works well on formalin-fixed and paraffin-embedded tissues (Bonfiglio and Feinberg, 1976). The latter advantage is also claimed for the mixed cell agglutination method, which, however, offers a low degree of resolution of histologic visualization since it employs the erythrocyte as an indicator (Davidsohn et al., 1966).

A. THE ABH ANTIGENS OF EMBRYO/FETUS OF THE FIRST TRIMESTER OF PREGNANCY

The antigens have been found in the earliest embryos available, those representing the fifth week of development. At this early stage there is a surprising abundance of cell wall-specific fluorescence outlining both the endothelium throughout the cardiovascular system and the epithelial cells of practically all organs or organ rudiments (Szulman, 1971). The ABH antigens are present in the blood islands of the yolk sac, in the erythropoietic foci of the liver, and in the erythrocytes inside the vessels. They are well and richly expressed at the cell surfaces of the epithelia forming the primitive digestive tube (Fig. 2) and its derivatives, the pharyngeal pouches, the thymus (Fig. 3), the pituitary (pars anterior), and the thyroid glands; the trachea and the bronchi (Fig. 3); the hepatic and pancreatic diverticula; the cloaca, the urachus, and the allantois. The mesonephros (Fig. 4) and later the metanephros are remarkable for the rich endowment of their respective ducts, while the secretory tubules (formed in situ from the mesenchymal cap) show no antigens (Szulman, 1964). The epithelium of the integument also evinces much antigen, as do the ducts and glands derived therefrom at somewhat later stages, e.g., the otic vesicle. However, the central nervous system the liver, and the adrenal gland show no ABH antigens (Szulman, 1964, 1971).

ARON E. SZULMAN

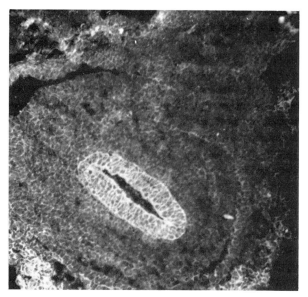

FIG. 2. Primitive gut of an human embryo 7 mm, 33 days postfertilization. Frozen section stained with anti-A conjugate (FITC). Note the surface outlining of the epithelial cells by the antigen. This antigenic endowment disappears toward the end of the first trimester; the mucus secretion of the gut will contain the ABH-specific glycoprotein from the very beginning of mucus production (compare with Fig. 5). ×300.

B. RECESSION OF ABH EPITHELIAL ANTIGENS; COMMENCEMENT OF ABH MUCUS-BOUND SECRETION

The end of the first trimester of pregnancy is marked by an orderly recession of the epithelial cell wall antigens of most primitive organs. This antigenic loss coincides with histologically recognizable steps of differentiation. The maturation is indicated by an increasing morphological complexity and by tokens of function in the organs concerned (Szulman, 1964). The establishment of the mucous secretion in the salivary glands and in the various segments of the gastrointestinal tract is one of such signs of organ function. The secretion contains the ABH and Lewis antigens from its very inception at 35–40 mm (total fetal length) 9–10 weeks menstrual age. Another example of antigenic loss is witnessed in the thyroid during its transition from a solid epithelial crescent to an organ with recognizable acini and one capable of concentrating iodine. A similar recession of antigens is also observed in the pituitary (anterior lobe) gland. Several organs—as previously referred to—have not been demonstrated to possess the antigens and it is impossible to decide whether they have gone through a positive stage

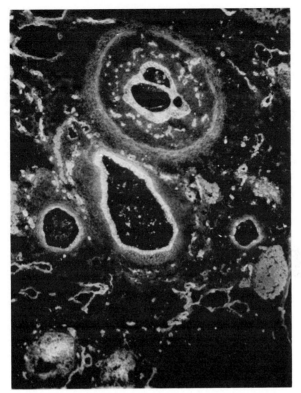

FIG. 3. Cross-section of lower neck. Human embryo 27 mm, 52 days postfertilization age. Esophagus (top), trachea, and thymus (bottom), now a spindle-shaped, paired organ of antigen-positive epithelium. Note positive epithelium lining the esophagus and trachea. Vessels, including the large arteries and veins of the neck, are very well visualized through endothelial staining. Cryostat section stained for A antigen. ×100.

during brief developmental periods that escaped investigation (Szulman, 1971). The adult, vestigial pattern of ABH cell wall antigens and the pattern of mucous secretions are established at 12–14 weeks menstrual age.

The biologic meaning of the antigenic disappearance is most likely bound with the function of the antigens or of the total substance—both of which remain unknown. The advent of the mucous secretion (Fig. 5), on the other hand, signifies the presence of soluble ABH substances in the fetal plasma—in anticipation of the active transfer of large amounts of IgG across the placenta in the latter half of pregnancy (Gitlin, 1974).

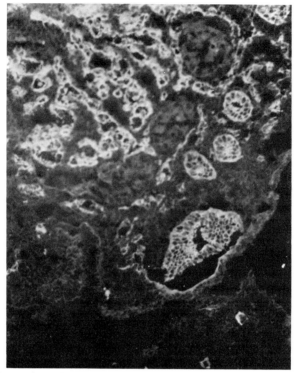

FIG. 4. Mesonephros, human embryo 19 mm, 46 days postfertilization age. High-power view to show the duct and branches (right side of photograph), negative tubules and a large glomerulus (left upper corner). Cryostat sections stained with anti-H conjugate. ×350.

C. THE ABH ANTIGENS OF THE PLACENTA

The placenta presents some unique features of special importance in feto-maternal relationships. While the ABH antigens are present in abundance in the embryo proper (Figs. 2, 3, and 4)—the epithelial trophoblastic covering of the villi remains negative (Fig. 6) as disclosed by immunofluorescence (Szulman, 1972) and by immunoelectron microscopy (Goto et al., 1976). The antigenic status of the trophoblastic barrier is still subject to dispute (Edwards et al., 1975), but it is fair to state that at least with respect to ABH antigens trophoblastic neutrality has been well established. This is further supported by the absence of the A and B antigens from the vessels of the villi and of the umbilical chord in A/B individuals while the H antigens (to which there is normally no antibody in the human) is fully expressed.

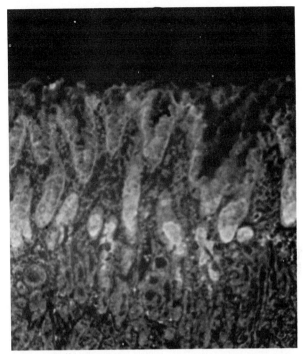

FIG. 5. Stomach of fetus, third trimester. Frozen section stained for A antigen. Specimen from a "nonsecretor" individual to illustrate persisting secretion of the A-specific glycoprotein in the deeper parts of mucosa. Note the negative epithelium elsewhere (compare Fig. 2). ×150.

The importance of trophoblastic neutrality can be illustrated by considering an example of an O group mother carrying an A or a B group conceptus. The maternal anti-A/B antibodies, both of the IgG and the IgM species, borne in maternal blood come into intimate contact with the trophoblast and it is the absence of the A/B antigens that avoids antigen–antibody union otherwise most likely to result in "immune coagulopathy," described in kidney transplantation (Starzl *et al.*, 1970). In fact, this is important in considering the biologic necessity for trophoblastic neutrality with respect to other antigens.

IV. Function and Biological Significance of ABH Antigens/Substances

The physiological functions of the blood group antigens remain virtually unknown (Gershowitz and Neel, 1970). In that respect the ABH are in company with other, much investigated cell-surface antigens, notably those of the major histocompatibility systems H-2 and HLA, of

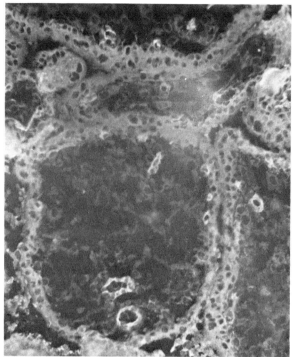

FIG. 6. Placenta from an embryo, 27 mm, 52 days postfertilization age, group A (same embryo as in Fig. 3). Cryostat sections stained with anti-A reagents fail to evince any antigens in both trophoblast and the villous capillaries. Pictured here is a villus stained with an anti-H conjugate which demonstrates the presence of the "species-antigen" H in the vessels. Other epithelia are well endowed with antigen A (and H) (compare Fig. 3). ×500.

the murine antigens of the T/t system (Bennett, 1975), and the related F9 antigen (Jacob, 1977). All these antigens contribute to the general molecular profile of the respective cell surfaces and the subject of their role in cell interaction is explored elsewhere in these volumes. In general the extreme polymorphism of the transplantation antigens and the moderate polymorphism of the ABH would—taken prima facie—fit them ill for a precise biological role in a universal process. One would expect the existence of a uniform code of cell communication embodying a minimum degeneracy (Bretcher and Raff, 1975). It could be argued from this premise that the constant moieties of the macromolecules in question qualify better in this respect, for example, the molecules underlying the variable carbohydrates of the ABH substances. A further circumstance arguing for the lack of involvement of the ABH carbohydrates is the existence of two amorphic genes concerned with their biosynthesis, viz. O of the ABO locus and h of the H/h locus that program for truncated versions of the oligosaccharidic chain—but which exert no known influence upon organogenesis or upon reproduction. In this context recent experiments illustrating the noninvolvement of the H-2 transplantation antigens in cell assembly *in vitro* should be recorded (McClay and Gooding, 1978; Zenzes *et al.*, 1978). Among the current theories on cell-to-cell interactions one (Shur and Roth, 1975) invokes the interlocking of cell-surface glycosyltransferases with their vis-à-vis substrate sugar molecules. This would seem the most economical hypothesis as applied to ABH for it implicates only a single gene in any given individual as responsible for cell linkage and allows for any degree of polymorphism.

In sum, it can be said that the ABH antigens are found on the cell surface and that they contribute to the hydrophilic status of the superficial segment of the proteins to which they are attached and to the locking-in (Bretcher and Raff, 1975) of the latter at the membrane bilayer. They fulfill these functions in a nonspecific way, again raising the unanswered question as to the reasons for their exquisite structural specificity and for the universal ABO polymorphism in the world populations (Gershowitz and Neel, 1970; Szulman, 1971).

V. The ABH Antigen in Feto-Maternal Relationships

While the functions of the ABH antigens still belong in the realm of speculation, feto-maternal erythrocytic ABO incompatibility is firmly established in the etiology of one of the syndromes of fetal erythroblastosis. This does not establish a physiological function for the A/B antigens but it points to the "tip of the iceberg" of their wider biological significance in reproduction. Thus, the finding of the ABH antigens as surface components of epithelial cells during the stages of active organogenesis led this author to the concept of feto-maternal ABO incompatibility at the tissue level. The epithelial A/B antigens of an early embryo are considered poised as targets for maternal transplacental antibodies (Szulman, 1964) the latter known to be capable of diffusion through the early placenta to a significant degree (Gitlin, 1974). In the absence of complement in the early embryo (Colten, 1972), antigen–antibody reactions at the cells' surface may induce a series of secondary changes that could result in functional "cell blindfolding," and lead to a significant disturbance of organogenesis. Enacted at a very early stage of development, interference with main organ formation causes gross disorganization and death of the embryo (Szulman, 1971, 1975).

Parental ABO incompatibility and hence feto-maternal conflict have long been subjects of genetic inquiries some leading to equivocal or contradictory results (recent brief reviews by Szulman, 1971, and by Lauritsen *et al.*, 1975). The latter difficulty is explicable as due to the fact that the ABO selective pressures are weak and the population samples necessary for ascertainment have to be much larger than those hitherto examined. Thus, for example, the incontestable effect of Rh(D) antigen parental incompatibility upon reproduction could not as yet be demonstrated in the various biometric studies (Sing *et al.*, 1971). More recently, however, two inquiries based on direct ABO typing of mothers and abortuses demonstrated a significant excess of fetuses incompatible with their mothers (Takano and Miller, 1972), especially in conceptuses without chromosomal anomalies (Lauritsen *et al.*, 1975).

The events leading to ABO fetal selection must be taking place in the very early stages of human pregnancy, in embryos of less than 10 mm in size, and well before the advent of the mucous secretions (Fig. 5) that provide the soluble ABH glycoprotein substances (Høstrup, 1963) capable of deflecting maternal transplacental antibodies from the A/B tissue targets. They are certainly of importance in later pregnancy when transplacental maternal IgG reaches the fetus in large quantities due to a special transportation mechanism (Gitlin, 1974). In the early stages under consideration, however, no such protection is available and the experimental efforts described in Section V, A inquire into the mechanisms of IgG anti-A/B action upon tissues during an *in vitro* assembly that mimic such simplified *in vivo* situation.

A. THE MODIFICATION OF EXPERIMENTAL *in Vitro* ORGANOGENESIS BY ANTIBODIES TO CELL-SURFACE ANTIGENS

Embryonal tissues have long been known to have the ability to reaggregate from an artificially disaggregated cell population and reform histotypically in the image of the organ of derivation (Moscona, 1962). Such reconstitution is generally accepted as representing true *in vivo* organogenesis that depends on mutual, like-cell cuing and on inductive cell dialogue between epithelium and mesenchyme (Grobstein, 1967). Since those phenomena are most likely dependent on information encoded on the cell surface it was feasible to investigate whether changes wrought upon the latter by IgG antibody directed to the A or B antigen would modify organogenesis in a disaggregation—reaggregation model. The idea was explored (Szulman, 1975) employing the chick embryo mesonephros (Fig. 7) whose duct and main branches—but not the secretory tubules—are equipped with the Forssman (F) antigen. In this morphologic respect the chick resembles

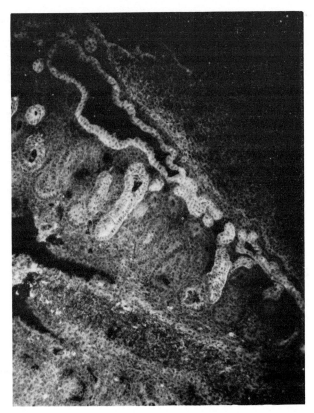

FIG. 7. Chick embryo, mesonephros 4.5 days incubation. Near longitudinal section to show the Forssman antigen of the duct and its main branches, as well as the negative tubules of the upper nephron. ×100.

the human embryo (Fig. 4), with the difference, however, that the Forssman is apparently a nonpolymorphic species antigen of *Gallus domesticus.*

The embryonal mesonephros is easily disaggregated by weak trypsin solution with no loss of antigen, as ascertained by immunofluorescence (Fig. 8). Reaggregation is accomplished in a technically simple hanging-drop tissue culture system (Grover, 1961) wherein solid conglomerates can be obtained as early as 18 hours after incubation. They show tubular formation (Fig. 9) resembling the original mesonephros of the 4- to 5-day-old embryo complete with antigenic reconstruction of F-positive and F-negative segments of the nephron. Such tubular reconstruction is interfered with by anti-Forssman sera or their FITC conjugates, administered in quantities such as to leave the culture

FIG. 8. Chick embryo mesonephros 4.5 days incubation. Trypsin disaggregated cells stained for Forssman antigen. Observe the F+ and F− elements as they begin to aggregate. ×300.

medium with a slight residual titer at the end of the experiment. The experiments result in the reformation of the F-negative segments of the nephron; however, the positive elements, deriving from the duct and its branches, remain unable to reorganize (Fig. 10). Control experiments employed Forssman antisera variously absorbed with antigen from sources other than sheep red cells used in the original immunization, e.g., guinea pig kidney, and gave satisfactory results.

Further information on events taking place *in vitro* will accrue from following the behavior of the antibody suitably tagged, through the various stages of aggregation and through administering it to cultures at various stages of aggregation and in varying quantities. Even though histologic reconstruction is rapid—less than 24 hours in these experiments—a certain degree of antibody and antigen turnover must be expected during the reaggregation process and the relationship between antibody availability and antibody consumption at the cell's

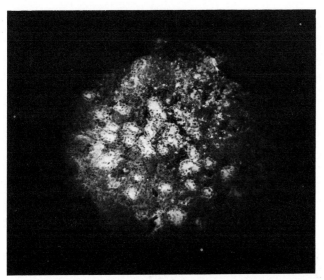

FIG. 9. Chick embryo mesonephros. An aggregate in a hanging-drop tissue culture employing cells represented in Fig. 8 grown in medium with normal rabbit serum. Note tubular reconstruction obtained in a 20-hour specimen. Some of the tubules are Forssman-positive, others F-negative, a recreation of the original antigenic constitution. ×75.

surface may hold an important key in understanding the embryo's self-defense.

The contrived system previously outlined can now be applied to the more direct study of human fetal tissues, typed for the A/B antigens. The experiments, albeit more difficult technically, follow the rationale of the chick experiments with the application of appropriate anti-A/B IgG sera; they thus follow more closely the prototype of the early embryo *in utero*. In the fetal lung, for example, the tracheobronchial epithelium is richly endowed with the A or B antigen. Disaggregation of lung fragments by proteolytic enzymes results in a single-cell population with an expected proportion of cells with their A/B antigens intact. Upon reaggregation it undergoes an organotypical reconstruction that preserves the A/B-positive identity of the newly formed tubules, the reorganization of which can be studied under the influence of appropriate antibodies of known molecular species.

B. MOLECULAR PROCESSES FOLLOWING SURFACE ANTIGEN–ANTIBODY REACTIONS

Experimental tissue reconstruction has been modified by whole cell-directed antibodies in the past (Moscona and Moscona, 1962; Lil-

142   ARON E. SZULMAN

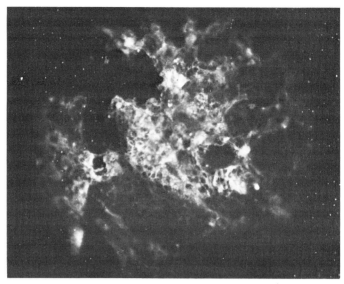

FIG. 10. Chick-embryo mesonephros, 4.5 days. A hanging-drop reaggregate grown in the presence of human anti-Forssman (anti-sheep RBC) serum. Observe the unimpeded reorganization of the F-negative elements and large areas of Forssman-positive cells forming solid sheets without tubular formation. Hog anti-human globulin stains the human anti-Forssman of the "blindfolded" cells. Similar results obtained in experiments employing culture medium containing rabbit anti-Forssman conjugate. ×300. (Reproduced by permission of Academic Press from Szulman, 1975.)

lien, 1969; McClay and Gooding, 1977). The compaction of mouse morula and development of blastula can be arrested by Fab fragments of antibody to F9 antigen (Kemler *et al.*, 1977). Fab fragments directed to specific preaggregation antigens (cs-A) inhibit the formation of slugs of *Dictyostelium discoideum* (Beug *et al.*, 1973; Gerisch, this volume). In all such experiments the underlying molecular mechanisms remain unknown, as do the nature of the molecules underlying the antigen, their relationships within the plasma membrane bilayer, and their cytoplasmic linkages.

The nature of some of the changes brought about by antibody is partly revealed by patch and cap formation followed by internalization or shedding of the antigen–antibody complex (Loor, 1977). Blood group antigens A/B can be capped on animal cells by whole antibody (Sundquist, 1972) and their disappearance and regeneration in human fetal tissue culture monolayers reacted with antibody were described (Högman, 1962) long before the idea of cell-surface modulation was established (Boyse *et al.*, 1967). The latter is an important phenomenon in the present context, for it most likely contributes to the fetal resistance to antibodies. The biological price, however, remains to be determined, one of the risks being the removal—however temporary—of physiologically indispensable molecules from the cell membrane. In this connection it is of interest that antibody-induced "modulation" (meaning insensitivity of a cell to further antibody plus complement) in some documented instances does not entail a total antigenic depletion (Loor *et al.*, 1975; Esmon and Little, 1976) and may designate a state of coexistence wherein the antibody supplied to the culture medium is continuously fixed by antigen and steadily turned over by the cell (Lesley and Hyman, 1974).

Most of the previously quoted data stem from investigations on lymphocytes and no information is available as to how similar changes at the cell surface may influence cell assembly. It is of interest here that the susceptibility of mouse embryo cells to immune lymphotoxicity can be much diminished in a three-dimensional situation of experimental organogenesis, in contrast to the vulnerability of the same cell population when grown as a tissue culture monolayer (Szulman and Johnson, 1978). Could cells, freely moving in a three-dimensional milieu have a different antigen topography from those encountered in standard tissue cultures?

The disaggregation–reaggregation techniques are employed by this author using human fetal tissues of known ABH types with the aim of *in vitro* isolation of some circumstances of the embryo *in utero*. Assuming that experimental organogenesis is equivalent in the relevant aspects to the process *in vivo*, further refinements are called for, especially with respect to antibody quality (IgG, IgM, Fab), dosage, turnover by the cells, and fate during the various stages of cell aggregation. Irrespective of the molecular mechanisms—remotely guessed at in previous paragraphs—the questions answerable at present remain at the cellular and tissue level.

VI. Concluding Remarks

The blood group antigens ABH are integral elements of the cell surface in the endothelium and in most epithelia of the human embryo during early organogenesis. They probably represent a variety of macromolecules, all associated with the surface of the cell membrane and subserve functions as yet unknown. Their biological significance, pointed to by the increased hazards in ABO incompatible feto-maternal matches, is interpreted in the light of an hypothesis that views the A/B antigens as potential targets for maternal IgG antibodies crossing by diffusion the early placental barrier. The injury caused by the surface

A/B antigen–antibody reactions is visualized as leading to interference with cell assembly causing early embryonic demise. Experimental organogenesis *in vitro* confirms the feasibility of this idea, since the histotypic reconstruction of tissues can be interfered with by cell-surface directed antibody.

REFERENCES

Bennett, D. (1975). *Cell* **6**, 441–454.
Beug, H., Katz, E. F., and Gerisch, G. J. (1973). *J. Cell Biol.* **56**, 647–658.
Bonfiglio, T. A., and Feinberg, M. R. (1976). *Arch. Pathol. Lab. Med.* **100**, 307–310.
Boyse, A. E., Stockert, E., and Old, L. J. (1967). *Proc. Natl. Acad. Sci. U.S.A.* **58**, 954–960.
Bretcher, M. S., and Raff, M. C. (1975). *Nature (London)* **258**, 43–49.
Colten, H. R. (1972). *J. Clin. Invest.* **51**, 725–732.
Davidsohn, I., Kovarik, S., and Lee, C. L. (1966). *Arch. Pathol.* **81**, 381–390.
Edwards, F. R., Howe, C. W., and Johnson, M. H. (1975). "Immunobiology of Trophoblast." Cambridge Univ. Press, London and New York.
Esmon, N. L., and Little, J. R. (1976). *J. Immunol.* **117**, 919–926.
Feltkamp-Vroom, T. M. (1975). *Ann. N.Y. Acad. Sci.* **254**, 21–26.
Gershowitz, H., and Neel, V. (1970). *In* "Blood and Tissue Antigens" (D. Aminoff, ed.), pp. 33–50. Academic Press, New York.
Gitlin, C. (1974). *In* "The Placenta" (K. S. Moghissi and E. S. E. Hafez, eds.), pp. 151–191. Thomas, Springfield, Illinois.
Goto, S., Hoshino, M., Tonodo, Y., and Ishizuka, N. (1976). *Lab. Invest.* **35**, 530–536.
Grobstein, C. (1967). *Natl. Cancer Inst. Monogr.* **26**, 279.
Grover, J. W. (1961). *Dev. Biol.* **3**, 555–568.
Hakamori, S., Watanabe, K., and Laine, R. A. (1977). *In* "Human Blood Groups" (J. F. Mohn, R. W. Plunkett, R. K. Cunningham, and R. M. Lambert, eds.), pp. 150–164. Karger, Basel.
Högman, C. F. (1962). *Acta Pathol. Microbiol. Scand.* **55**, 241–249.
Horowitz, M. I. (1978). *In* "The Glycoconjugates" (M. I. Horowitz and W. Pigman, eds.), Vol. 2, pp. 387–436. Academic Press, New York.
Høstrup, H. A. (1963). *Vox Sang.* **8**, 557–566.
Jacob, F. (1977). *Immunol. Rev.* **33**, 3–32.
Kemler, R., Babinet, C., Eisen, H., and Jacob, F. (1977). *Proc. Natl. Acad. Sci. U.S.A.* **74**, 4449–4452.
Lauritsen, J. G., Grunet, N., and Jensen, M. (1975). *Clin. Genet.* **7**, 308–316.
Lawler, S. D., and Marshall, R. (1961). *Vox Sang.* **6**, 541–546.
Lesley, J., and Hyman, R. (1974). *Eur. J. Immunol.* **4**, 732–739.
Lillien, J. E. (1969). *Curr. Top. Dev. Biol.* **4**, 169–195.
Lloyd, K. O., Kabat, E. A., and Licerio, E. (1968). *Biochemistry* **7**, 2976–2990.
Loor, F., Block, N., and Little, J. R. (1975). *Cell. Immunol.* **17**, 351–365.
Loor, R. (1977). *Prog. Allergy* **23**, 3–153.
McClay, D. R., and Gooding, L. R. (1977). *J. Cell Biol.* **75**, 56–66.
McClay, D. R., and Gooding, L. R. (1978). *Nature (London)* **274**, 367–368.
Marchesi, V. T., Tillack, T. W., Jackson, R. L., Segrest, J. P., and Scott, R. E. (1972). *Proc. Natl. Acad. Sci. U.S.A.* **69**, 1445–1449.
Moscona, A. A. (1962). *J. Cell. Comp. Physiol.* **60**, 65–80.
Moscona, A. A., and Moscona, M. (1962). *Anat. Rec.* **142**, 319 (abstr.).

Shur, B. D., and Roth, S. (1975). *Biochim. Biophys. Acta* **415,** 473–515.

Sing, C. F., Shreffler, D. C., Neel, J. V., and Napier, J. A. (1971). *Am. J. Hum. Genet.* **23,** 164–172.

Starzl, T. E., Boehmig, H. J., Amemiya, H., Wilson, C. B., Dickson, F. J., Gilles, G. R., Simpson, C. M., Holgrimson, C. G. (1970). *N. Engl. J. Med.* **283,** 383–390.

Sundquist, K. G. (1972). *Nature (London), New Biol.* **239,** 147–149.

Szulman, A. E. (1960). *J. Exp. Med.* **111,** 785–800.

Szulman, A. E. (1962). *J. Exp. Med.* **115,** 977–996.

Szulman, A. E. (1964). *J. Exp. Med.* **119,** 503–516.

Szulman, A. E. (1971). *Hum. Pathol.* **2,** 575–584.

Szulman, A. E. (1972). *N. Engl. J. Med.* **286,** 1028–1031.

Szulman, A. E. (1975). *Dev. Biol.* **43,** 101–108.

Szulman, A. E. (1977). *In* "Human Blood Groups" (J. F. Mohn, R. W. Plunkett, R. K. Cunningham, and R. M. Lambert, eds.), pp. 426–436. Karger, Basel.

Szulman, A. E., and Johnson, M. H. (1978). *J. Anat.* **127,** 273–276.

Szulman, A. E., and Marcus, D. M. (1973). *Lab. Invest.* **28,** 565–574.

Takano, K., and Miller, J. R. (1972). *J. Med. Genet.* **9,** 144–150.

Taylor, C. R. (1978). *Arch. Pathol. Lab. Med.* **102,** 113–121.

Watkins, W. M. (1974). *In* "The Red Blood Cell" (D. MacN. Surgenor, ed.), 2nd ed., Vol. 1, pp. 293–360. Academic Press, New York.

Watkins, W. M. (1978). *Proc. R. Soc. London, Ser. B* **202,** 31–53.

Zenzes, M. T., Wolf, U., Gunther, E., and Engel, W. (1978). *Cytogenet. Cell Genet.* **20,** 365–372.

CHAPTER 7

CELL-MEDIATED IMMUNE RESPONSES TO MOUSE EMBRYONIC CELLS: DETECTION AND CHARACTERIZATION OF EMBRYONIC ANTIGENS

Suzanne Ostrand-Rosenberg

DEPARTMENT OF BIOLOGICAL SCIENCES
UNIVERSITY OF MARYLAND BALTIMORE COUNTY
CATONSVILLE, MARYLAND

I. Introduction

Many authors have suggested that the cell surface macromolecules of embryonic cells play a major role in differentiation of the embryo (see Bennett *et al.,* 1971; Owen, 1965). This theory is an attractive one in that it accounts readily for the specificity of cellular associations that are probably mandatory during embryonic development. According to such a theory, the various precursor cells display surface receptors or surface macromolecules that are unique to that cell type. Other cells in the developing organism which are destined to interact or associate with these cells are able to do so via complementary surface structures on their cell membranes. In addition, those cells which are influenced to differentiate by soluble factors or hormones, possess on their surfaces receptors appropriate for interaction with the soluble factor. Therefore, new cell surface moieties or receptors should continually appear during the course of development, and developing systems should display tissue-specific, as well as stage-specific surface moieties characteristic of a given time or period of development.

Numerous cell surface specificities characteristic of embryonic cells have been described. In most cases these macromolecules are identified as antigens by their ability to stimulate an antibody response in

*CURRENT TOPICS IN
DEVELOPMENTAL BIOLOGY, VOL. 14*

syngeneic or xenogeneic adults. The immune system is well suited to detect embryonic antigens because it will perceive as immunogenic most cell membrane specificities that are not found in the normal adult and to which it is not tolerant.

Both the humoral (antibody) and the cell-mediated immune systems should be stimulated by embryonic antigens. Studies of the immune system indicate that certain antigens stimulate antibody production (B cells) while other antigens preferentially stimulate effector lymphocyte (T cells) responses. Therefore, some embryonic antigens may effectively stimulate both the T- and the B-cell arms of the immune system, while certain classes of embryonic antigens may be undetected by antibody production and defined only by cell-mediated immune responses.

Embryonic antigens capable of stimulating cell-mediated or humoral immune responses can be divided into three categories: (a) alloantigens on the embryo derived from the paternal genotype and genetically foreign to the mother, (b) embryo-specific antigens representing stage-specific or tissue-specific markers of embryonic cells which may or may not be independent of the embryo's genotype, and (c) other antigens expressed on embryonic cells. This chapter will briefly review some of the antigenic systems (both alloantigens and embryo-specific antigens) expressed on embryonic mouse cell surfaces that may be capable of stimulating cell-mediated immunity and functionally involved in embryogenesis, and then present recent studies that utilize the cell-mediated immune system to recognize and characterize antigens of early embryonic mouse development.

II. Some Cell Surface Antigens of Early Mouse Embryos

This section will briefly describe some of the cell surface antigens found in early mouse embryos. This listing is by no means complete and the reader is referred to other articles in this series for more complete listings and details on individual antigens (Volume 13, chapters by Monroy and Rosati, Jacob, Solter, Wiley, and Schachner). The reason for briefly reviewing some embryonic antigens here is to focus on those that may trigger cell-mediated immune reactions in adult immunocompetent cells.

A. Alloantigens (Category I Antigens)

1. Major Histocompatibility-2 (H-2) Antigens

Early studies in many laboratories using indirect immunofluorescence (Palm *et al.*, 1971; Heyner, 1973; Muggleton-Harris and Johnson,

1976), transplantation methods (Simmons and Russell, 1962, 1966; Edidin et al., 1971; Vandeputte and Sobis, 1972; Searle et al., 1975), and cell-mediated cytolysis (Jenkinson and Billington, 1974) indicated that H-2 antigens do not appear embryonically prior to approximately day 6 of gestation. At this time they are found on the embryo proper, but are absent on the trophectoderm. However, more recent reports, using more sensitive techniques, describe H-2 antigens on pre-day 6 embryos. Using the highly sensitive immunoperoxidase labeling technique Searle et al. (1976) have found H-2 antigens on preimplantation mouse blastocysts.

Krco and Goldberg (1977), using well-defined antisera to paternal and maternal H-2 antigens and complement-dependent cytotoxicity, obtained lysis of embryos as early as the eight-cell stage. On the other hand, Webb et al. (1977) monitored H-2 antigen synthesis by assaying for immunoprecipitable H-2 from embryos grown in radiolabeled amino acids and found H-2 synthesis commencing in the late blastocyst inner cell mass (ICM) and not detectable in the early blastocyst. The trophoblast apparently does not contain H-2 antigens at or immediately following implantation (Simmons and Russell, 1962, 1966; Palm et al., 1971; Heyner, 1973; Jenkinson and Billington, 1974; Muggleton-Harris and Johnson, 1976; Vandeputte and Sobis, 1972; Searle et al., 1975; Webb et al., 1977), although paternal and maternal H-2 antigens are clearly found on the trophoblast of 14-, 16-, and 18-day-old mouse embryos (Chatterjee-Hasrouni and Lala, 1979).

Searle et al. (1976) have noted a transient appearance of H-2 antigens on preimplantation blastocyst trophectoderm and a subsequent absence of H-2 on later stage trophoblast. These authors suggest that the preimplantation expression may be the result of antigen carry-over from earlier stages and that there is no H-2 antigen synthesis during cleavage. Other investigators (Hakansson and Sundqvist, 1975; Hakansson et al., 1975) have noted the presence of H-2 antigens on blastocysts and the subsequent loss of these antigens from blastocysts activated for implantation by estradiol. The techniques for detection used by these authors did not distinguish between ICM and trophoblast in H-2 expression.

In summary, the onset of H-2 antigen expression in the mouse embryo is questionable, although those studies performed with specific congeneic antisera and highly sensitive assay procedures indicate H-2 antigens first appear in cleavage to blastocyst stage embryos. H-2 expression on trophoblast cells is also controversial, although the consensus is that H-2 antigens are absent on trophoblast of embryos immediately after implantation.

2. Ia Antigens

Only one study to date has examined mouse embryos for the presence of Ia antigens (Delovitch et al., 1978). Ia antigens were found by immunoprecipitation of solubilized, radiolabeled embryonic antigens to first appear at day 11 of gestation and to be restricted to fetal liver until day 16.

3. Other Alloantigens

Many of the early studies aimed at detecting H-2 antigens on embryos were performed with noncongeneic or uncharacterized antisera. Such antisera contain anti-H-2 as well as non-anti-H-2 antibodies. As a result, numerous non-H-2 antigens of undefined etiology have been found on preimplantation mouse embryos. These antigens are readily detectable by indirect immunofluorescence, mixed hemabsorption, transplantation methods, and immunoperoxidase staining, although the exact stage at which they first appear (from two-cell to blastocyst) is controversial (Heyner et al., 1969; Vandeputte and Sobis, 1972; Heyner, 1973; Searle et al., 1975, 1976).

Non-H-2 antigens are also expressed on trophoblast cells. Using a mixed hemadsorption assay, Sellens (1977) found reactivity of an antiserum containing antibodies to non-H-2 antigens with the trophoblast of blastocyst outgrowths. Likewise, a specific xenogeneic antiserum directed against ectoplacental cone trophoblast and rendered specific for trophoblast by absorption was found strongly reactive by immunoperoxidase staining with trophectoderm of postimplantation mouse embryos (7.5 day) and very weakly and sporadically reactive with eight-cell embryos (Searle and Jenkinson, 1978). Preimplantation mouse embryos and trophoblast therefore express numerous undefined antigens.

B. Embryo-Specific Antigens (Category II Antigens)

1. Teratocarcinoma Tumor-Defined Antigens

Teratocarcinomas are malignant tumors which consist of metastatic embryonal carcinoma cells and nontumorigenic differentiated cells which have been derived from the three embryonic germ layers. They resemble very closely the multipotential cells of early embryos in that the embryonal carcinoma cells can give rise to a multitude of differentiated tissues (Stevens, 1967; Damjanov and Solter, 1974). A single embryonal carcinoma cell cloned in vitro when reintroduced into a recipient will give rise to tumors composed of cells derived from all three germ layers, indicating the pluripotency of a single embryonal carinoma cell (Kleinsmith and Pierce, 1964). In addition, teratocarcinoma cells can participate in normal fetal development and give rise to normal adult tissues when implanted into allogeneic mouse blastocysts (Brinster, 1975, 1976; Mintz and Illmensee, 1975; Mintz et al., 1975; Papaioannou et al., 1975; Illmensee and Mintz, 1976).

Several recent reviews have appeared on teratocarcinoma-defined antigens (Hogan, 1977; Jacob, 1977; Gachelin, 1978) and this topic is covered in several other articles in these volumes (see chapters by Solter, Jacob, and Wiley, Volume 13), therefore, the teratocarcinoma-defined surface antigens will only be briefly reviewed here.

Edidin et al. (1971) originally showed that a heterologous antiserum made against the 129 strain murine teratocarcinoma 402AX also reacted with the inner cell mass of normal mouse embryos, but not with trophoblast cells, and hence defined an oncofetal antigen. Further studies demonstrated that the antiserum detected at least three specificities, one of which was termed Antigen I and was shown by cocapping studies to be physically associated with H-2 antigens on the cell surface of a mouse L cell fibroblast (Gooding and Edidin, 1974). Antigen I is present on fertilized eggs through the blastocyst stage of development, adult ovary, and on numerous murine tumor cell lines in addition to the immunizing teratocarcinoma (Edidin et al., 1974; Gooding and Edidin, 1974; Edidin and Gooding, 1975; Edidin, 1976a,b; Gooding et al., 1976). Antigen I is also present on two human teratocarcinoma cell lines (Ostrand-Rosenberg et al., 1977a; Edidin et al., 1978; S. Ostrand-Rosenberg, unpublished). Recent studies with a syngeneic 129 anti-402AX antiserum (C. Hammerberg and S. Ostrand-Rosenberg, unpublished) demonstrate a narrower reactivity of this antiserum as compared to the xenogeneic antiserum. Specifically, the syngeneic antiserum reacts with zygote, two-cell, and four- to eight-cell embryos, but reacts poorly with blastocysts, suggesting that the moiety detected is only weakly expressed at the blastocyst stage. Studies by Bartlett et al. (1978) and Edidin et al. (1978) indicate that the teratocarcinoma 402AX has the ability to prime syngeneic lymphocytes both in vitro and in vivo and that such sensitized lymphocytes can inhibit growth of the sensitizing cells as well as numerous other malignant cell lines that serologically express Antigen I. In addition, 129 splenic lymphocytes primed to teratocarcinoma 402AX growth inhibit random bred CD-1 blastocyst outgrowths at high ratios of effector lymphocytes to target cells (Edidin et al., 1978), while at low ratios appear to stimulate blastocyst outgrowths (B. Fenderson and M. Edidin, personal communication).

A second 129 strain teratocarcinoma has also been extensively examined for oncofetal antigens. Artzt *et al.* (1973) have prepared a
syngeneic antiserum against the F9 teratocarcinoma, a subline of
OTT6050, which reacts only with the immunizing teratocarcinoma,
cleavage stage embryos, and sperm. Absorption experiments with normal sperm and with sperm from $t^{12}/+$ mice indicate that the F9 antigen
may be the wild-type product of the $+^{t12}$ allele (Artzt *et al.*, 1974;
Marticorena *et al.*, 1978). Immunofluorescence localization studies
(Babinet *et al.*, 1975) indicate that the F9 antigen is expressed on both
ICM and trophectoderm. The F9 antigen appears to be a marker of undifferentiated embryonal carcinoma cells because a teratocarcinoma line
capable of differentiation in culture loses the F9 antigen with *in vitro*
differentiation (Jacob, 1977). Because of the reciprocal relationship between the F9 antigen and H-2 antigens (Jakob *et al.*, 1973; Artzt and
Jacob, 1974) and because of the structural similarities between the H-2
and F9 antigens, it has been suggested that the F9 antigen may serve
as a precursor molecule for H-2 (Artzt and Bennett, 1975; Babinet *et
al.*, 1975; Vitetta *et al.*, 1975). The small 12,000-molecular weight subunit of the F9 antigen, however, does not appear to be β_2-microglobulin,
as one would expect if the F9 antigen were a structural precursor of the
H-2 antigen (Dubois *et al.*, 1976). F9 antigen expression is also found on
human spermatozoa (Buc-Caron *et al.*, 1974; Fellous *et al.*, 1974), precursor stages in sperm maturation of both human and murine sperm
(Gachelin *et al.*, 1976), and on human teratocarcinoma cell lines
(Hogan *et al.*, 1977; Holden *et al.*, 1977). The ability of F9 cells to sensitize
syngeneic lymphocytes and serve as targets in a cell-mediated lympholysis assay (CML) is questionable. Early studies (Forman and
Vitetta, 1975) indicated no CML response, while later studies (Wagner
et al., 1978) indicated a strong CML of F9 targets by F9 primed 129
splenic lymphocytes. A recent report by these same authors, however
(Golstein *et al.*, 1978), indicates that the effector lymphocytes may be
recognizing artifactual xenogeneic (fetal calf) serum determinants of
the F9 cells rather than specific developmental antigens.

    Solter and Knowles (1978) have defined a stage-specific mouse em-
bryonic antigen (SSEA-1) with a monoclonal antibody derived from a
mouse myeloma cell fused to a spleen cell from a BALB/c mouse immunized with the F9 teratocarcinoma. SSEA-1 is first expressed on
eight-cell mouse embryos and is found on most ICM cells through the
blastocyst stage (see Solter, Volume 13).

    Other antigens apparently independent of F9 antigens but also de-
fined by teratocarcinoma cells have also been described. Antiserum to
PCC4, a multipotential teratocarcinoma subline of OTT6050, defines

an antigen expressed on the immunizing cells, ICM of preimplantation mouse embryos, and adult sperm, but not on trophectoderm (Gachelin et al., 1977). In addition Artzt et al. (1976) have described what they call a "quasi-endodermal" antigen which is found on embryonic cells of endodermal origin (liver), cleavage stage embryos, adult sperm, and some tumor cells of ectodermal and mesodermal origin. The teratocarcinoma defining this antigen is endodermal and was also derived from the OTT6050 teratocarcinoma.

Using another teratocarcinoma cell line Stern and co-workers (1975) prepared a syngeneic antiserum against the SIKR teratocarcinoma cell ("C" antigen) which by indirect immunofluorescence reacts with the undifferentiated embryonal carcinoma cells of the teratocarcinoma culture, 4- to 32-cell stage mouse embryos, as well as with sperm, adult kidney, and adult brain. Subclones of the SIKR teratocarcinoma clearly undergo differentiation in vitro (Evans and Martin, 1975; Martin and Evans, 1974, 1975a,b). The differentiation process can readily be followed antigenically on the teratocarcinoma cells by noting the disappearance of the "C" antigen and the appearance of H-2 and Thy-1 antigens with differentiation (Stern et al., 1975).

Dewey and co-workers (1977) have described a syngeneic antiserum directed against the totipotent OTT6050 teratocarcinoma also of 129 strain origin. The antiserum detects an antigen that is found by indirect immunofluorescence on trophoblast and ICM of cleavage stage mouse embryos and on the ectoderm and endoderm of postimplantation mouse embryos (no stages later than day 6 were assayed). Absorption studies indicated that sperm and unfertilized eggs were nonreactive, while adult brain, liver, kidney, spleen, ovary, and testes cells could absorb out some of the antiserum activity. In addition, all mouse tumors except a hepatoma were negative for the antigen. These authors also compared their antiserum to that produced by Artzt and co-workers (1974) by reacting the anti-OTT6050 serum with a pool of day 2 embryos from $+/t^{12} \times +/t^{12}$ matings. No indication was found that their antiserum detected the product of the $+/t^{12}$ wild-type allele.

2. T/t Complex

The T-complex of the mouse is a genetic region of chromosome 17 that maps to the left of the H-2 region. T factors fall into two phenotypic categories: those that are dominant (T) and those that are recessive (t) (reviewed by Bennett, 1975; Klein and Hammerberg, 1977). T/t embryos die early on in development, while T/+ animals are phenotypically normal except for having a short tail. Heterozygotes for recessive t factors develop normally and have normal tails. The survival of t homozygotes, however, depends on the type of t factor: lethal, semilethal, or viable. The recessive t factors that have been described to date have been identified because of the tailless phenotype expressed in T/t heterozygotes. Aside from this taillessness $t/+$ animals are phenotypically normal. The lethal and semilethal effects of the recessive t factors can be associated with gross pathological and morphological abnormalities in the t bearing embryos. The numerous t factors have been catalogued into six complementation groups based on the period during embryogenesis in which the homozygotes die and the embryonic structures affected. In addition to embryonic development the T/t complex is also involved in sperm cell differentiation (Bennett and Dunn, 1967, 1971), sperm behavior as measured by transmission ratios at fertilization (Chesley and Dunn, 1936), and suppression of crossing over between T and H-2 (Hammerberg and Klein, 1975).

It has been suggested that the T/t complex codes for cell surface antigens which are expressed in the embryo during early development (Gleucksohn-Waelsch and Erickson, 1970; Bennett et al., 1971; Artzt and Bennett, 1975) and are responsible for the appropriate cell–cell interactions necessary for normal embryogenesis to proceed. There is some evidence to support this hypothesis. Serologically detectable cell surface antigens coded for by a T allele (Bennett et al., 1972) and by the T/t complex (Yanagisawa et al., 1974) have been identified on sperm. Also, four T/t complex alloantigens have been shown by immunofluorescence to be expressed on preimplantation mouse embryos (Kemler et al., 1976). However, the evidence is contradictory that the cell surface gene products of the T/t complex are directly responsible for given cell–cell interactions during embryogenesis. The work of Kemler et al. (1976) has shown that the T/t factors are uniformly expressed through cleavage regardless of the time of action of the T/t haplotype during embryogenesis. Also, Wudl and co-workers (1977; Wudl and Sherman, 1976) have shown that the homozygous presence of a particular t factor in in vitro blastocyst cultures is lethal for all of the cells in the culture and is not restricted to only the cells which fail to organize properly in vivo.

C. Other Embryonic Antigens (Category III Antigens)

1. H-Y Antigens

Female mice of most strains will reject skin grafts from males of the same inbred strain due to the presence of the histocompatibility-Y (H-Y) or male antigen (reviewed by Gasser and Silvers, 1972). The extent of rejection and the capacity of various inbred strains to reject male skin grafts is apparently controlled by an immune response (IR) gene that is closely linked to the *H-2* complex (reviewed by Silvers and Wachtel, 1977; Wachtel, 1977). On the other hand, cytotoxic anti-H-Y antibodies are always produced in females grafted with interstrain male skin regardless of the fate of the male skin graft (Goldberg *et al.*, 1972). H-Y antigen is also expressed on male spleen, thymus, lymph node, and bone marrow cells (Goldberg *et al.*, 1971), and is independent of androgen responsiveness (reviewed by Silvers and Wachtel, 1977; Wachtel, 1977). Using complement-dependent cytotoxicity, Krco and Goldberg (1976) have demonstrated the expression of H-Y antigen on the cells of eight-cell mouse embryos.

2. Forsmann Antigen

Recent studies (Stern *et al.*, 1978; Willison and Stern, 1978) using monoclonal antibodies derived from a hybridoma of a mouse myeloma cell fused to a spleen cell from a rat immunized with mouse spleen cells indicate the presence of Forsmann antigen on preimplantation embryos. The antigen is found on the ICM as well as on the trophectoderm of early blastocysts, and disappears from the trophectoderm after *in vivo* implantation.

The expression of other cell surface antigens in mouse embryo cells is described elsewhere in these volumes (see chapters by Solter, Wiley, and Schachner, Volume 13).

III. Cell-Mediated Immune Responses to Early Mouse Embryos

This section will briefly review some of the data on cell-mediated immune responses to embryos and embryonic cells *in vivo* and *in vitro* and will then present a brief review of unpublished studies from the author's laboratory on *in vitro* cell-mediated immune responses as a method of analyzing embryonic antigens.

A. MATERNAL CELL-MEDIATED IMMUNE RESPONSE TO THE EMBRYO

Most allogeneic pregnancies progress to term in immunocompetent females who are carrying histoincompatible fetuses. Histoincompatible allografts are usually rejected by the cell-mediated immune system (T cells) of an immunocompetent host. Why the allogeneic and presumably immunogenic fetus is not rejected as an allograft is not understood. Reasons for the lack of rejection have been grouped into three categories: (*a*) the mother is tolerant and, hence, unreactive to the alloantigens of her fetus, (*b*) the fetus does not express its full complement of alloantigens and, hence, is not seen as an allograft by the mother, and (*c*) the uterine environment is an immunologically privileged site to which the immune system of the mother does not have access (Medawar, 1953, as quoted by Edidin, 1972). Several review articles have covered this topic (Beer and Billingham, 1971, 1976; Edidin, 1972; Barker and Billingham, 1977) and this author will, therefore, not review this subject further, except to mention some very recent studies involving maternal cell-mediated immune responses generated in syngeneic pregnancies and, hence, involving embryo-specific (category II) cell surface antigens.

1. Growth Enhancement of Embryos and Tumor Cells Sharing Embryonic Antigens

Because oncofetal antigens are shared between embryos and various tumor cells, the question arises whether immunoreactivity toward fetal antigens is developed during pregnancy. If so, is such reactivity subsequently recalled during a challenge of pregnant (or once pregnant) animals with tumor cells? Chism et al. (1978) have recently reviewed this controversial and interesting subject and, hence, this author will only address studies reported subsequently.

Several recent studies indicate significant enhancement of growth of embryonic cells by maternal cells. Peritoneal exudate cells (PEC, a mixture of lymphocytes and macrophages) from random bred pregnant CD-1 females stimulate the in vitro growth of blastocyst outgrowths, while PEC from virgin females have no effect (B. Fenderson and M. Edidin, personal communication). In addition, PEC from pregnant 129 females relative to virgin females stimulate teratocarcinoma 402AX cell growth in vitro. This effect is apparently due to a non-T-cell population because nylon wool treatment of the PEC prior to incubation with 402AX targets removes the stimulatory capacity (B. Fenderson and M. Edidin, personal communication). These experiments further suggest that the 402AX teratocarcinoma-defined antigens (see Section II, B, 1) can serve as targets on embryonic cells for lymphocyte sensitization, and may aide in enhancing embryo growth in utero. Such enhancement may be the result of the induction of specific regulatory cells (non-T cells) by the embryonic cells. Another study suggests that embryonic cells have the capacity to suppress an otherwise normal cellular immune response. Globerson and Umiel (1978) have demonstrated that embryonic liver, spleen, and thymus cells from 16- and 17-day fetuses can inhibit allogeneic mixed lymphocyte cultures regardless of the genotypes of fetal and stimulator cells.

2. Lymphocyte Sensitization to Embryonic Antigens

A series of studies by Chism and co-workers (1975, 1976a,b, 1978) have demonstrated by chromium release assay, in vitro sensitization of splenic lymphocytes to an oncofetal antigen expressed on 14-day fetal liver cells. Specificity of the sensitized effectors was determined by inhibition tests with cold competitors and indicated that the sensitizing antigen was also expressed on a large number of adult tumors.

B. *In Vitro* CELL-MEDIATED IMMUNE RESPONSES TO EMBRYONIC CELLS

As discussed in Section I, the cell-mediated immune system may recognize cell surface antigens that go undetected by serum antibodies. Therefore, a thorough testing of embryonic cells for the ability to stimulate cellular immune responses may reveal moieties on embryonic cell surfaces that are important in early mammalian development and that have not been described in studies using humoral antibodies.

The following section will describe some recent studies in the author's laboratory involving cell-mediated immune responses to embryonic cells. The goal of these experiments is to define, characterize, and assess the functional involvement of these antigens in early mouse development.

1. *Experimental Design*

All of the experiments described in the following have been performed using lymphocytes that are syngeneic (genetically matched) with the embryonic cells. In such a syngeneic system only antigens that are restricted to the embryonic cells and absent from the adult lymphocytes (category II embryo-specific antigens; see Section I) will be detected. Any background antigens (e.g., H-2 antigens category I alloantigens; see Section I) will be shared between the lymphocytes and embryonic cells and hence will be unnoticed by the lymphocytes.

2. *Mouse Blastocyst Cell Lines (MB Cells)*

Established cell lines have recently been derived from (SWR/J × SJL/J)F1 4-day-old mouse blastocysts (MB cells, Sherman, 1975a,b). The MB cell lines (MB2, MB21, MB31, MB4) have characteristic levels of alkaline phosphatase, acid phosphatase, N-acetyl-β-D-hexosaminidase, and β-glucuronidase which suggest that particular lines may be expansions of specific embryonic tissue types. The MB cell lines are morphologically diverse and cloning studies indicate that within each line there is a heterogeneous population of cells (Sherman, 1975a,b). H-2 antigen expression on MB cells is quantitatively different from that on any adult tissue or cell population. It has been suggested that this variance reflects the embryonic nature of the MB cells (Ostrand-Rosenberg *et al.*, 1977b). The H-2 variation is apparently not due to the mixture of different cell types in each line because

H-2 analyses of clones derived from one of the lines show the clones are similar to their parent line (S. Ostrand-Rosenberg and H. Nguyen, unpublished). A further indication of the embryonic nature of the MB cell lines is their expression of teratocarcinoma-defined antigens as detected by both serological and cell-mediated immune reactions. Both xenogeneic (Ostrand-Rosenberg *et al.*, 1977b; S. Ostrand-Rosenberg and A. Twarowski, unpublished) and syngeneic (S. Ostrand-Rosenberg and A. Twarowski, unpublished) antiteratocarcinoma antisera react with MB2, MB21, MB31, and MB4 by indirect immunofluorescence. In addition, 129 strain splenic lymphocytes sensitized to teratocarcinoma 402AX growth inhibit up to 80% of all of the MB lines at effector to target ratios of 100:1 (Bartlett *et al.*, 1978).

3. Mixed Cell Culture Experiments

Genetically homogeneous lymphocytes when maintained *in vitro* do not proliferate or incorporate tritiated thymidine. If genetically incompatible immunocompetent lymphocytes are mixed *in vitro,* however, the normally resting lymphocytes will be stimulated by the incompatible antigens to undergo blast transformation and subsequent proliferation characteristic of lymphocyte activation. This reaction is called a mixed lymphocyte response (MLR) and classically T lymphocytes were shown to be the predominant responding cells and the reactivity was mapped to the major histocompatibility complex in the mouse. However, it is now generally agreed that there are numerous lymphocyte activating determinants which map within the *I* region of the *H-2* complex, as well as another locus, the *M* locus that governs mixed lymphocyte reactions.

Recent reports indicate that immunocompetent lymphocytes can also respond to cell surface antigens of nonlymphoid cells in mixed cell cultures (MCC). For example, T lymphocytes can readily be specifically sensitized to undergo blast transformation and subsequent proliferation in combination with syngeneic stimulating cells that are virally infected (Gardner *et al.*, 1975; Schrader *et al.*, 1975), chemically substituted (Shearer *et al.*, 1975), or of tumor origin (Bartlett *et al.*, 1977, 1978; Chism *et al.*, 1976a,b). Responder-stimulator cell combinations that are syngeneic, but differ in their stage of development (e.g., adult lymphocytes and MB cells of the same genotype, respectively), also induce lymphocyte proliferation specific for stage-specific antigens of the MB cells.

MCC experiments using (SWR/J × SJL/J)F1 lymphocytes as responder cells and the various different MB lines as the stimulator cells have been performed as follows. Responder lymphocytes were isolated from the spleens of adult SWR/J × SJL/J)F1 animals and incubated with irradiated (5000 R) MB stimulator cells. Cells were cocultured in 96 well flat bottomed trays at varying ratios of stimulator to responder cells ranging from 50 : 1 to 400 : 1 responders to stimulators, respectively. In all cases the number of responding lymphocytes was kept constant ($5 \times 10^5/100$ μl/well) and the number of stimulating MB cells was varied from $1 \times 10^4/100$ μl/well to $1.25 \times 10^3/100$ μl/well. On the morning of the fifth day of coculture each well was pulsed with 0.1 μCi of tritiated thymidine in growth medium (RPMI-1640 supplemented with 10% fetal calf serum, 1% antibiotic–antimycotic, and 5×10^{-5} M 2-mercaptoethanol), and the cultures harvested 6 hours later onto glass fiber filter paper using a semiautomatic multiwell harvester. The filter paper discs carrying the radiolabel for each culture well were then counted by standard scintillation counting techniques. Because the stimulator MB cells have been irradiated, they should not incorporate significant amounts of tritiated thymidine and hence the counts per minute (cpm) per well should reflect the level of lymphocyte proliferation or the extent to which the normally resting lymphocytes have been triggered by antigens of the stimulating MB cells. The following controls are run routinely. Responder lymphocytes are run alone to obtain background levels in the absence of stimulating cells, and irradiated stimulator MB cells are run alone to determine the contribution of the stimulating cells to total cpm.

Figure 1 shows the results of a MCC experiment using (SWR/J × SJL/J)F1 responding lymphocytes and irradiated MB31 stimulator cells. Stimulation is seen at all ratios of stimulator : responder cells and appears to be most efficient at high concentrations of stimulating MB31 cells. Irradiated stimulators alone and unstimulated responder lymphocytes alone show background levels of tritiated thymidine uptake. The absolute stimulation (that is cpm of responders + stimulators in experimental wells) varies from experiment to experiment depending on the background level of responding lymphocytes alone. Therefore, in order to normalize and compare experiments performed on different days with the different MB cell lines, a stimulation index (S.I.) is computed as follows:

$$\text{S.I.} = \frac{\text{cpm (responders + stimulators)}}{\text{cpm (responders alone)}}$$

Figure 2 shows the results of MCC experiments using the four different MB cell lines. The different MB cell lines (MB2, MB21, MB31, and MB4) all produce different stimulation indices. To demonstrate that stimulation in this system is the result of specific MB cell surface

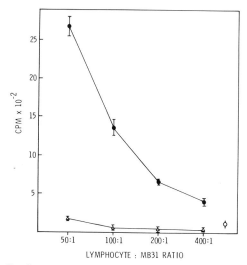

FIG. 1. Mixed cell culture experiment using (SWR/J × SJL/J)F1 splenic lymphocytes as responders and 5000 R irradiated MB31 cells as stimulators. The ordinate shows the counts per minute (cpm) ± standard error of tritiated thymidine incorporated into the splenic lymphocytes, and the abscissa shows the ratio of responding lymphocytes to stimulating MB cells. ●, (SWR/J × SJL/J)F1 lymphocytes + irradiated MB31 cells; △, irradiated MB31 cells alone; ○, (SWR/J × SJL/J)F1 lymphocytes alone.

antigens primary fibroblasts from 19-day-old (SWR/J × SJL/J)F1 fetuses, as well as syngeneic (SWR/J × SJL/J)F1 lymphocytes were used as stimulator cells in mixed cell cultures. As shown in Fig. 2, these cells are unable to stimulate the responding syngeneic splenic lymphocytes. Because of the syngeneic nature of the stimulating and responding cells, stimulation must be the result of MB cell embryonic antigens. The different stimulation indices observed with the different MB cell lines probably indicate that each MB line expresses quantitatively and/or qualitatively different embryonic antigens. This possibility will be explored further in Section III, B, 4 dealing with growth inhibition studies.

To determine the immunologic basis of the MCC stimulation splenic lymphocytes were separated by standard procedures into purified populations of B cells and T cells (Bartlett *et al.*, 1978) and cocultured as per the normal MCC procedure with irradiated MB stimulator cells. In these experiments both subpopulations (B and T cells) of lymphocytes are stimulated indicating that MB cells stimulate both cell-mediated and humoral immune responses (S. Ostrand-Rosenberg and A. Twarowski, unpublished).

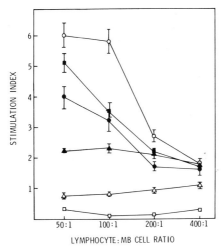

Fig. 2. Comparison of stimulation indices ± standard error of (SWR/J × SJL/J)F1 splenic lymphocytes by MB2, MB21, MB31, MB4, (SWR/J × SJL/J)F1 19-day primary fibroblasts, and (SWR/J × SJL/J)Fl splenic lymphocytes. Each line represents (SWR/J × SJL/J)F1 responder lymphocytes + irradiated ●, MB2 stimulators; ○, MB21 stimulators; ■, MB31 stimulators; ▲, MB4 stimulators; □, (SWR/J × SJL/J)F1 primary fibroblast stimulators; △, (SWR/J × SJL/J)F1 splenic lymphocyte stimulators. Note the variable stimulation depending on the particular MB cell line and the absence of stimulation by the control primary fibroblast and syngeneic lymphocytes.

4. Lymphocyte-Mediated Growth Inhibition (GRI)

In most systems lymphocytes sensitized in a 5-day mixed cell culture reaction can be harvested and used as specifically sensitized killer cells in a standard cell-mediated lympholysis (CML) assay to determine the cytotoxicity of the lymphocytes for target cells. However, in certain systems, specific target cells are not lysed by specifically sensitized lymphocytes. Some authors have attributed this lack of killing to an absence of histocompatibility antigens on the target cells (Forman and Vitetta, 1975; Zinkernagel and Oldstone, 1976; Tursz et al., 1977). Because of the quantitative and qualitative variability of H-2 antigens on MB cells (Ostrand-Rosenberg et al., 1977b; see Section III, B, 2 for details), we have used a lymphocyte-mediated growth inhibition assay (GRI) (Bartlett et al., 1977, 1978) rather than the CML assay to measure the ability of specifically sensitized lymphocytes to affect the growth of embryonic target cells.

Recent studies have indicated that in some syngeneic tumor systems sensitized lymphocytes specifically inhibit the growth of target cells (Bartlett et al., 1977, 1978). Although earlier reports suggested that growth inhibition was the effect of the nonspecific action of macrophages (Germain *et al.*, 1975; Kirchner *et al.*, 1975), more recent studies have demonstrated that the inhibition is the effect of specific T lymphocytes (Barlett *et al.*, 1977, 1978).

Growth inhibition studies should be informative in two areas. (*a*) The cross-reactivity of antigens detected on different cell lines can be assessed by comparing the reactivity of lymphocytes sensitized to one MB cell line on that line and other MB lines. (*b*) The involvement of particular antigens in embryonic cell proliferation can be monitored by determining the growth of MB cells in the presence of specifically sensitized lymphocytes.

Responder lymphocytes and irradiated stimulator MB cells were cocultured at a ratio of $20:1$ [4×10^7 (SWR/J $\times$ SJL/J)F1 lymphocytes $+ 2 \times 10^6$ irradiated MB cells in 10 ml culture medium] for 5 days in T flasks. The supernatant containing the lymphocytes was harvested (the MB cells attached to the flask) and the lymphocyte number adjusted to 2.5×10^5 viable lymphocytes/100 μl medium. Aliquots (100 μl) of effector lymphocytes containing 2.5×10^5, 1.25×10^5, 6.25×10^4, or 3×10^4 cells were then cocultured in 96 well flat bottomed plates with 5×10^3 fresh MB target cells in a total volume of 200 μl/well in culture medium. After 48 hours of culture the wells were pulsed with 0.1 μCi of tritiated thymidine and harvested 24 hours later. Samples were processed as described for the mixed cell culture system. Percentage growth inhibition (GRI) was calculated by:

$$\% \text{GRI} = 100\% \left[1 - \frac{\text{cpm (effector lymphocytes + MB targets)} - \text{cpm (effector lymphocytes alone)}}{\text{cpm (MB targets alone)}} \right]$$

Two controls were routinely included in the GRI assay to ascertain effector cell specificity. (*a*) Fresh, noncultured (SWR/J $\times$ SJL/J)F1 splenic lymphocytes, and (*b*) (SWR/J $\times$ SJL/J)F1 splenic lymphocytes cultured in T flasks with irradiated (SWR/J $\times$ SJL/J)F1 lymphocytes were used as effector cells. This latter control determines the nonspecific activity directed against fetal calf serum antigens. Figure 3 shows the results of a growth inhibition experiment with (SWR/J $\times$ SJL/J)F1 splenic lymphocytes sensitized in a mixed cell culture to irradiated MB31 stimulator cells and tested on fresh MB31 target cells. Note the very high inhibition (96%) of MB31 target cells all the way out to a $12:1$ ratio of effector lymphocytes to MB31 target cells. In this particular experiment there is obvious nonspecific inhibition against what is probably fetal calf serum antigens as seen by the inhibitory capacity of (SWR/J $\times$ SJL/J)F1 effectors sensitized against them-

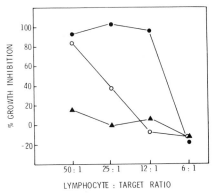

FIG. 3. Lymphocyte-mediated growth inhibition assay of (SWR/J × SJL/J)F1 splenic lymphocytes sensitized *in vitro* in a mixed cell culture to irradiated MB31 cells and subsequently tested for growth inhibition on fresh MB31 target cells. ●, (SWR/J × SJL/J)F1 lymphocytes sensitized to MB31, + MB31 target cells; ○, (SWR/J × SJL/J)F1 lymphocytes sensitized to syngeneic lymphocytes, + MB31 target cells; ▲, Fresh, nonsensitized (SWR/J × SJL/J)F1 lymphocytes, + MB31 target cells.

selves. Fresh splenic lymphocytes show no inhibition. Similar antifetal calf serum activity has been demonstrated in cell-mediated lympholysis experiments against teratocarcinoma targets (Golstein *et al.*, 1978). It is, therefore, essential in these types of experiments to perform the self-sensitized effector lymphocyte controls. One can then calculate the absolute growth inhibition by subtracting the nonspecific inhibition (effectors sensitized to themselves) from the specific inhibition (effectors sensitized to MB cells).

A comparison of the embryonic cell surface antigens of the different MB cell lines can be made by sensitizing (SWR/J × SJL/J)F1 splenic lymphocytes to one MB line and then assessing their ability to inhibit

TABLE I

ABSOLUTE GROWTH INHIBITION OF MB4 AND MB31 CELLS BY
(SWR/J × SJL/J)F1 SPLENIC LYMPHOCYTES SENSITIZED
TO MB4 CELLS

Lymphocyte : target ratio	MB4 targets (% growth inhibition)	MB31 targets (% growth inhibition)
50 : 1	30	20
25 : 1	41	20
12 : 1	19	0
6 : 1	0	2

growth in other lines. Table I shows the results of MB4-sensitized lymphocytes tested on MB4 and MB31 target cells. Both MB lines are growth inhibited, although MB31 cells are less affected than the MB4 cells. These results suggest that some but not all of the surface antigens being recognized by the effector lymphocytes on the sensitizing MB4 cells are shared with the MB31 cells. Effector lymphocytes sensitized to a MB line and then tested for growth inhibition of (SWR/ J × SJL/J)F1 19-day primary fibroblasts have no effect, indicating that the antigens detected on the MB lines are early embryonic moieties (Ostrand-Rosenberg and Twarowski, unpublished). Growth inhibition studies of the other MB lines give similar results (S. Ostrand-Rosenberg and A. Twarowski, unpublished), suggesting that there are embryonic antigens shared by all of the MB lines as well as embryonic antigens that are probably unique to particular MB lines.

IV. Concluding Remarks

Preimplantation mouse embryos clearly express on their cell surfaces a multitude of specific alloantigens, embryo-specific antigens, and antigens of as yet undefined etiology that are readily detected by both humoral (antibody) and cell-mediated immune responses. The functional involvement of these many antigens in early mouse development is unclear at present, although one can easily speculate that they are somehow involved in cell–cell recognition, interaction, and organization of the evolving embryo.

This chapter has been restricted to cell surface antigens of early mouse embryos and specifically has attempted to describe moieties that are detected by the cell-mediated immune system. The specificities described by the mixed cell culture (MCC) and growth inhibition (GRI) assays employed in the author's laboratory are probably stage-specific embryonic antigens that are independent of the embryonic antigens described by others. Two lines of evidence support this hypothesis. (a) Because of the syngeneic nature of the experiments, alloantigens are not involved, thus eliminating category I antigens (Section II, A). (b) The different stimulation indices and degrees of growth inhibition (Sections III, B, 3 and III, B, 4) suggest that different antigens on the various MB cell lines are activating the syngeneic lymphocytes.

If the same antigen(s) were present on all of the MB cell lines, then lymphocyte stimulation in the mixed cell culture (MCC) and growth inhibition (GRI) experiments should be uniform for all four of the cell lines. As shown in Fig. 2 and Table I different stimulation indices and degrees of growth inhibition are found depending on the MB cell line being tested. Therefore, it seems likely that a variety of embryonic antigens are being detected on the different MB cell lines. The exact identity of the embryonic antigens being detected in these experiments is unclear at present; however, it seems unlikely that stimulation and growth inhibition are due exclusively to the currently recognized category II-type antigens (see Section II, B) (teratocarcinoma-defined and T/t complex antigens). It is possible that the different MB lines are selectively expressing one or a few of the teratocarcinoma-defined antigens and hence variable reactivity is due to differential expression of the various antigens. Serologically, however, all of the MB lines express at least one teratocarcinoma-defined antigen (S. Ostrand-Rosenberg and A. Twarowski, unpublished); therefore, unless other embryonic antigens are also involved in the reactivity seen, it is difficult to explain why all the MB cells do not show equal reactivity. The most likely explanation for the varying reactivities of the four different MB cell lines in cell-mediated immune responses is therefore that each line is expressing different stage-specific embryonic antigens that can activate immunocompetent lymphocytes to varying extents.

It is apparent that the cell-mediated immune response is a sensitive and specific tool for detecting embryonic antigens. We have established an experimental system for using cell-mediated immune responses to characterize and define embryonic antigens. The aim of this research is to determine the molecular identity of the cell surface antigens that trigger these cell-mediated immune reactions and to assess the involvement of these molecules in normal mammalian development.

We hope that by understanding the molecular nature and functional involvement of these antigens in early mouse development, we will gain some further insight into the very complex processes of differentiation and development of early mammalian embryos.

ACKNOWLEDGMENTS

The author thanks Dr. B. Bradley of this department for his help with the statistical analyses, Alexandra Twarowski for very capable technical assistance, and Carol Ferrigno for typing the manuscript. Original work reported in this manuscript was supported by American Cancer Society, Maryland Chapter #78-31, and by National Science Foundation #PCM-15989 grants to the author.

REFERENCES

Artzt, K., and Jacob, F. (1974). *Transplantation* **17**, 632–634.
Artzt, K., and Bennett, D. (1975). *Nature (London)* **256**, 545–547.
Artzt, K., Dubois, P., Bennett, D., Condamine, H., Babinet, C., and Jacob, F. (1973).*Proc. Natl. Acad. Sci. U.S.A.* **70**, 2988–2992.
Artzt, K., Bennett, D., and Jacob, F. (1974). *Proc. Natl. Acad. Sci. U.S.A.* **71**, 811–814.
Artzt, K., Hamburger, L., Jakob, H., and Jacob, F. (1976). *Dev. Biol.* **51**, 152–157.

Babinet, C., Condamine, H., Fellous, M., Gachelin, G., Kemler, R., and Jacob, F. (1975). *In* "Teratomas and Differentiation" (M. I. Sherman and D. Solter, eds.), pp. 101–107. Academic Press, New York.

Barker, C. F., and Billingham, R. E. (1977). *Adv. Immunol.* **25**, 1–54.

Bartlett, P. F., Fenderson, B. A., and Edidin, M. (1977). *Fed. Proc., Fed. Am. Soc. Exp. Biol.* **36**, 1290.

Bartlett, P. F., Fenderson, B. A., and Edidin, M. (1978). *J. Immunol.* **120**, 1211–1217.

Beer, A. E., and Billingham, R. E. (1971). *Adv. Immunol.* **14**, 1–84.

Beer, A. E., and Billingham, R. E. (1976). "The Immunobiology of Mammalian Reproduction." Prentice-Hall, Englewood Cliffs, New Jersey.

Bennett, D. (1975). *Cell* **6**, 441–454.

Bennett, D., and Dunn, L. C. (1967). *J. Reprod. Fertil.* **13**, 421.

Bennett, D., and Dunn, L. C. (1971). *In* "Immunogenetics of the H-2 System" (A. Lengerová and M. Vojtísková, eds.), pp. 90–103. Karger, Basel.

Bennett, D., Boyse, E. A., and Old, L. J. (1971). *In* "Cell Interactions" (L. G. Silvestri, ed.), pp. 247–263. North-Holland Publ., Amsterdam.

Bennett, D., Goldberg, E., Dunn, L. C., and Boyse, E. A. (1972). *Proc. Natl. Acad. Sci. U.S.A.* **69**, 2076–2080.

Brinster, R. L. (1975). *In* "Teratomas and Differentiation" (M. I. Sherman and D. Solter, eds.), pp. 51–58. Academic Press, New York.

Brinster, R. L. (1976). *Cancer Res.* **36**, 3412–3414.

Buc-Caron, M., Gachelin, G., Hofnung, M., and Jacob, F. (1974). *Proc. Natl. Acad. Sci. U.S.A.* **71**, 1730–1733.

Chatterjee-Hasrouni, S., and Lala, P. K. (1979). *J. Exp. Med.* **149**, 1238–1253.

Chesley, P., and Dunn, L. C. (1936). *Genetics* **21**, 525–536.

Chism, S. E., Burton, R. C., and Warner, N. L. (1975). *Nature (London)* **257**, 594–596.

Chism, S. E., Burton, R. C., and Warner, N. L. (1976a). *J. Natl. Cancer Inst.* **57**, 377–387.

Chism, S. E., Wallis, S., Burton, R. C., and Warner, N. L. (1976b). *J. Immunol.* **117**, 1870–1877.

Chism, S. E., Burton, R. C., and Warner, N. L. (1978). *Clin. Immunol. Immunopathol.* **11**, 346–373.

Damjanov, I., and Solter, D. (1974). *Curr. Top. Pathol.* **59**, 69–130.

Delovitch, T. L., Press, J. L., and McDevitt, H. O. (1978). *J. Immunol.* **120**, 818–824.

Dewey, M. J., Gearhart, J. D., and Mintz, B. (1977). *Dev. Biol.* **55**, 359–374.

Dubois, P., Fellous, M., Gachelin, G., Jacob, F., Kemler, R., Pressman, D., and Tanigaki, N. (1976). *Transplantation* **22**, 467–473.

Edidin, M. (1972). *In* "Transplantation Antigens" (B. D. Kahan and R. Reisfeld, eds.), pp. 75–113. Academic Press, New York.

Edidin, M. (1976a). *In* "The Cell Surface in Animal Embryogenesis and Development" (G. Poste and G. L. Nicolson, eds.), pp. 127–143. North-Holland Publ., Amsterdam.

Edidin, M. (1976b). *Ciba Found. Symp.* **40** (new ser.), 177–197.

Edidin, M., and Gooding, L. R. (1975). *In* "Teratomas and Differentiation" (M. I. Sherman and D. Solter, eds.), pp. 109–121. Academic Press, New York.

Edidin, M., Patthey, H. L., McGuire, E. J., and Sheffield, W. D. (1971). *In* "Proceedings of the First Conference and Workshop on Embryonic and Fetal Antigens in Cancer" (N. G. Anderson and J. H. Coggin, Jr., eds.), pp. 239–248. Oak Ridge Natl. Lab., Oak Ridge, Tennessee.

Edidin, M., Goodling, L. R., and Johnson, M. (1974). *In* "Karolinska Symposia on Research Methods in Reproductive Endocrinology" (E. Diczfalusy, ed.), 7th Symp., pp. 336–356. Bogtrykkeriet Forum Press, Copenhagen.

Edidin, M., Ostrand-Rosenberg, S., and Bartlett, P. F. (1978). *In* "Cell Differentiation and Neoplasia" (G. F. Saunders, ed.), pp. 67–79. Raven Press, New York.

Evans, M. J., and Martin, G. R. (1975). *In* "Teratomas and Differentiation" (M. I. Sherman and D. Solter, eds.), pp. 237–250. Academic Press, New York.

Fellous, M., Gachelin, G., Buc-Caron, M., Dubois, P., and Jacob, F. (1974). *Dev. Biol.* **41**, 331–337.

Forman, J., and Vitetta, E. S. (1975). *Proc. Natl. Acad. Sci. U.S.A.* **72**, 3661–3665.

Gachelin, G. (1978). *Biochim. Biophys. Acta* **516**, 27–60.

Gachelin, G., Fellous, M., Guenet, J. L., and Jacob, F. (1976). *Dev. Biol.* **50**, 310–320.

Gachelin, G., Kemler, R., Kelly, F., and Jacob, F. (1977) *Dev. Biol.* **57**, 199–209.

Gardner, I. D., Bowern, N. A., and Blanden, R. V. (1975). *Eur. J. Immunol.* **5**, 122–127.

Gasser, D. L., and Silvers, W. K. (1972). *Adv. Immunol.* **15**, 215–247.

Germain, R. N., Williams, R. M., and Benacerraf, B. (1975). *J. Natl. Cancer Inst.* **54**, 709–720.

Gluecksohn-Waelsch, S., and Erickson, R. (1970). *Curr. Top. Dev. Biol.* **5**, 281–316.

Globerson, A., and Umiel, T. (1978). *Transplantation* **26**, 438–442.

Goldberg, E. H., Boyse, E. A., Bennett, D., Scheid, M., and Carswell, E. A. (1971). *Nature (London)* **232**, 478–480.

Goldberg, E. H., Boyse, E. A., Scheid, M., and Bennett, D. (1972). *Nature (London), New Biol.* **238**, 55–57.

Golstein, P., Luciani, M., Wagner, H., and Rollinghoff, M. (1978). *J. Immunol.* **121**, 2533–2538.

Gooding, L. R., and Edidin, M. (1974). *J. Exp. Med.* **140**, 61–78.

Gooding, L. R., Hsu, Y., and Edidin, M. (1976). *Dev. Biol.* **49**, 479–486.

Hakansson, S., and Sundqvist, K. (1975). *Transplantation* **19**, 479–484.

Hakansson, S., Heyner, S., Sundqvist, K.-G., and Bergstrom, S. (1975). *Int. J. Fertil.* **20**, 137–140.

Hammerberg, C., and Klein, J., (1975). *Nature (London)* **258**, 296–299.

Heyner, S. (1973). *Transplantation* **16**, 675–678.

Heyner, S., Brinster, R. L., and Palm, J. (1969). *Nature (London)* **222**, 783–784.

Hogan, B. M. (1977). *Int. Rev. Biochem.* **15**, 333–376.

Hogan, B., Fellous, M., Avner, P., and Jacob, F. (1977). *Nature (London)* **270**, 515–518.

Holden, S., Bernard, O., Artzt, K., Whitmore, W. F., and Bennett, D. (1977). *Nature (London)* **270**, 518–520.

Illmensee, K., and Mintz, B. (1976). *Proc. Natl. Acad. Sci. U.S.A.* **73**, 549–553.

Jacob, F. (1977). *Immunol. Rev.* **33**, 3–32.

Jakob, H., Boon, T., Gaillard, J., Nicolas, J.-F., and Jacob, F. (1973). *Ann. Microbiol. Paris* **124**, 269–282.

Jenkinson, E. J., and Billington, W. D. (1974). *Transplantation* **18**, 286–289.

Kemler, R., Babinet, C., Condamine, H., Gachelin, G., Guenet, J. L., and Jacob, F. (1976). *Proc. Natl. Acad. Sci. U.S.A.* **73**, 4080–4084.

Kirchner, H., Holden, H., and Herberman, R. (1975). *J. Natl. Cancer Inst.* **55**, 971–975.

Klein, J., and Hammerberg, C. (1977). *Immunol. Rev.* **33**, 70–104.

Kleinsmith, L. J., and Pierce, G. B. (1964). *Cancer Res.* **24**, 1544–1548.

Krco, C. J., and Goldberg, E. H. (1976). *Science* **193**, 1134–1135.

Krco, C. J., and Goldberg, E. H. (1977). *Transplant. Proc.* **9**, 1367–1370.

Marticorena, P., Artzt, K., and Bennett, D. (1978). *Immunogenetics* **7**, 337–347.

Martin, G. R., and Evans, M. J. (1974). *Cell* **2**, 163–172.

Martin, G. R., and Evans, M. J. (1975a). *Cell* **6**, 467–474.

Martin, G. R., and Evans, M. J. (1975b). *Proc. Natl. Acad. Sci. U.S.A.* **72**, 1441–1445.

Medawar, P. B. (1953). *Symp. Soc. Exp. Biol.* **7,** 320–338.

Mintz, B., and Illmensee, K. (1975). *Proc. Natl. Acad. Sci. U.S.A.* **72,** 3585–3589.

Mintz, B., Illmensee, K., and Gearhart, J. D. (1975). *In* "Teratomas and Differentiation" (M. I. Sherman and D. Solter, eds.), pp. 59–82. Academic Press, New York.

Muggleton-Harris, A. L., and Johnson, M. H. (1976). *J. Embryol. Exp. Morphol.* **35,** 59–72.

Ostrand-Rosenberg, S., Edidin, M., and Jewett, M. A. S. (1977a). *Dev. Biol.* **61,** 11–19.

Ostrand-Rosenberg, S., Hammerberg, C., Edidin, M., and Sherman, M. I. (1977b). *Immunogenetics* **4,** 127–136.

Owen, R. D. (1965). *In* "Isoantigens and Cell Interactions" (J. Palm, ed.), pp. 1–5. Wistar Institute, Philadelphia.

Palm, J., Heyner, S., and Brinster, R. L. (1971). *J. Exp. Med.* **133,** 1282–1293.

Papaioannou, V. E., McBurney, M. W., Gardner, R. L., and Evans, M. J. (1975). *Nature (London)* **258,** 70–73.

Schrader, J. W., Cunningham, B. A., and Edelman, G. M. (1975). *Proc. Natl. Acad. Sci. U.S.A.* **72,** 5066–5070.

Searle, R. F., and Jenkinson, E. J. (1978). *J. Embryol. Exp. Morphol.* **43,** 147–156.

Searle, R. F., Jenkinson, E. J., and Johnson, M. H. (1975). *Nature (London)* **255,** 719–720.

Searle, R. F., Sellens, M. H., Elson, J., Jenkinson, E. J., and Billington, W. D. (1976). *J. Exp. Med.* **143,** 348–359.

Sellens, M. H. (1977). *Nature (London)* **269,** 60–61.

Shearer, G. M., Rehn, T. G., and Garbarino, C. A. (1975). *J. Exp. Med.* **141,** 1348–1364.

Sherman, M. I. (1975a). *Cell* **5,** 343–349.

Sherman, M. I. (1975b). *Differentiation* **3,** 51–67.

Silvers, W. K., and Wachtel, S. S. (1977). *Science* **195,** 956–960.

Simmons, R. L., and Russell, P. S. (1962). *Ann. N.Y. Acad. Sci.* **99,** 717–732.

Simmons, R. L., and Russell, P. S. (1966). *Ann. N.Y. Acad. Sci.* **129,** 35–45.

Solter, D., and Knowles, B. B. (1978). *Proc. Natl. Acad. Sci. U.S.A.* **75,** 5565–5569.

Stern, P., Martin, G. R., and Evans, M. J. (1975). *Cell* **6,** 455–465.

Stern, P., Willison, K. R., Lennox, E., Galfré, G., Milstein, C., Secher, D., Ziegler, A., and Springer, T. (1978). *Cell* **14,** 775–783.

Stevens, L. C. (1967). *Adv. Morphog.* **6,** 1–31.

Tursz, T., Fridman, W. H., Senik, A., Tsapis, A., and Fellous, M. (1977). *Nature (London)* **269,** 806–808.

Vandeputte, M., and Sobis, H. (1972). *Transplantation* **14,** 331–338.

Vitetta, E. S., Artzt, K., Bennett, D., Boyse, E. A., and Jacob, F. (1975). *Proc. Natl. Acad. Sci. U.S.A.* **72,** 3215–3219.

Wachtel, S. S. (1977). *Immunol. Rev.* **33,** 3–58.

Wagner, H., Starzinski-Powitz, A., Rollinghoff, M., Golstein, P., and Jakob, H. (1978). *J. Exp. Med.* **147,** 251–264.

Webb, C. G., Gall, W. E., and Edelman, G. M. (1977). *J. Exp. Med.* **146,** 923–932.

Willison, K. R., and Stern, P. L. (1978). *Cell* **14,** 785–793.

Wudl, L. R., and Sherman, M. I. (1976). *Cell* **9,** 523–531.

Wudl, L. R., Sherman, M. I., and Hillman, N. (1977). *Nature (London)* **270,** 137–140.

Yanagisawa, K., Bennett, D., Boyse, E. A., Dunn, L. C., and Dimeo, A. (1974). *Immunogenetics* **1,** 57–67.

Zinkernagel, R., and Oldstone, M. B. (1976). *Proc. Natl. Acad. Sci. U.S.A.* **73,** 3666–3670.

CHAPTER 8

IMMUNOLOGICAL METHODS IN THE STUDY OF CHONDROITIN SULFATE PROTEOGLYCANS

Albert Dorfman, Barbara M. Vertel,[1] *and Nancy B. Schwartz*

DEPARTMENTS OF PEDIATRICS AND BIOCHEMISTRY
JOSEPH P. KENNEDY, JR., MENTAL RETARDATION RESEARCH CENTER
PRITZKER SCHOOL OF MEDICINE
UNIVERSITY OF CHICAGO
CHICAGO, ILLINOIS

I. Introduction

Multicellular organisms are characterized by the presence of extracellular matrix. The role of matrix in the organization and support of tissues is obvious, but recently the possible interactions of matrix components with cell surfaces have received increasing attention. The principal matrix components now recognized are collagens, elastin, fibronectin, proteoglycans, and hyaluronic acid. The concept that these substances are primarily connective tissue components and products of connective tissue cells (e.g., fibroblasts, chondrocytes, and osteocytes) has undergone revision as a result of the demonstration that at least some of these are synthesized by nonconnective tissue cells.

Additionally, it has become clear that matrix components, particularly collagens, vary in structure. Specific gene products are characteristic of individual tissues and developmental stages. In the case of collagen, at least five different proteins have now been identified (for

[1] Present address: Department of Biology, Syracuse University, Syracuse, New York.

169

CURRENT TOPICS IN
DEVELOPMENTAL BIOLOGY, VOL. 14

170   ALBERT DORFMAN *et al.*

review, see Miller, 1976; Fessler and Fessler, 1978). There is evidence
that a similar diversity may exist for proteoglycans. From a developmental point of view, sufficient information has already accumulated
to indicate that specific matrix components are present at certain
stages and, as differentiation proceeds, an orderly succession of products appears. These changes raise two related problems: (*a*) What are
the mechanisms responsible for successive changes in gene expression?
and (*b*) What are the consequences to cell behavior and tissue organization of the appearance of the specific products?

In the case of the collagens, a number of gene products are now
characterized and considerable success has been achieved in the production of specific antibodies for the individual collagens. This has
made possible the development of immunohistochemical methods for
the identification of individual collagens in tissues (reviewed by Timpl
et al., 1977).

The principal carbohydrate components of matrix, the glycosaminoglycans, are now reasonably well characterized both as to chemical structure and pathways of biosynthesis. Whereas earlier studies have focused on the carbohydrate portions of proteoglycans,
more recently the specific proteins to which glycosaminoglycans are
attached (designated core proteins) have been the subject of investigation. Unfortunately, technical problems in obtaining these proteins
completely free of carbohydrate have hampered elucidation of structure.

Since it has been difficult to define the structure of core proteins by
conventional techniques of protein chemistry, a number of investigators have attempted to use immunological approaches to answer
certain structural, biosynthetic, and biological questions: (*a*) Does cartilage chondroitin sulfate proteoglycan core protein contain more than
one antigenic site? (*b*) Can immunological methods be used to establish
the relationship of cartilage chondroitin sulfate proteoglycan to chondroitin sulfate proteoglycans of other tissues? (*c*) What is the extent of
cross-reactivity of proteoglycans of different species? (*d*) To what extent
are available antisera specific for core protein? (*e*) Can immunological
methods be used for quantitation of core proteins? (*f*) Can immunological methods be used for tissue localization of proteoglycans? and (*g*)
Can immunological methods be used for the study of biosynthesis of
core protein to define the biosynthetic product, mRNA, and the involved genes? The application of immunological techniques to the
study of these proteins is still in an early stage of development so that
this chapter can be considered only a progress report. It is hoped, however, that it may serve to bring together currently available informa-

tion and indicate certain critical problems and possible future directions of research. In order to provide an appropriate context for the immunological studies to be discussed, the structure of proteoglycans will be considered first.

II. Structure of Proteoglycans

A. CARTILAGE PROTEOGLYCANS

Studies conducted over the past 35 years have extensively documented the fact that the glycosaminoglycans, chondroitin sulfate, keratan sulfate, dermatan sulfate, heparan sulfate, and heparin occur in tissues covalently bound to proteins. Yet, despite considerable effort, there is no clearcut resolution of the question of whether or not hyaluronic acid is covalently bound to protein although the preponderance of evidence indicates that if binding occurs, it is not to a large core protein.

A number of recent excellent reviews have summarized the current state of knowledge of the structure of proteoglycans (Rosenberg, 1975; Hascall, 1977; Hascall and Heinegård, 1979). Accordingly, this topic will be reviewed primarily from the point of view of the most important considerations necessary for interpretation of immunological and developmental studies.

Progress in the understanding of the structure of proteoglycan has accelerated following the development by Sajdera and Hascall (1969) of the method of nondisruptive extraction employing 4 M guanidinium chloride, 3 M MgCl$_2$, or 6 M LiCl. They discovered that isopycnic centrifugation, in CsCl in the presence of 4 M guanidinium chloride, resulted in sedimentation of proteoglycans as a single component. At lower guanidinium chloride concentrations, larger aggregates were formed. This separation, which depends on the fact that the carbohydrate-containing molecules have a higher buoyant density than do proteins, has been adopted by many investigators. Preparations are generally identified on the basis of these methods, the term A1 referring to aggregates obtained at the bottom of an associative gradient (in the presence of 0.5 M guanidinium chloride) and the term A1-D1 for preparations obtained when the A1 fraction is subsequently separated in a dissociative gradient (4 M guanidinium chloride). Other fractions obtained may be accordingly designated as A2–5 or A1D2–5, depending on the number of fractions collected.

Because a substance present at the top of the dissociative gradient was required for reaggregation of material recovered from the bottom of the gradient, it was postulated that under dissociative conditions, subunits or monomers were separated from factors required for aggregation. Subsequent studies by Keiser *et al.* (1972) demonstrated the presence of two proteins (now referred to as link proteins) in the A1-D4 fractions. Details of current knowledge of the link proteins have been recently reviewed by Baker and Caterson (1979). The nature of the aggregation phenomenon was clarified by the important discovery by Hardingham and Muir (1972) of the role of hyaluronic acid in aggregation. Studies by Gregory (1973) and Hascall and Heinegård (1974a) confirmed and extended these findings. The interaction of hyaluronic acid with proteoglycans has been recently reviewed by Muir and Hardingham (1979). Of a variety of related polymers, only hyaluronic acid was found to participate in this reaction (Hascall and Heinegård, 1974b). Oligosaccharides derived from hyaluronic acid, five or more disaccharide repeating units in length, displace the monomer from the aggregate (Hardingham and Muir, 1973; Hascall and Heinegård, 1974b).

The discovery of the role of hyaluronic acid in aggregation opened the way for further elucidation of the structure of both the monomer and aggregates. There is now considerable evidence that although monomers interact with hyaluronic acid in a presumably reversible fashion, the aggregates formed are stabilized by the presence of link protein.

As a result of these studies, a model of the proteoglycan monomer and its aggregation with hyaluronic acid and link protein has been constructed. The detailed evidence supporting this structure has been reviewed by Hascall (1977) and Hascall and Heinegård (1979). This model, presented in Fig. 1, is based primarily on studies carried out on proteoglycans derived from bovine nasal septum and porcine tracheal cartilage, although many studies of proteoglycans from human articular cartilage, Swarm rat tumor cartilage, and embryonic chick cartilage appear to support the generality of most aspects of the model.

It is suggested that an average proteoglycan molecule has a size of 2.5×10^6 daltons with a core protein of 200,000 daltons. To each core protein are attached approximately 100 chondroitin sulfate chains, of approximately 20,000 daltons, and 30–60 keratan sulfate chains, each 4000–8000 daltons. The hyaluronic acid binding region of about 60,000–80,000 daltons is at one end of the molecule; next to this is a region of 20,000–25,000 daltons, relatively, rich in keratan sulfate. The remainder of the molecule (approximately 100,000 daltons) contains the attached chondroitin sulfate chains as well as a fraction of the keratan sulfate chains (Heinegård, 1977). In monomers obtained from Swarm chondrosarcoma, keratan sulfate is absent and the hyaluronic

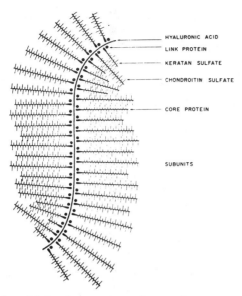

FIG. 1. Proposed model for the structure of proteoglycan aggregate. (Taken from Rosenberg, 1975, with permission from the author.)

acid attachment region was estimated to be 50,000 daltons (Oegema *et al.*, 1975). The hyaluronic acid binding region differs from the chondroitin sulfate containing region in amino acid composition in that it has more aspartic acid, methionine, cysteine, tyrosine, phenylalanine, and arginine, while the chondroitin sulfate substituted region contains relatively higher concentrations of serine and glycine (Rosenberg *et al.*, 1976; Heinegård, 1977).

The proposed model has received support from several electron microscopic studies utilizing the Kleinschmidt technique. Earlier studies involved visualization of monomers (Rosenberg *et al.*, 1970; Wellauer *et al.*, 1972; Thyberg *et al.*, 1975) while more recently Rosenberg *et al.* (1975) and Kimura *et al.* (1978) have studied aggregates.

In general, the various chemical and electron microscopic studies conform well to the proposed model. However, a number of structural problems remain unresolved. From a biosynthetic point of view, the gene product would be expected to be a defined polypeptide of a specific size unless the core protein is made up of subunits which are assembled after translation.

Almost all studies of cartilage chondroitin sulfate proteoglycan have indicated considerable polydispersity. However, it is somewhat difficult to interpret the individual investigations in view of the variation of extraction techniques and tissues studied. A number of different questions may be raised regarding this problem: (*a*) What is the chemical basis of polydispersity of cartilage proteoglycans? (*b*) What is the structural basis for lack of aggregation with hyaluronic acid of a certain fraction of proteoglycans found in cartilage extracts? (*c*) Are those chondroitin sulfate proteoglycans which contain small core proteins structurally different from that of the main bulk of cartilage proteoglycans?

The polydispersity of proteoglycans of bovine nasal septum has recently been examined in considerable detail by Rosenberg *et al.* (1976) and Heinegård (1977). They concluded that the isolated proteoglycans consist of a series of compounds of varying size with differing lengths of core protein. Unlike the conclusions of Hopwood and Robinson (1975), no evidence was found that polydispersity was due to variation in size of chondroitin sulfate chains. In accord with the model illustrated in Fig. 1, they concluded that all the molecules contain the hyaluronic acid binding region, but segments of core protein linked to chondroitin sulfate chains were of variable length. Since preparations utilized for this study were derived from an A1 fraction (proteoglycan associated with hyaluronic acid), no information was obtained with respect to the nature of molecules not aggregated with hyaluronic acid.

In summary, it is difficult to draw final conclusions as to the existence of more than one type of chondroitin sulfate proteoglycan core protein in adult cartilage. The finding of small proteoglycans containing only chondroitin sulfate taken together with finding proteoglycans with variable length chondroitin sulfate regions could well indicate that both derive from a larger proteoglycan as a result of cleavage. Since some studies on heterogeneity (e.g., Rosenberg *et al.*, 1976; Heinegård, 1977) have utilized preparations first isolated by associative gradients, proteoglycans lacking the hyaluronic acid binding regions would be missed. If both the small chondroitin sulfate proteoglycans and the proteoglycans containing binding region derive from the same molecule, the problem of biosynthesis would be more in accord with accepted concepts of protein synthesis. On the basis of biosynthetic experiments, it now seems likely that the core protein of the principal proteoglycan is synthesized as a single peptide of high molecular weight (vide infra).

B. Noncartilage Chondroitin Sulfate Proteoglycans

The possibility of the existence of chondroitin sulfate proteoglycans which contain protein cores different from that of cartilage proteoglycan has received support from developmental studies as well as from the study of proteoglycans of other tissues. Biosynthetic studies have established that dermatan sulfate is formed from chondroitin sulfate following polysaccharide synthesis (Fransson et al., 1973). Since chondroitin sulfate synthesis is dependent on core protein synthesis (Telser et al., 1966), it follows that all proteoglycans containing dermatan sulfate must derive from chondroitin sulfate proteoglycans. Lowther et al. (1970) reported the isolation of a proteoglycan with a molecular weight of 4.2×10^4–6.5×10^4 from bovine heart valves. Conditions of extraction, however, were probably not adequate for extraction of high-molecular-weight proteoglycans. Kresse et al. (1971) isolated a polydisperse proteoglycan from bovine arterial tissue with a molecular weight of 2×10^6 which contained both chondroitin sulfate and dermatan sulfate. Eisenstein et al. (1975) isolated from bovine aorta a proteoglycan containing 20% protein and both chondroitin and dermatan sulfates, but were unable to demonstrate aggregation with hyaluronic acid, perhaps for technical reasons.

Recently S. Gardell, J. Baker, B. Caterson, D. Heinegård, and L. Rodén (personal communication) have extracted material from bovine aorta which is similar in size to cartilage proteoglycan and appears to contain the hyaluronic acid binding region on the basis of immunological studies (vide infra for immunological methods; Wieslander and Heinegård, 1977). They have also identified link protein in such extracts by immunological methods. Oegema et al. (1979) have prepared a polydisperse chondroitin sulfate–dermatan sulfate proteoglycan with a molecular weight of 1.5–2.0×10^6 based on equilibrium sedimentation and consisting of approximately 18% protein. At least 10% of this proteoglycan appears to interact with hyaluronic acid. Norling et al. (1978) isolated a chondroitin sulfate proteoglycan from cultured human glial cells with a molecular size similar to cartilage chondroitin sulfate proteoglycan. A portion of this material appeared to aggregate with hyaluronic acid.

A proteoglycan which acts as a carrier for platelet factor 4 has been isolated by Barber et al. (1972), but whether this is synthesized as such by platelets has not been demonstrated. Chondroitin sulfate has been demonstrated in chick vitreous humor (Smith and Newsome, 1978), but the nature of the proteoglycan has not been elucidated. A chondroitin sulfate proteoglycan isolated from Kurloff cells by Dean and Muir (1970) showed a low protein content and chondroitin sulfate chains larger than those of cartilage proteoglycan. Whether this material is synthesized by the Kurloff cells was not clearly established.

Öbrink (1971) isolated a polydisperse dermatan sulfate proteoglycan from pig skin which contained 58% protein and had a molecular weight of 2.9×10^6 (light scattering). Only traces of heparan sulfate and chondroitin sulfate were contained in this complex. More recently, Damle *et al.* (1978) have also isolated a dermatan sulfate proteoglycan from pig skin which contained only 4–5% protein and did not aggregate with hyaluronic acid. The exact size was not specified, but it was reported to be considerably smaller than proteoglycan subunit of cartilage. A chondroitin sulfate proteoglycan isolated from adult rat brains by Margolis *et al.* (1976) appeared to contain a relatively small amount of chondroitin sulfate and was closely associated with a glycoprotein. Whether the glycoprotein is covalently linked to the same core protein as the chondroitin sulfate chains was not clearly established.

Recently Yanagishita *et al.* (1979) characterized a proteoglycan in porcine ovarian follicular fluid which contains 50% hybrid chondroitin sulfate–dermatan sulfate chains (56,000 daltons), 20% protein, and 20% oligosaccharides rich in sialic acid, galactose, mannose, glucosamine, and galactosamine. The protein, estimated to be 400,000 daltons, was significantly different from cartilage core protein in amino acid composition and the proteoglycan did not aggregate with hyaluronic acid. The detailed studies of this material perhaps establish with greater certainty than any previous study the existence of a proteoglycan clearly different from cartilage proteoglycan. J. R. Hassell and D. A. Newsome (personal communication) have reported the presence of a chondroitin sulfate proteoglycan of 170,000 daltons in monkey corneal stroma with only one or two chondroitin sulfate chains of 60,000 daltons each and with one or more glycoprotein-type oligosaccharide side chains of 2500 daltons. S. DeLuca, V. C. Hascall, and A. Caplan (personal communication) have reported the presence of mannose- and sialic acid-containing oligosaccharides in proteoglycans isolated from chick limb bud chondrocyte cultures. K. Sugahara and A. Dorfman (unpublished results) have found a small proteoglycan containing very few chondroitin sulfate chains in embryonic chick calvarium. This material was isolated in the presence of proteolytic inhibitors.

C. PROTEOGLYCANS IN DEVELOPMENT

Recently, a number of studies have been concerned with changing patterns of structure of proteoglycans during development. Most available information stems from studies of differentiation of embryonic cartilage and of the nanomelic chick. Palmoski and Goetinck (1972) observed that chromatography of a hyaluronidase-sensitive proteoglycan produced by cultured chondrocytes derived from embryonic chick sternae resulted in the separation of two different sized proteoglycans.

The larger proteoglycan was absent in the material synthesized by BrdUrd-treated cells and cells derived from nanomelic chicks. They concluded that the smaller species represents a nonspecific proteoglycan while the larger species represents a cartilage-specific proteoglycan. In a subsequent publication (Pennypacker and Goetinck, 1976), small amounts of the larger proteoglycan were found to be produced by cultures of chondrocytes from nanomelic chicks. Levitt and Dorfman (1973, 1974) found evidence for two different sized proteoglycans in cultures of limb bud mesenchyme which differentiate to cartilage. Almost complete inhibition of synthesis of the larger species, but not the smaller, occurred following inhibition of cartilage differentiation by BrdUrd. A portion of the smaller proteoglycan contains heparan sulfate (P.-L. Ho and A. Dorfman, unpublished results). The smaller species, but not the larger, was present before differentiation. Similar results were reported by Goetinck et al. (1974). It was concluded that on differentiation the chondrocyte acquires the capacity to form large amounts of a cartilage-specific proteoglycan. The capacity to synthesize the more ubiquitous small proteoglycan is present before differentiation or in BrdUrd-inhibited cells. Lash and Vasan (1978) have studied the nature of proteoglycans formed by somites when cultured in the presence of a variety of agents which stimulate chondrogenesis. During chondrogenesis, they found an increase in the size of proteoglycan monomers and an increase in the synthesis of aggregates.

The detailed structure of proteoglycans synthesized by chick limb bud mesenchyme cultures recently has been studied by DeLuca et al. (1977, 1978) and Kimura et al. (1978). Proteoglycans of 2- to 3-day-old cultures were smaller than those isolated from older cultures and contained two components. A significant portion of these proteoglycans contained heparan sulfate. The proteoglycans of earlier cultures did not aggregate with hyaluronic acid.

Okayama et al. (1976) have investigated the behavior on centrifugation in sucrose gradients of proteoglycans extracted by 4 M guanidinium chloride from a variety of embryonic chick tissues. On the basis of sedimentation velocity, four fractions of $^{35}SO_4^{2-}$-labeled proteoglycan were separated. A characteristic larger proteoglycan was found to be synthesized by embryonic vertebral chondrocytes, limb bud chondrocytes, and somite chondrocytes. In contrast, fibroblasts, blastodisc cells, spinal cord cells, and BrdUrd-treated chondrocytes produced only smaller proteoglycans. It was concluded that only chondrocytes (chondroblasts in the authors' terminology) have the capacity to produce a cartilage-specific proteoglycan. Somewhat similar findings were reported by Kitamura and Yamagata (1976).

Another developmental approach has recently been used by Reddi *et al.* (1978). Following the implantation of bone matrix powder in rats there is a sequential development of cartilage and bone. Proteoglycans synthesized 7 days after implantation of bone powder were similar in size to those obtained from rat femoral heads, but contained little keratan sulfate. Association with hyaluronic acid was demonstrated by the presence of aggregates when an associative extraction was used or carrier proteoglycan was added. On day 11 when osteogenesis begins, a smaller proteoglycan is synthesized. The smaller type of proteoglycan has larger chondroitin sulfate chains and does not aggregate.

III. Antigenicity of Proteoglycans

A. GENERAL COMMENTS

From the earliest studies of the immunology of connective tissue components, particularly polysaccharides and collagen, the view prevailed that they were either nonantigenic or poorly so. Failure to produce antibodies in rabbits immunized with hyaluronate isolated from connective tissues or bacteria was reported (Kendall *et al.*, 1937; Seastone, 1939; Humphrey, 1943; Quinn and Singh, 1957). Using highly purified polysaccharide, Boake and Muir (1955) reported the nonantigenicity of chondroitin sulfate, while the apparent lack of antigenicity of collagen was also observed (Kirrane and Robertson, 1968).

Later studies necessitated modification of these views. Probably the major reason for this change was the utilization of milder methods for the isolation of antigens. Formerly, definition of the chemical structure of polysaccharides was the primary objective, with consequent use of disruptive conditions including enzymic or chemical means (particularly alkali treatment), to remove as much (contaminant) protein as possible. Once it was firmly established that anionic polysaccharides, with the possible exception of hyaluronate, are covalently bound to noncollagenous protein to form protein–polysaccharides or proteoglycans, more gentle nondisruptive extraction procedures were developed which preserved the integrity of the protein moiety.

B. NATURE OF ANTIGENIC DETERMINANTS

Several investigators discovered during the period 1960–1970 that protein–polysaccharides of cartilage are antigenic. In 1962 Saunders *et al.* reported the development of skin sensitivity in rats immunized with bovine cartilage protein–polysaccharides. DiFerrante (1964) described precipitating antibodies against protein–polysaccharide complexes extracted from bovine nasal septa, as well as against a "light" (PP-L) fraction obtained according to the techniques described by Shubert and co-workers (Gerber et al., 1960). White et al. (1963a,b) produced both precipitating and agglutinating antibodies to human cartilage protein–polysaccharide, and showed that antigenicity was closely associated with the protein moiety. By the technique of indirect hemagglutination, DiFerrante and Pauling (1964) demonstrated the production of two different types of antibodies in rabbits following injections of a protein–polysaccharide extracted from bovine nasal septa. One type, directed against the protein–polysaccharide, appeared to be species specific, while the other type, directed against chondroitin 4-SO$_4$ was not species specific. It was postulated that the species-specific antigenic determinants depend on the amino acid sequence or the conformation of peptides contiguous to the carbohydrate moiety. Loewi (1965) produced precipitating and agglutinating antibodies to porcine cartilage protein–polysaccharides, and later Loewi and Muir (1965) reported that the cross-reacting antigenic determinant in porcine cartilage protein–polysaccharide was not chondroitin sulfate. One constituent was found to be shared with chondroitin sulfate proteoglycans from several other species, while additional constituents of the antigen were revealed only following hyaluronidase digestion.

Once the antigenicity of the protein–polysaccharide from cartilage was firmly etablished, specific questions, including the number and nature of the antigenic determinants of cartilage protein–polysaccharide, were examined. Sandson et al. (1966) prepared antisera in rabbits to bovine, human, and porcine PP-L. The antisera to PP-L from each species were studied by both precipitation and agglutination techniques. Their results indicated that PP-L contained a minimum of two antigenic determinants; one is species specific, and the other is not. Both antigenic determinants appeared to be in, or closely associated with, the protein moiety of PP-L. In subsequent studies (Sandson et al., 1969; Hammerman and Sandson, 1970), cartilage protein–polysaccharides from 11 different species were shown to cross-react. Inhibition studies using tanned sheep red blood cells indicated that the cartilage protein–polysaccharides from these 11 species share at least one common antigenic determinant. It was not ascertained, however, whether this common component and the species-specific component previously reported (Sandson et al., 1966) are both present on the same or different molecules. The reactive components could be separated by hyaluronidase digestion of the protein–polysaccharide; immunoelectrophoresis then showed that the common component migrated more rapidly than the species-specific component (Sandson et al., 1966; Pankovich and Korngold, 1967). DiFerrante (1970) fractionated hyaluronidase-treated proteoglycan isolated from bovine nasal septa on DEAE-Sephadex. This material was found to be a mixture of various fragments, some inactive and some immunologically more active than nondegraded proteoglycan. The method of preparation of the immunologically active fragments suggested that the possible occurrence of electrostatic bonds may result in shielding of antigenic sites. The possibility remained that the carbohydrate chains played a role in the structure of the antigenic sites since the immunologically active fractions of the proteoglycan digests contained substantial amounts of chondroitin sulfate.

Tsiganos and Muir (1969b) and Brandt et al. (1970) fractionated and characterized by chemical and immunological methods protein-polysaccharides from pig laryngeal cartilage. Proteoglycans, extracted with neutral isoosmotic sodium acetate, were separated by gel filtration on 6% agarose into two fractions which differed in chemical composition and in antigenic determinants. The retarded fraction possessed a single antigen, while the excluded fraction contained the same antigen as the starting material and the antigen found in the retarded fraction. Five different N-terminal amino acids were identified in the excluded fraction, only two of which were present in the retarded material. Additional differences in amino acid composition were detected while polysaccharide chain length and keratan sulfate content were similar in both. It was concluded that these preparations were heterogeneous and selection of certain types of molecules takes place during extraction and purification.

Most of the studies of the immunological properties of cartilage proteoglycans described during this period used relatively crude material derived by ultracentrifugation of cartilage homogenates. The introduction of the nondisruptive extraction procedure (Sajdera and Hascall, 1969) coupled with fractionation by CsCl density-gradient centrifugation (Hascall and Sajdera, 1969) led to the preparation of new and more clearly defined proteoglycan fractions.

The first reports of immunological studies of proteoglycan components derived from cartilage by the method of Hascall and Sajdera were by DiFerrante et al. (1970). These investigators coated glutaraldehyde-fixed erythrocytes with bovine proteoglycan subunit and glycoprotein link fraction and used antisera to disruptively prepared bovine and human PP-L fraction in hemagglutination and inhibition assays. On the basis of their results, they concluded that the glycoprotein link fraction contained most of the species-specific antigenic determinants whereas the proteoglycan subunits contained most of the cross-reacting ones.

In a subsequent and more exhaustive study, Keiser *et al.* (1972) prepared precipitating antibodies by immunization of rabbits with bovine cartilage proteoglycan aggregate, subunit and link fractions. The antisera were used to identify an antigenic component in bovine subunit preparations which displayed rapid mobility on immunoelectrophoresis and was also found in human, porcine, chicken, and rat proteoglycan. Bovine proteoglycan aggregate and link fractions were shown to have antigenic components in addition to the subunit-associated components which characteristically formed the precipitin line nearest the antibody well on immunodiffusion. The bovine link-associated antigens had slower mobility on immunoelectrophoresis and were not identified in proteoglycan preparations from the four other species tested. The subunit or core protein-associated antigen appeared to be identical with the previously described fast determinant of PP-L fraction, whereas the slow species-specific determinant of PP-L fraction appeared to be associated with the link fraction (Sandson *et al.*, 1966). Similar results were obtained with human articular cartilage proteoglycans prepared by nondisruptive extraction (Keiser and Sandson, 1974).

In a subsequent study, DiFerrante *et al.* (1972) showed that immunological and concanavalin A affinity reagents failed to detect the glycoprotein link component in nondisruptive preparations of proteoglycan complex. This finding led to the hypothesis that in native cartilage, glycoprotein link may represent a segregated antigen which is shielded by the dense cloud of negative charges and large domain occupied by proteoglycan subunit molecules. This model fitted well with the postulated organization of proteoglycan complex consisting of proteoglycan subunits bound together via noncovalent interactions by glycoprotein molecules and was dramatically illustrated by the "sunburst" pattern in the early electron microscopic studies of Rosenberg *et al.* (1970).

Another currently popular view during this period involved the substructure of proteoglycan core protein. A segment of core protein of approximately 10 amino acids remained resistant to digestion by trypsin and chymotrypsin. This segment contained two adjacent chondroitin sulfate chains and thus was often referred to as "doublets" (Mathews, 1971). Hemagglutination and inhibition studies indicated that doublets derived from bovine and porcine proteoglycan contain at least one species common antigenic determinant (Sandson *et al.*, 1970; Baxter and Muir, 1972). Since doublets from various species have the same glycosidic linkage and similar amino acid residues, either the glycoside, the peptide, or both, could be determinants of a species common antigen. Baxter and Muir (1972) and Muir *et al.* (1973) showed that proteoglycan subjected to the Smith degradation procedure, which removes the chondroitin sulfate side chains and neutral sugar bridge from the serine hydroxyl group, retained species common immunologic reactivity. The Smith degraded bovine proteoglycan reacted with antisera to pig proteoglycan and the reaction was inhibited by "doublets" from pig proteoglycans, suggesting that the amino acid sequence of the doublet peptide is the determinant of a species common antigen. The possibility was not excluded, however, of there being additional antigenic determinants, species common or species specific, related to other portions of the proteoglycan subunit.

The study of link protein is presently being approached by immunological methods. B. Caterson and J. Baker (personal communication) have recently developed a highly sensitive radioimmunoassay for link protein and A. R. Poole, A. Reiner, H. Choi, and L. C. Rosenberg (personal communication) have also reported specific antibodies for link proteins.

A model of the proteoglycan subunit differing from the early conceptions has been proposed. As discussed in Section I, the proteoglycan subunit has structural and functional polarity: one end consisting of core protein and predominantly chondroitin sulfate chains, and the other ends which includes the hyaluronic acid binding region and core protein predominantly containing keratan sulfate chains (Hascall and Heinegård, 1974a). Fragments from either end of the molecule can be obtained by proteolytic digestion of proteoglycan subunit followed by Sepharose or DEAE-cellulose chromatography (Hascall and Heinegård, 1974a; Keiser and DeVito, 1974). Immunological analysis of these fragments has revealed that the proteoglycan subunit contains at least two different antigenic determinants, one present in both chondroitin sulfate and keratan sulfate containing peptide fragments and a second found only in keratan sulfate containing peptide fragments (Keiser and DeVito, 1974). These studies were followed by an immunological characterization of the functionally distinct fragments of proteoglycan complex produced by Heinegård and Hascall's method (1974) of chondroitinase-trypsin digestion and Sepharose 2B chromatography. The immunological results support the finding (Keiser, 1975) that the initial Sepharose 2B peak contains the keratan sulfate-containing portion of proteoglycan subunit and one link protein, while the second peak contains these two components in addition to the expected chondroitin sulfate-containing fragments. All of these results indicate that proteoglycan subunit is not uniform in structure, but instead contains two or more segments which differ in the type of polysaccharide side chain, in amino acid composition of the associated portion of core protein and in immunological properties. Thus, the previous results of Brandt et al. (1973) on the proteoglycans of different hydrodynamic size in cartilage homogenates, which also differ in immunologic activity, are not necessarily inconsistent with the existence of a single proteoglycan core protein which was modified during extraction to yield intact molecules with differing proportions of chondroitin and keratan sulfate chains.

Some of the early studies reviewed above suggest the possibility of the presence of two antigenic sites, one of which is species cross-reactive. This question has recently been examined by Wieslander and Heinegård (1977, 1979) who utilized trypsin- and chondroitinase-digested monomers to separate hyaluronic acid binding region from the chondroitin sulfate-containing portion of the proteoglycan. On rocket electrophoresis, it was found that each fraction produced specific antibodies, both of which reacted with the proteoglycan monomer. Antibodies to the hyaluronic acid binding region were found to be species specific while those to the chondroitin sulfate-containing region are species nonspecific. Antibodies prepared to link protein did not cross-react with either region of the proteoglycan monomer. Further evidence for a species-specific antigenic site has been obtained by Sugahara and Dorfman (1979). Reduction and alkylation of hyaluronidase-treated proteoglycan obtained from embryonic chick epiphyses or rat chondrosarcoma markedly alters reactivity with antisera to nonreduced core protein. Species-specific reactivity was almost totally abolished. Reduction and alkylation is known to alter the hyaluronic acid binding region (Hardingham et al., 1976).

Recently, A. R. Poole, A. Reiner, H. Choi, and L. C. Rosenberg (person communication) have used double immunodiffusion, rocket, and crossed immunoelectrophoresis to study an antisera raised in sheep to bovine nasal cartilage proteoglycan. With double immunodiffusion, two lines of equal intensity were observed with proteoglycan subunit from purified nasal cartilage, but only one with subunit from bovine epiphyseal or articular cartilage. No cross-reaction was observed with subunit prepared from human hyaline cartilage or chondrosarcomas. Antiserum prepared against human chondrosarcoma proteoglycan, absorbed with human serum, showed two lines when reacted against the preparation used as immunizing antigen and did not react with bovine nasal septum subunit. When reacted with preparations from other chondrosarcomas, two lines were obtained with some and one line with others. With preparations from human adult cartilage, two lines were obtained while preparations from fetal articular or epiphyseal cartilages yielded only one line. No cross-reaction of these sera with link protein or type II collagen was observed. It was concluded that in some cartilage there are two immunologically distinct core proteins. One question remains unanswered: Is core protein a single polypeptide chain, or does there exist more than one species of core protein in cartilage and other tissues? Studies using either chondroitinase or testicular hyaluronidase to remove enzymically chondroitin sulfate side chains from the proteoglycan subunit have yielded conflicting results. In one recent study, Keiser and Hatcher (1977) showed that a chondroitinase-produced core protein preparation isolated as a single peak on Sepharose gel chromatography contained at least two immunologically distinct components. Hyaluronidase-produced core protein from the same proteoglycan subunit fraction was found to contain multiple components nearly all of which were smaller than the components in the chondroitinase digest. These investigators suggested that the multiple components result from proteolytic degradation of the core protein in the course of the enzymic removal of chondroitin sulfate. In fact, they detected the presence of small amounts of protease contaminants in several commercial chondroitinase and hyaluronidase preparations by a sensitive radioassay. They concluded that until proteases can be rigorously excluded from enzyme preparations, it will not be possible to determine whether the proteoglycan consists of a single or several different core proteins. However, in more recent studies, antigens prepared by digestion with testicular hyaluronidase or chondroitinase ABC gave similar results in the radioimmunoassay and on double diffusion studies in agarose (P.-L. Ho and A. Dorfman, unpublished results.) It seems likely that a distinction between antigenically different components and multiple antigenic sites will be resolved by the use of clonal antibodies. A. Dorfman, T. Hall, P.-L. Ho, and F. Fitch (unpublished results) have recently succeeded in preparing antibody-producing clones by hybridizing mouse myeloma cells with spleen cells from rats immunized with core protein. Clonal antibodies have been obtained which react in the radioimmunoassay (vide infra).

C. RADIOIMMUNOASSAY

Recently, more sensitive immunological methods have been utilized to study core protein. Keiser and DeVito (1974) utilized ^{125}I-labeled purified bovine proteoglycan subunit for a radioimmunoassay. Nevo and Michaeli (1975) have used ^{125}I-labeled antigen for a radioimmunoassay of Swarm rat chondrosarcoma. Iodination permits the preparation of an antigen of high specific radioactivity, but has the disadvantage of possible lack of specificity since adequate criteria for the determination of purity of core protein have not been established. For this reason, Ho et al. (1977) utilized $^{35}SO_4^{2-}$-labeled antigen. This method is based on the assumption that chondroitin sulfate proteoglycan represents the only $^{35}SO_4^{2-}$-containing substance in cartilage. The labeled antigen was prepared from differentiating chick limb bud mesenchyme cultures exposed to $^{35}SO_4^{2-}$. Proteoglycan subunit was isolated in the presence of proteolytic inhibitors by an associative and two dissociative CsCl gradients. The labeled antigen was treated with highly purified testicular hyaluronidase and the released oligosaccharides were separated from the core protein by chromatography on Sephadex G-200. Although hyaluronidase removes approximately 85% of the radioactivity, the $^{35}SO_4^{2-}$ linked to keratan sulfate and the remaining stubs of chondroitin sulfate permit the preparation of an antigen of sufficiently high specific activity for a radioimmunoassay. Antisera were prepared in rabbits by injecting hyaluronidase-treated nonradioactive antigen prepared from epiphyseal cartilage of 13-day-old chick embryos in the same manner as previously described. Utilizing the $(NH_4)_2SO_4$ method of Farr (1958), a direct precipitation method was developed. In early studies, the method gave linearity up to approximately 60% precipitation of antigen, but more recently precipitation of up to 85% of radioactive antigen is usually observed. The method has been modified to utilize formalinized Staphylococcus aureus for precipitation of antibody–antigen complex. A disadvantage of $^{35}SO_4^{2-}$-labeled antigen is the decay of $^{35}SO_4^{2-}$. To overcome this problem, labeling with [^{3}H]acetate has been used. Results similar to those with $^{35}SO_4^{2-}$ have been obtained. However, since acetate may label other components, this antigen has not been used regularly. Antisera prepared in rabbits show detectable antibodies at a dilution of serum as great as 1 : 6000.

When antisera produced against proteoglycan subunit (prepared as previously described) was tested by the double diffusion method, up to three lines have been observed. In order to determine whether the lines were due to a $^{35}SO_4^{2-}$-labeled antigen, a usual double diffusion reaction was carried out followed by autoradiography. Two major lines containing radioactive label were observed. These results suggest that at least two $^{35}SO_4^{2-}$-containing substances are present in the antigen. Absorption of serum by embryonic liver powder produced no change in pattern (T. Hall and A. Dorfman, unpublished results). Antisera contained no antibodies to type I or type II collagen as measured by radioimmunoassay or hemagglutination (Vertel and Dorfman, 1979).

The radioimmunoassay permits the conclusion that the antiserum contains antibodies to a protein containing covalently linked ester sulfate. When proteoglycan monomer is used, the extent of contamination by counts due to heparan sulfate is low, but even a small contamination becomes more significant following hyaluronidase treatment, which removes approximately 85% of the counts. This error becomes particularly significant with noncartilage cells or BrdUrd-treated cells, for heparan sulfate may constitute a significant portion of the $^{35}SO_4^{2-}$ counts. In proteoglycan prepared from limb bud cells inhibited from differentiation it has recently been found (P.-L. Ho and A. Dorfman, unpublished results) that heparan sulfate may account for 50% of the radioactivity.

A radioimmunoinhibition method based on these reagents may be used to detect nonradioactive core protein in the concentration range of 5–50 μg. Radioimmunoinhibition assays are not only useful because of their sensitivity and capacity to detect nonradioactive antigen, but the observed slope usually permits conclusions regarding identity or cross-reactivity.

The inhibition assay has been used to demonstrate the increase of synthesis of core protein of chondroitin sulfate proteoglycan during the differentiation of chick limb bud mesenchyme in high-density cultures and the inhibition of this synthesis as a result of treatment of such cultures with BrdUrd (Ho et al., 1977). The method has also been used to demonstrate that although β-xylosides prevent normal synthesis of proteoglycan in cultured chondrocytes, no inhibition of core protein synthesis occurs (Schwartz et al., 1976).

The immunological approach was also employed to examine the secretion process of the under-glycosylated core protein produced by β-xyloside-treated cells. In order to compare the rate of secretion of core protein from treated and control cells, methods for determining intracellular and extracellular cartilage core protein by radiolabeling and immunochemistry were developed (N. B. Schwartz and B. M. Vertel, unpublished results). Immunohistochemical procedures (vide infra) were used to monitor the removal of extracellular proteoglycan by hyaluronidase treatment of unfixed control and treated cells which had been labeled with either $^{35}SO_4^{2-}$, [^{3}H]glucosamine, or [^{3}H]serine. By comparing radioactivity remaining after hyaluronidase digestion with that present initially, an estimate of intracellular and extracellular matrix-associated proteoglycan was possible. In all cases, more of the material labeled with any of the three isotopes remained after hyaluronidase digestion of β-xyloside-treated cells than in controls, indicating that the partially glycosylated proteoglycan is not as efficiently exported from the cell as is completely glycosylated material (Schwartz, 1979). The intracellular and extracellular distribution of core protein has also been quantitiated for both types of cultures by radioimmunoinhibition assays. In agreement with isotope incorporation studies, the intracellular accumulation of core protein in β-xyloside-treated cells was also demonstrated. There was also an indication that these cells may be synthesizing more total core protein than do untreated control cells.

The radioimmunoassay has been used successfully for the study of proteoglycan prepared from Swarm rat chondrosarcoma. Antigen may be labeled with $^{35}SO_4^{2-}$ by incubating cell suspensions with $^{35}SO_4^{2-}$ or by labeling the purified antigen with ^{125}I (N. B. Schwartz, K. Ellis, C. Coudron, unpublished results). The $^{35}SO_4^{2-}$-labeled antigen purified and prepared by hyaluronidase treatment, and the ^{125}I-labeled antigen purified and digested prior to iodination were compared by radioimmunoinhibition assays using each as the competing antigen with the other. Inhibition levels of 80–90% were observed with both, indicating iodination does not significantly alter the antigenic properties of the core protein.

D. CROSS-REACTIVITY OF CHONDROITIN SULFATE PROTEOGLYCANS

In subsequent studies using ^{125}I-labeled rat chondrosarcoma antigen in inhibition assays with antisera prepared against rat chondrosarcoma proteoglycan, the nature of core proteins from cartilage sources from different species as well as from different tissues from the same species was studied. Embryonic chick cartilage, rat fibrosarcoma, and cultured rat glioma (RG-6) cell core proteins competed with this rat chondrosarcoma antigen, indicating cross-reactivity between cartilage proteoglycan core protein and core proteins from different tissues (N. B. Schwartz, unpublished results).

K. Sugahara and A. Dorfman (unpublished results) observed competition of a radioactive antigen prepared from embryonic chick epiphyses with antisera prepared against proteoglycan subunits of both chick epiphyses and rat chondrosarcoma. However, there is a marked difference between relative potency of the antisera when measured against homologous and heterologous antigens.

K. Sugahara and A. Dorfman (unpublished results) have also studied the cross-reactivity of proteoglycan prepared from embryonic chick calvaria with cartilage proteoglycans. Preparations derived from chick calvaria inhibited the reaction of chick antiserum with radioactive chick $^{35}SO_4^{2-}$ antigen, as well as the reaction of rat serum with chick radioactive $^{35}SO_4^{2-}$ antigen. Such preparations also inhibited reaction of chick serum with rat ^{125}I-labeled antigen, but did not inhibit the reaction of rat serum with rat ^{125}I-labeled antigen. Perhaps some of these apparent differences are due to the nature of ^{125}I- and $^{35}SO_4{}^{2-}$-labeled antigens. Cross-reactivity of chick calvarium and cartilage antigens was also demonstrated by double immunodiffusion.

E. EFFECT OF CHEMICAL MODIFICATION ON IMMUNOGENICITY

The immunoreactivity of deglycosylated proteoglycans, used as xylosyltransferase acceptors, was also examined. Chondroitin sulfate was removed from rat chondrosarcoma proteoglycan by purified hyaluronidase digestion followed by treatment with hydrogen fluoride in pyridine or by Smith degradation. The latter two procedures produced excellent xylosyltransferase acceptors. However, quantitative radioimmune inhibition assay indicated a 50-fold decrease in immunoreactivity of the proteoglycan preparations deglycosylated by either treatment (N. B. Schwartz, K. Ellis, C. Coudron, and L. Philipson, unpublished results). These results suggest some structural alteration is induced by complete removal of carbohydrate as measured by reaction with antibodies prepared against proteoglycans containing minimal amounts of carbohydrate. Reduction and alkylation of either chick or rat proteoglycan subunit results in a marked decrease of capacity to compete in the respective homologous inhibition assays. Slightly more activity is retained when the reduced and alkylated preparations are assayed in heterologous systems. On double diffusion studies, reduction and alkylation abolished all reactivity of the chick antigen. In the case of rat antigen, a major precipitin line disappeared while minor lines were still present (Sugahara and Dorfman, 1979).

F. IDENTIFICATION OF PRODUCTS OF CELL-FREE SYNTHESIS

Studies of chondroitin sulfate proteoglycan biosynthesis have relied almost exclusively on post-translational properties of the macromolecule for identification. Using this approach it has not been possible to examine adequately the nascent core protein prior to glycosylation. Upholt et al. (1977, 1979) are presently utilizing immunological techniques in the isolation and identification of core protein synthesized in cell-free translation systems. It has been demonstrated that RNA isolated from embryonic chick sternae or differentiated limb bud cultures is translated in a wheat germ system into a protein with an apparent molecular weight of 340,000. This protein, not translated using liver or calvaria RNA, is immunoprecipitated by antibodies to core protein. Furthermore, the same component is immunoprecipitated by a monoclonal antibody which also immunoprecipitates the $^{35}SO_4$-labeled core protein antigen (A. Dorfman, B. M. Vertel, and W. B. Upholt, unpublished results). RNA isolated from Swarm rat chondrosarcoma is translated into a protein with a slightly lower apparent molecular weight (B. M. Vertel, W. B. Upholt, and A. Dorfman, unpublished results).

G. IMMUNOHISTOCHEMISTRY

The availability of specific antisera for core protein permits localization of proteoglycan in tissues by a variety of immunohistochemical methods. Loewi and Muir (1965) were among the first to use immunofluorescent localization of proteoglycans in tissue sections. Loewi (1965) and Barland et al. (1966) also examined the localization of protein–polysaccharides in tissues by indirect immunofluorescent techniques. When cartilage sections were studied with antiserum to cartilage protein–polysaccharides, fluorescence was observed primarily in the lacuna of the chondrocyte in the perilacunar area. If cartilage was pretreated with testicular hyaluronidase, fluorescence was diffusely distributed throughout the matrix. Fluorescence with an antiserum to cartilage protein–polysaccharide was also found in other tissues, including basement membrane of glomerulus and renal tubule, sarcolemma of cardiac and skeletal muscle, basement membrane of tracheal mucosa and thyroid, and endothelium and basement membrane of blood vessels. However, it is difficult to draw conclusions concerning the cross-reactivity of proteoglycans in different tissues from these earlier experiments because of the poor characterization of the antisera used.

Vertel and Dorfman in immunohistochemical studies (1978, 1979, and unpublished results) have analyzed chondrogenesis in vitro. Rabbit anti-core protein IgG was used in indirect immunohistochemical reactions in conjunction with goat anti-rabbit IgG coupled to fluorescein isothiocyanate, peroxidase, or hemocyanin to analyze the extracellular accumulation and distribution of chondroitin sulfate proteoglycan. Immunohistochemical reaction products were localized to alcian blue staining regions in differentiating limb bud cultures. High-density cultures which were incubated with the antibody probes demonstrated an increasing reaction after 2 days of culture. Analogous immunofluorescence patterns were obtained with antibodies specific for type II collagen (B. M. Vertel and A. Dorfman, unpublished results). Areas of noncartilage cells in the same cultures did not react with anti-core protein or anti-type II collagen sera. Instead, type I collagen antibodies were extensively localized in early limb bud cultures as well as in regions of noncartilage mesenchyme in increasingly older cultures (B. M. Vertel and A. Dorfman, unpublished results). Cultures blocked from differentiation to cartilage by BrdUrd reacted with anti-type I collagen, but failed to react with anti-core protein or anti-type II collagen.

Scanning electron microscopy of preparations reacted with core protein antibodies and hemocyanin goat anti-rabbit IgG revealed that hemocyanin–antibody complexes completely covered the filamentous cartilage matrix, even at early stages of differentiation (Vertel and Dorfman, 1978). The extensive binding of hemocyanin obscured detail of matrix substructure.

All of the hemocyanin–antibody complexes appeared to be associated with filamentous (presumably type II collagen) components in the matrix. This close association between proteoglycan aggregates and type II collagen filaments probably represents a condensation of aggregate along the structural collagen frame resulting from fixation and dehydration and/or drying procedures necessary for preparation for scanning electron microscopy. Presumably, in hydrated tissue, proteoglycan aggregates are associated with the collagen structural framework, but also extend to fill spaces between filaments. In contrast to the extensive binding of hemocyanin in matrix surrounding chondrocytes, no hemocyanin–antibody complexes were observed in matrix synthesized by high-density limb bud cultures blocked from differentiation to cartilage by BrdUrd.

In order to examine the intracellular localization of core protein in chondrocytes in the transmission electron microscope, ferritin–IgG complexes were prepared with anti-core protein IgG and with normal rabbit IgG as described by Kishida *et al.* (1975). Chondrocytes were trypsinized from 16-day-old chick embryo sternae, allowed to recover from enzyme treatment, fixed, and homogenized as described by Olsen *et al.* (1975) prior to immunohistochemical reaction and processing for electron microscopy. Ferritin–anti-core protein IgG complexes were observed predominantly in the rough endoplasmic reticulum and sometimes in Golgi vesicles of sternal chondrocytes, whereas ferritin–normal rabbit IgG complexes were not specifically localized (B. M. Vertel and A. Dorfman, unpublished results).

The relationship of synthesis of type I collagen (characteristic of noncartilage connective tissue) and synthesis of the cartilage matrix components, chondroitin sulfate proteoglycan and type II collagen, has been examined in individual cells during chondrogenesis by simultaneous indirect immunofluorescence reactions using fluorescein- and rhodamine-coupled antibodies (Vertel and Dorfman, 1979). Unfixed cells were used for antibody localization in extracellular matrix (B. M. Vertel and A. Dorfman, unpublished results). The fine fibrillar meshwork of type II collagen surrounding chondrocytes grown in the presence of ascorbate was distinguishable from the more uniform distribution of core protein immunofluorescence in cartilage matrix and from the coarser type I collagen fibers surrounding flattened noncartilage cells in low-density limb bud cultures. It is particularly useful to study the structure of matrix surrounding unfixed cells, for under these conditions the matrix retains its water content, and fixation and dehydration artifacts will not be created.

In order to visualize both intra- and extracellular localization of antibodies, cultures grown at low densities were fixed and treated to permit antibody entrance into the cells (Vertel and Dorfman, 1979). Simultaneous staining revealed extensive accumulation of core protein around chondrocytes and intracellular accumulation of type II collagen. Extracellular core protein immunofluorescence obscured the intracellular reaction product, but could be removed by brief digestion with purified testicular hyaluronidase prior to fixation.

Subsequent to enzymic digestion, core protein and type II collagen were usually observed in the same chondrocytes within discrete, sometimes identical cytoplasmic regions (Fig. 2). These results directly demonstrate simultaneous localization of core protein and type II collagen within the same cartilage cells. Cycloheximide reversibly inhibited the intracellular localization of these products, thereby establishing that the cytoplasmic immunofluorescence truly reflects a biosynthetic process.

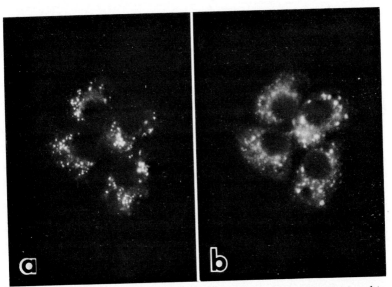

Fig. 2. Simultaneous immunofluorescence localization of core protein (a) and type II collagen (b) in sternal chondrocytes cultured for 4 days and digested with purified testicular hyaluronidase prior to fixation. Immunofluorescence is observed in discrete cytoplasmic regions which are sometimes coincident.

Although the specific cytoplasmic sites and intensity of immunofluorescence for type II collagen and core protein varied for individual chondrocytes, between days 3 and 10 of cell culture, equivalent intracellular staining for both cartilage products was observed in greater than 85% of the cells identifiable as chondrocytes by cell morphology. Most of the remaining 15% stained for both products, but stained more intensely for one or the other. Flattened, fibroblast-like cells in differentiating cartilage cultures and in cultures blocked from differentiation by BrdUrd did not react with antibodies to the cartilage-specific products. However, intracellular localization of type I collagen antibodies was demonstrated for these cells. Simultaneous staining of differentiating cartilage cultures with type I collagen antibodies and either type II collagen or core protein antibodies established these two distinct cell populations.

As discussed previously, chondrocytes grown at low density in culture accumulated only chondroitin sulfate proteoglycan extracellularly. In contrast, chondrocytes grown for several days in 50 μM ascorbate accumulated both chondroitin sulfate proteoglycan and type II collagen in the extracellular matrix. [Ascorbate is important in collagen fibrillogenesis, but its specific role in this process is unclear (see Fessler and Fessler, 1978, for recent discussion).] Extracellular core protein immunofluorescence was more intense in ascorbate-treated cultures. When these cultures were digested with testicular hyaluronidase, extracellular immunoreactive material was no longer completely removed. Core protein and type II collagen remained in the identical extracellular matrix. Presumably an interaction between type II collagen and the proteoglycan macromolecule prevented its complete removal from matrix by hyaluronidase digestion.

Another distinct class of chondrocytes, described by von der Mark *et al.* (1977) and Müller *et al.* (1977), also could be identified (B. M. Vertel and A. Dorfman, unpublished results). In 1- to 8-week-old chondrocyte cultures, a small number of cells of chondrocyte morphology were stained by type I and not by type II collagen antibodies. Rarely did an individual cell localize both collagen types simultaneously. These observations suggested that the switch in synthesis involves a reciprocal cessation of synthesis of type II collagen accompanied by the onset of synthesis of type I collagen.

A similar relationship between synthesis of core protein and type I collagen was observed (B. M. Vertel and A. Dorfman, unpublished results). Detectable amounts of type I collagen and core protein were observed in less than 5% of chondrocytes, and, of these, most cells contained predominantly core protein or type I collagen and trace amounts of the second product. Less than 1 to 2% stained moderately for both products. Thus, the switch is not solely a switch in collagen type, but is instead a switch from synthesis of cartilage to noncartilage cell products. Neither cell morphology nor position in a nodule was sufficient to identify chondrocytes in the process of switching.

The correct interpretation of observations of immunofluorescence is entirely dependent upon specific reactivity of the antibodies with the macromolecules in question and not with any other cellular components. Immunochemical determinations of core protein antibody specificity has been discussed in previous sections. Immunofluorescence data provide further evidence for specificity. Antibodies to type II collagen and core protein reacted with morphologically identifiable chondrocytes, and not fibroblasts. The localization of core protein was equivalent to the localization of alcian blue stain in cartilage nodules. Prior incubation of antibodies with purified cartilage core protein completely blocked core protein immunofluorescence without effect on collagen immunofluorescence. In contrast, prior to incubation of antibodies with purified link protein did not interfere with either immunofluorescence reaction. Digestion with collagenase blocked reaction with anti-type II collagen, but did not affect anti-core protein immunofluorescence. The localization of fibronectin antibodies in chrondrocytes cultures was quite different from localization of core protein and collagen antibodies (Dessau et al., 1978; B. M. Vertel, unpublished results). Thus, as far as has been determined, the antibodies to core protein and type II collagen used in immunofluorescence experiments are specific and contain no identifiable contaminating species.

The relationships between intracellular synthesis and processing and deposition in an extracellular matrix on the level of individual cells thus can be examined by immunofluorescence for several components simultaneously and thereby provide a better understanding of coordinate gene expression during differentiation.

IV. Concluding Remarks

The material previously presented indicates the verity of the statement in Section I, that any review at this time represents a progress report and can only serve to direct the reader to some of the difficult questions still to be addressed. Although the model for proteoglycan structure is attractive for the explanation of a great deal of data, certain important questions remain unanswered. The molecular weight of chondroitin sulfate proteoglycan is generally considered to be approximately 2.5×10^6 with a protein content of 10%, but all published data indicate considerable polydispersity. While undoubtedly a significant amount of polydispersity could be accounted for by variation in length and number of chondroitin sulfate chains on individual protein molecules, in the absence of isolation of a pure monodisperse protein, the actual size of core protein remains undetermined. Important in this respect is whether the protein core consists of one continuous peptide with polysaccharide chains present on this single peptide. Investigations (Upholt *et al.*, 1977, 1979) using immunological techniques for the study of cell-free synthesis indicate that the nascent core protein is a high-molecular-weight product which may be a precursor of the core protein in cartilage.

The findings of Rosenberg *et al.* (1976) and of Heinegård (1977) of the existence of chains of various lengths all of which contain the hyaluronic acid binding region may be explained as follows: (*a*) The hyaluronic acid binding region represents the amino terminal portion of the peptide and variation in size of chains represents incompletely formed molecules. (*b*) Polydispersity results from partial degradation of molecules originally of uniform size. (*c*) The protein core does not represent a uniform biosynthetic product, but rather it arises by a post-translational junction of independently synthesized peptides. The first explanation cannot be ruled out at present, but seems unlikely in that synthesis of incomplete peptides could occur only as a result of improperly placed termination signals unless a sizable number of ribosomes do not complete their task. Although such a process *in vivo* has not been demonstrated, this may not be as easily observed with non-carbohydrate-containing proteins. This explanation is, however, contrary to the pulse-chase experiments reported by DeLuca *et al.* (1978) which indicate that the chondroitin sulfate-containing portion of the molecule represents the amino terminal end. Polydispersity due to degradation cannot be completely ruled out despite precautions taken since degradation may occur in the normal course of metabolism in the tissue even before extraction. This possibility is particularly true of tissue culture material derived from cells cultured in the presence of serum. Some proteoglycans containing only the chondroitin sulfate region may be scission products of a large proteoglycan.

Given the uncertainty of the structure of core proteins, we may examine to what extent the questions that have been addressed by immunological methods have been answered. The problems of the number of antigenic sites remain imperfectly resolved. The findings previously detailed leading to the conclusion that the hyaluronic acid binding and the chondroitin sulfate containing region are the species-specific and species-nonspecific regions, respectively, neatly fit the model and explain certain data. However, recent experiments with reduced and alkylated material indicate marked reduction in antigenic activity. It is, however, difficult to compare results obtained by radioimmunoassay with those obtained with other methods because of the differences in sensitivity and nature of relationships that are studied. Reduction and alkylation may alter tertiary structure of the entire molecules. The effect of removal of carbohydrate by either hydrogen fluoride or Smith degradation suggests the carbohydrate side chains play some role in the structure of the molecule which affects antibody–antigen reaction. The problem of multiple antigenic sites should be resolved with further use of monoclonal antibodies.

The relationship of noncartilage proteoglycans to those of cartilage remains unclear. Reports concerning aortic proteoglycans have reached variable conclusions although the most recent studies (Oegema et al., 1979; S. Gardell, personal communication) indicate the presence of large molecular weight proteoglycans in aorta which may aggregate with hyaluronic acid. The large molecular weight material in porcine ovarian follicular fluid appears to be quite different than that of cartilage (Yanagishita et al., 1979). The demonstration of small proteoglycans in both cartilage and noncartilage tissues in earlier studies and the possibility of their origin as a result of degradation has already been discussed. More recently, such low-molecular-weight proteoglycans have been observed in cornea by J. R. Hassell and D. A. Newsome (personal communication) and by K. Sugahara and A. Dorfman (unpublished results) in calvaria. In the latter case, proteolytic inhibitors were used not only during extraction, but also in the course of incubation of tissue to produce radioactive material. The available data suggest that chondroitin sulfate linked to protein is certainly present in tissues other than cartilage. The limited immunological evidence demonstrates cross-reactivity of proteoglycans from noncartilage cells (calvaria, sarcoma, and glial tumors) with cartilage proteoglycans. Perhaps, when sufficient data are available, multiple but related proteins, as in the case of collagen, will be found to be produced in different tissues. These may arise as a result of separately evolving duplicated genes, processing of mRNA with elimination of different introns, or gene rearrangement as shown for immunoglobulin synthesis by Brack et al. (1978).

Despite the unresolved problems, it is clear that specific antibodies for core protein from cartilage proteoglycans can be effectively used for localization of proteoglycans in cell and tissues. Furthermore, it has been possible to measure core protein biosynthesis independent of chondroitin sulfate synthesis and to begin to identify the nascent core protein prior to post-translational modification. It seems likely that immunological methods will contribute to the resolution of the critical problems which still remain.

ACKNOWLEDGMENTS

Original research in this article was supported by U.S. Public Health Service grants HD-09402, HD-04583, and AM-05996. B. M. V. was supported by U.S. Public Health Service postdoctoral fellowship HD-05363. N. B. S. is an Established Investigator of the American Heart Association.

We deeply appreciate the assistance of Ms. Pei-Lee Ho in several aspects of the work. We thank Ms. Michele Borucki for typing this manuscript.

REFERENCES

Baker, J., and Caterson, B. (1979). In "Glycoconjugate Research" (J. D. Gregory and R. W. Jeanloz, eds.), Vol. 1, p. 329. Academic Press, New York.

Barber, A. J., Kaser-Glanzman, R., Jacabova, M., and Luscher, E. F. (1972). Biochim. Biophys. Acta 286, 312.

Barland, P., Janis, R., and Sandson, J. (1966). Ann. Rheum. Dis. 25, 156.

Baxter, E., and Muir, H. (1972). Biochim. Biophys. Acta 279, 276.

Boake, W. C., and Muir, H. (1955). Lancet 2, 1222.

Brack, C., Herama, M., Lenhard-Schuler, R., and Tonegawa, S. (1978). Cell 15, 1.

Brandt, K. D., Tsiganos, C. P., and Muir, H. (1970). In "Chemistry and Molecular Biology of the Intercellular Matrix" (E. A. Balazs, ed.), Vol. 3, p. 1579. Academic Press, New York.

Brandt, K. D., Tsiganos, P., and Muir, H. (1973). Biochim. Biophys. Acta 320, 453.

Damle, S. P., Kieras, F. J., Tzeng, W.-K., and Gregory, J. D. (1978). Fed. Proc., Fed. Am. Soc. Exp. Biol. 37, 1729.

Dean, M. F., and Muir, H. (1970). Biochem. J. 118, 783.

DeLuca, S., Heinegård, D., Hascall, V. C., Kimura, J. H., and Caplan, A. I. (1977). J. Biol. Chem. 252, 6600.

DeLuca, S., Caplan, A. I., and Hascall, V. C. (1978). J. Biol. Chem. 253, 4713.

Dessau, W., Sasse, J., Timple, R., Jilek, F., and von der Mark, K. (1978). J. Cell Biol. 79, 342.

DiFerrante, N. (1964) Science 143, 250.

DiFerrante, N. (1970). In Chemistry and Molecular Biology of the Intercellular Matrix" (E. A. Balazs, ed.), Vol. 3, p. 1551. Academic Press, New York.

DiFerrante, N., and Pauling, M. (1964). J. Lab. Clin. Med. 63, 945.

DiFerrante, N., Connelly, P. V., and Gregory, J. D. (1970). FEBS Lett. 9, 149.

DiFerrante, N., Connelly, P. V., and Sajdera, S. W. (1972). J. Lab. Clin. Med. 80, 364.

Eisenstein, R., Larsson, S.-E., Kuettner, K. E., Sorgente, N., and Hascall, V. C. (1975). Arteriosclerosis 22, 1.

Farr, R. S. (1958). J. Infect. Dis. 103, 239.

Fessler, H. H., and Fessler, L. I. (1978). Annu. Rev. Biochem. 47, 129.

Fransson, L. Å., Malmstrom, A., Lindahl, U., and Höök, M. (1973). In "Biology of Fibroblast" (E. Kulonen and I. Pikkarainen, eds.), p. 443. Academic Press, New York.

Gerber, B. R., Franklin, E. C., and Schubert, M. (1960). J. Biol. Chem. 235, 2870.

Goetinck, P. F., Pennypacker, J. P., and Royal, P. D. (1974). Exp. Cell Res. 87, 241.

Gregory, J. D. (1973). Biochem. J. 133, 383.

Hammerman, D., and Sandson, J. (1970). Mt. Sinai J. Med., N.Y. 37, 453.

Hardingham, T. E., and Muir, H. (1972). Biochim. Biophys. Acta 279, 401.

Hardingham, T. E., and Muir, H. (1973). *Biochem. J.* **135**, 905.
Hardingham, T. E., Ewins, R. J. E., and Muir, H. (1976). *Biochem. J.* **157**, 127.
Hascall, V. C. (1977). *J. Supramol. Struct.* **7**, 101.
Hascall, V. C., and Heinegård, D. (1974a). *J. Biol. Chem.* **249**, 4232.
Hascall, V. C., and Heinegård, D. (1974b). *J. Biol. Chem.* **249**, 4242.
Hascall, V. C., and Heinegård, D. (1979). In "Glycoconjugate Research" (J. D. Gregory and R. W. Jeanloz, eds.). Academic Press, New York.
Hascall, V. C., and Sajdera, S. W. (1969). *J. Biol. Chem.* **244**, 2384.
Heinegård, D. (1977). *J. Biol. Chem.* **252**, 1980.
Heinegård, D., and Hascall, V. C. (1974). *J. Biol. Chem.* **249**, 4250.
Ho, P.-L., Levitt, D., and Dorfman, A. (1977). *Dev. Biol.* **55**, 233.
Hopwood, J. J., and Robinson, H. C. (1975). *Biochem. J.* **151**, 581.
Humphrey, J. H. (1943). *Biochem. J.* **37**, 460.
Keiser, H. (1975). *Arch. Biochem. Biophys.* **168**, 622.
Keiser, H., and DeVito, J. (1974). *Connect. Tissue Res.* **2**, 273.
Keiser, H., and Hatcher, V. B. (1977). *Connect. Tissue Res.* **5**, 147.
Keiser, H., and Sandson, J. I. (1974). *Arthritis Rheum.* **17**, 219.
Keiser, H., Shulman, H., and Sandson, J. I. (1972). *Biochem. J.* **126**, 163.
Kendall, F. E., Heidelberger, M., and Dawson, M. H. (1937). *J. Biol. Chem.* **118**, 61.
Kimura, J. H., Osdoby, P., Caplan, A. I., and Hascall, V. C. (1978). *J. Biol. Chem.* **253**, 4721.
Kirrane, J. A., and Robertson, W. van B. (1968). *Immunology* **14**, 139.
Kishida, Y., Olsen, B. R., Berg, R. A., and Prockop, D. J. (1975). *J. Cell Biol.* **64**, 331.
Kitamura, K., and Yamagata, T. (1976). *FEBS Lett.* **71**, 337.
Kresse, H., Heidel, H., and Buddecke, E. (1971). *Eur. J. Biochem.* **22**, 557.
Lash, J. W., and Vasan, N. S. (1978). *Dev. Biol.* **66**, 151.
Levitt, D., and Dorfman, A. (1973). *Proc. Natl. Acad. Sci. U.S.A.* **70**, 2201.
Levitt, D., and Dorfman, A. (1974). *Curr. Top. Dev. Biol.* **8**, 103.
Loewi, G. (1965). *Ann. Rheum. Dis.* **24**, 528.
Loewi, G., and Muir, H. (1965). *Immunology* **9**, 119.
Lowther, D. A., Preston, B. N., and Meyer, F. A. (1970). *Biochem. J.* **118**, 595.
Margolis, R. U., Lalley, K., Kiang, W.-L., Crockett, C., and Margolis, R. K. (1976). *Biochem. Biophys. Res. Commun.* **73**, 1018.
Mathews, M. B. (1971). *Biochem. J.* **125**, 37.
Miller, E. J. (1976). *Mol. Cell. Biochem.* **13**, 165.
Muir, H., and Hardingham, T. E. (1979). In "Glycoconjugate Research" (J. D. Gregory and R. W. Jeanloz, eds.), Vol. 1, p. 375. Academic Press, New York.
Muir, H., Baxter, E., and Brandt, K. D. (1973). *Biochem. Soc. Trans.* **1**, 223.
Müller, P. K., Lemmen, C., Gay, S., Gauss, V., and Kühn, K. (1977). *Exp. Cell Res.* **108**, 47.
Nevo, F., and Michaeli, D. (1975). *Isr. J. Med. Sci.* **11**, 1225.
Norling, B., Glimeluis, G., Vestermark, B., and Wasteson, Å. (1978). *Biochem. Biophys. Res. Commun.* **84**, 914.
Öbrink, E. (1971). Thesis, Department of Medical Chemistry, Uppsala, Sweden.
Oegema, T., Hascall, V. C., and Dziewiatkowski, D. D. (1975). *J. Biol. Chem.* **250**, 6151.
Oegema, T., Hascall, V. C., and Eisenstein, R. (1979). *J. Biol. Chem.* **254**, 1312.
Okayama, M., Pacifici, M., and Holtzer, H. (1976). *Proc. Natl. Acad. Sci. U.S.A.* **73**, 3224.
Olsen, B. R., Berg, R. A., Kishida, Y., and Prockop, D. J. (1975). *J. Cell Biol.* **64**, 340.
Palmoski, M. J., and Goetinck, P. F. (1972). *Proc. Natl. Acad. Sci. U.S.A.* **69**, 3385.
Pankovich, A. M., and Korngold, L. (1967). *J. Immunol.* **99**, 431.

Pennypacker, J. P., and Goetinck, P. F. (1976). *Dev. Biol.* **50**, 35.
Quinn, R. W., and Singh, K. P. (1957). *Proc. Soc. Exp. Biol. Med.* **95**, 290.
Reddi, A. H., Hascall, V. C., and Hascall, G. K. (1978). *J. Biol. Chem.* **253**, 2429.
Rosenberg, L. (1975). *In* "Dynamics of Connective Tissue Macromolecules" (P. M. C. Burleigh and A. R. Poole, eds.), p. 114. Am. Elsevier, New York.
Rosenberg, L., Hellman, W., and Kleinschmidt, A. K. (1970). *J. Biol. Chem.* **245**, 4123.
Rosenberg, L., Hellman, W., and Kleinschmidt, A. K. (1975). *J. Biol. Chem.* **250**, 1877.
Rosenberg, L., Wolfenstein-Todel, C., Margolis, R., Pal, S., and Streder, W. (1976). *J. Biol. Chem.* **251**, 6439.
Sajdera, S. W., and Hascall, V. C. (1969). *J. Biol. Chem.* **244**, 77.
Sandson, J., Rosenberg, L., and White, D. (1966). *J. Exp. Med.* **123**, 817.
Sandson, J., Damon, H., and Mathews, M. B. (1969). *Fed. Proc., Fed. Am. Soc. Exp. Biol.* **28**, 605.
Sandson, J., Damon, H., and Mathews, M. B. (1970). *In* "Chemistry and Molecular Biology of Intracellular Matrix" (E. A. Balazs, ed.), Vol. 3, p. 1563. Academic Press, New York.
Saunders, A. M., Mathews, M. B., and Dorfman, A. (1962). *Fed. Proc., Fed. Am. Soc. Exp. Biol.* **21**, 26.
Schwartz, N. B. (1979). *J. Biol. Chem.* **254**, 2271.
Schwartz, N. B., Ho., P.-L., and Dorfman, A. (1976). *Biochem. Biophys. Res. Commun.* **71**, 851.
Seastone, C. V. (1939). *J. Exp. Med.* **70**, 361.
Smith, G. M., Jr., and Newsome, D. A. (1978). *Dev. Biol.* **62**, 65.
Sugahara, K., and Dorfman, A. (1979). *Biochem. Biophys. Res. Commun.* **89**, 193.
Telser, A., Robinson, H. C., and Dorfman, A. (1966). *Arch. Biochem. Biophys.* **116**, 458.
Thyberg, J., Lohmander, S., and Heinegård, D. (1975). *Biochem. J.* **151**, 157.
Timpl, R., Wick, G., and Gay, S. (1977). *J. Immunol. Methods* **18**, 165.
Tsiganos, C. P., and Muir, H. (1969). *Biochem. J.* **113**, 885.
Upholt, W. B., Vertel, B. M., Ho, P.-L., and Dorfman, A. (1977). *Fed. Proc., Fed. Am. Soc. Exp. Biol.* **36**, 650.
Upholt, W. B., Vertel, B. M., and Dorfman, A. (1979). *Proc. Natl. Acad. Sci. U.S.A.* **76**, 4847.
Vertel, B. M., and Dorfman, A. (1978). *Dev. Biol.* **62**, 1.
Vertel, B. M., and Dorfman, A. (1979). *Proc. Natl. Acad. Sci. U.S.A.* **76**, 1261.
von der Mark, K., Gauss, V., von der Mark, H., and Müller, P. (1977). *Nature (London)* **267**, 531.
Wellauer, P., Wyler, T., and Buddecke, E. (1972). *Hoppe-Seyler's Z. Physiol. Chem.* **353**, 1043.
Wieslander, J., and Heinegård, D. (1977). *Upsala J. Med. Sci.* **82**, 161.
Wieslander, J., and Heinegård, D. (1979). *Biochem. J.* **179**, 35.
White, D., Sandson, J., Rosenberg, L., and Schubert, M. (1963a). *Arthritis Rheum.* **6**, 305.
White, D., Sandson, J., Rosenberg, L., and Schubert, M. (1963b). *J. Clin. Invest.* **42**, 992.
Yanagishita, M., Rodbard, D., and Hascall, V. C. (1979). *J. Biol. Chem.* **254**, 911.

CHAPTER 9

IMMUNOLOGICAL STUDIES ON COLLAGEN TYPE TRANSITION IN CHONDROGENESIS

Klaus von der Mark

MAX-PLANCK-INSTITUT FÜR BIOCHEMIE
MARTINSRIED, FEDERAL REPUBLIC OF GERMANY

I. Introduction

The differentiation of a cartilage cell from an embryonic precursor cell is morphologically characterized by a dramatic increase in the cytoplasmic volume, the amount of rough endoplasmic reticulum, and the Golgi apparatus. As a consequence, the secretion of the macromolecular constituents of the cartilage matrix, collagen and chondroitin sulfate proteoglycans, increases steeply during differentiation of mesenchymal cells to chondroblasts. The number of intercellular associations also increases, temporarily reaching a maximum in the condensation phase. With maturation of the cartilage blastema, cells become separated by the secreted extracellular matrix, losing all intercellular contacts in mature hyaline cartilage (Searls, 1973; Levitt and Dorfman, 1974; Thorogood and Hinchliffe, 1975).

This classical concept of cartilage differentiation considering chondrogenesis as a quantitative event was challenged by the finding that

199

differentiated chondrocytes synthesize a collagen, the so-called type II collagen or $[\alpha 1(II)]_3$ (Miller and Matukas, 1969; Trelstad *et al.*, 1970), that is genetically different from the collagen synthesized by the mesenchymal precursor cells of chondroblasts. Linsenmayer *et al.* (1973a) have shown that undifferentiated mesenchyme in the limb bud of a stage 24 chick embryo synthesizes type I collagen or $[\alpha 1(I)]_2\alpha 2$, the collagen of skin, bone, and tendon, while *de novo* synthesis of type II collagen begins with the appearance of metachromatically staining cartilage matrix. This finding indicated that cartilage differentiation does not only involve a quantitative increase in matrix synthesis, but primarily a qualitative change in the pattern of gene expression (for review, see von der Mark and Conrad, 1979).

Types I and II collagen differ in about one-third of their amino acid sequence, resulting in charge differences, different chromatographic behavior, and different peptide patterns produced by cyanogen bromide cleavage (for review, see Miller, 1976; Fietzek and Kühn, 1976). These differences allow a biochemical and immunological separation and identification of the collagen types in normal and pathological tissues and in developing systems. While the rationale for the transition in collagen types during chondrogenesis remains to be established, as the particular functions of the various collagen types are yet unclear, the immunological and biochemical determination of type II collagen synthesis during development opened the possibility of following cartilage differentiation unambiguously *in vivo* and *in vitro* with a tissue-specific parameter. This chapter will describe applications of immunological assays for collagen types to problems of chondrogenic differentiation, attempting to demonstrate the advantages and limitations of these assays. I would like to emphasize that the immunological assays for collagen types in tissue culture are of greatest use when supplemented with biochemical data. Finally, an attempt is made to elucidate the particular role of the genetically distinct collagen types in embryonic development.

II. Biochemistry and Immunochemistry of Collagen Types

A. STRUCTURE AND OCCURRENCE OF COLLAGEN TYPES

The monomeric molecules of types I, II, and III collagen consist of three subunits, called α chains, that fold into a triple-helical structure. The molecules are approximately 280 nm in length, corresponding to about 1000 amino acid residues per α chain. Every third position in the sequence is occupied by glycine, and proline and hydroxyproline constitute 18–22% of the residual amino acids. Although the sequences of most α chains are homologous, there is a 30% difference between the amino acid sequences of $\alpha 1(I)$ and $\alpha 1(II)$ (Fietzek and Kühn, 1976; Butler *et al.*, 1974). Similar data were reported for the difference between $\alpha 1(I)$ and $\alpha 1(III)$ (Fietzek *et al.*, 1977).

Each connective tissue is composed of a characteristic pattern of one or several collagen types. The most common collagen type I or $[\alpha 1(I)_2]\alpha 2$ is found in skin, bone, tendon, vessel walls, and dentin, and in most other connective tissues except hyaline cartilage which contains type II collagen $[\alpha 1(II)]_3$ as the main collagenous constituent, small amounts of AB collagen (Rhodes and Miller, 1978), and three other collagen chains (Burgeson and Hollister, 1979).

Type III collagen is present in skin, vessel walls, and reticular fibers (Chung and Miller, 1974; Epstein, 1974) and codistributes largely with type I collagen except in bone and corneal stroma (Gay *et al.*, 1975; von der Mark *et al.*, 1977b). Type IV collagen designates a collagen or a class of collagens present in basement membranes (Kefalides, 1973). Recently, in human fetal membranes, placenta, and skeletal muscle two new collagen chains, called A and B chains, were described (Burgeson *et al.*, 1976; Chung *et al.*, 1976); these either form separate triple-helical molecules of the composition A_3 or B_3 (Rhodes and Miller, 1978) or combine in one molecule of the composition AB_2 (Bentz *et al.*, 1978). The amino acid composition, however, is more related to basement membrane collagen (Burgeson *et al.*, 1976; Chung *et al.*, 1976).

The various collagen types can be separated by fractional salt precipitation with sodium chloride (Trelstad *et al.*, 1972; Chung and Miller, 1974) and identified by their elution pattern on CM-cellulose chromatography (Miller, 1971a; Epstein, 1974), or, most reliably, on the basis of a fingerprint pattern produced by the separation of cyanogen bromide-derived peptides on CM-cellulose chromatography (Miller, 1971b; Mayne *et al.*, 1975) or on SDS gel electrophoresis (Byers *et al.*, 1974). Type I collagen may be extracted from skin or tendons with acetic acid or citrate buffer. Only a small percentage of the total collagen is solubilized, the amount depending upon the age of the tissue. More collagen is obtained by digestion of the tissues with pepsin. At temperatures that maintain the molecules in the native state (usually 4–15°C) this enzyme removes amino- and carboxy-terminal peptides bearing intra- and intermolecular crosslinks.

Type II collagen can be obtained by pepsin digestion of hyaline cartilage (usually xyphoid, nasal, or articular cartilage) after the majority of the proteoglycans have been extracted with 4 M guanidinium chloride. Redisual proteoglycans can be removed from type II collagen by precipitation with cetylpyridinium chloride or by DEAE-cellulose chromatography (Miller and Matukas, 1969; Trelstad *et al.*, 1970; Miller, 1971a).

Although hyaline cartilage is the only parenchymal tissue presently known to contain type II collagen, this collagen is also produced by several epithelia such as embryonic chick notochord (Linsenmayer *et al.*, 1973b; H. von der Mark *et al.*, 1976), sturgeon notochord (Miller and Matthews, 1974), embryonic chick cornea epithelium (Linsenmayer *et al.*, 1977; von der Mark *et al.*, 1977b), and neural retina (Smith *et al.*, 1976; von der Mark *et al.*, 1977b) which secretes type II collagen into the vitreous body (Newsome *et al.*, 1976).

B. Biosynthesis of Collagen

Collagen is synthesized on the polysomes of the rough endoplasmic reticulum (Olsen and Prockop, 1974; Nist *et al.*, 1975) as a precursor molecule called procollagen (for reviews, see Bornstein, 1974; Grant and Jackson, 1976; Fessler and Fessler, 1978). The pro-α chains carry peptide extensions of 150 and 350 amino acid residues at the amino and carboxy terminus, respectively. Hydroxylation of proline to hydroxyproline and of lysine to hydroxylysine occurs on the nascent chains before assembly into a triple-helical molecule. After or during secretion into the extracellular space, procollagen is converted to collagen by specific proteases that remove the N- and C-terminal extensions, allowing the collagen molecules to aggregate to collagen fibrils in the interstitial space.

Chondrocytes synthesize and secrete type II procollagen *in vitro* when liberated from embryonic xyphoid cartilage with trypsin and collagenase (Dehm and Prockop, 1973; Uitto, 1977). In suspension culture the secreted procollagen is not converted to collagen for at least 24 hours; in monolayer culture of chondrocytes, extracellular type II collagen is deposited after several days in culture (Dessau *et al.*, 1978). However, under monolayer conditions a transition to type I collagen synthesis occurs (see Section VI) concomitantly with a morphologic modulation of the phenotype.

C. Immunochemistry

The collagen molecule carries principally three types of antigenic determinants: (*a*) terminal, sequential determinants at the C- and N-terminal telopeptides that are pepsin-labile; (*b*) central, conformation-dependent antigenic sites that are destroyed upon denaturation; and (*c*) central sequential antigenic sites that are conformation-independent (for reviews see Timpl, 1976; Furthmayr and Timpl, 1976). Both non-triple-helical extensions of the procolla-

gens carry additional antigenic determinants that are of higher immunogenic activity than those of collagen; antibodies directed against
procollagen extensions do not bind to antigenic determinants of the
collagen molecule (Furthmayr et al., 1972; von der Mark et al., 1973).

Specific immunohistological localization of collagen types was possible since Hahn et al. (1974) could show that antibodies specific to type
I collagen from calf can be prepared which do not cross-react with type
II collagen and vice versa (Hahn et al., 1975). Since then, numerous immunofluorescence studies on the distribution of collagen types in normal and pathological tissues as well as in cell cultures have been published (for review, see Timpl et al., 1977). From these studies it became
evident that there is a closer immunologic relationship among
homologous collagen types of different species than among different
collagen types of the same species. For example, antibodies prepared
against chick type II collagen react with type II collagen from quail,
mouse, rat, rabbit, dog, cat, calf, human, and shark (K. von der Mark,
unpublished). This evolutionary relation between collagen types is
confirmed by comparison of partial amino acid sequences of homologous
collagen types of different species, which revealed fewer exchanges
than between heterologous types of the same species (Fietzek and
Kühn, 1976).

The extent of interspecies cross-reactivity depends on the animal in
which antibodies are raised. Similarly, different species respond to different antigenic sites of the collagen molecule (Timpl, 1976; Furthmayr
and Timpl, 1976).

1. Preparation of Type-Specific Antibodies

Antibodies to types I, II, or III collagen have been raised in rabbits
(Hahn et al., 1974, 1975; H. von der Mark et al., 1976; Nowack et al.,
1976) by several injections of 5–10 mg of collagen. This relatively high
amount of protein is required because of the low immunogenic activity
of collagen. Type-specific antibodies were also raised in guinea pigs (H.
von der Mark et al., 1976) and goats (Nowack et al., 1976). The crude
antisera which normally show a titer against several collagen types in
the passive hemagglutination test (Beil et al., 1972) have to be purified
further by absorption to heterologous collagen types and affinity
chromatography on the homologous collagen type, covalently linked to
sepharose (H. von der Mark et al., 1976). The specificity of the anti-type
I collagen immunoglobulin can be checked by passive hemagglutination or radioimmunoassay (Adelmann et al., 1973).

Figure 1 shows a radioimmunoassay, testing the specificity of rabbit
antibodies to chick type II collagen. The antibodies bind more than

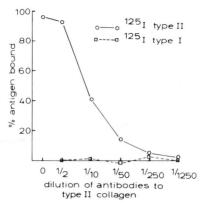

F<small>IG</small>. 1. Radioimmunoassay of rabbit anti-type II collagen antibodies with ¹²⁵I-labeled type I and type II collagen. The antibodies bind more than 90% of the type II collagen but less than 5% of the type I collagen. The antigen–antibody complex is precipitated with goat anti-rabbit immunoglobulin.

90% of ¹²⁵I-labeled type II collagen but less than 10% of ¹²⁵I-labeled type I collagen. Similarly, antibodies to type I collagen do not bind to radioactively labeled types II or III collagen; however, they bind more than 90% of type I collagen (Nowack *et al.,* 1976; Herrmann *et al.,* 1980).

The antibody specificity may also be tested by immunofluorescence on tissues known to contain only one collagen type. For example, collagen antibodies specific for type I collagen will stain bone and tendon, but not the matrix of hyaline cartilage, whereas the opposite staining pattern proves the specificity of antibodies against type II collagen. Mature cartilage matrix reacts with anti-type II collagen only after treatment with testicular hyaluronidase or 4 *M* guanidinium chloride, which apparently demask collagen fibers by removing chondroitin sulfate proteoglycans. For similar reasons, type I collagen specific fluorescence of bone shows only after decalcification with EDTA (H. von der Mark *et al.,* 1976).

Recently, the preparation of monoclonal antibodies to chick type I collagen was reported, revealing high specificity and extremely high titers (Linsenmayer *et al.,* 1979). By fusion of mouse myeloma cells with spleen cells from a mouse immunized with chick type I collagen, hybridoma cell clones were obtained which produced an IgG immunoglobulin directed against native chick type I collagen. The antibodies produced were specific by radioimmunoassay, passive hemagglutination, and immunofluorescence and were produced in large quantities in mass cultures of hydridoma cells, or obtained in ascites fluid in mice injected intraperitoneally with the clone. Similarly, monoclonal antibodies against chick type II collagen were prepared that were able to stain embryonic chick cartilage in a dilution of 1:200,000 using the immunofluorescence test (Linsenmayer and Hendrix, 1980). Such antibodies generally are species-specific.

2. Immunoprecipitation

Radioactively labeled collagens synthesized in cell culture can be determined quantitatively and specifically by immunoprecipitation with an excess of collagen type specific antibodies (von der Mark and von der Mark, 1977a). As collagen–anticollagen immunocomplexes are soluble, precipitation of the antigen–antibody complex with goat anti-immunoglobulin or with protein A from Staphylococcus aureus (Kessler, 1975) is necessary. The specificity of the collagen–antibody reaction can be controlled by identification of the precipitated collagen by SDS–gel electrophoresis and fluorography (Dessau et al., 1978). This approach, the quantitative determination of collagen types in cell culture, is better than classical techniques in terms of speed and sensitivity; however, it requires considerable amounts of specific antibodies and complete solubility of the tested collagens or procollagens. The synthesis of types I and IV collagen in the developing mouse embryo was shown by immunoprecipitation in an elegant study by Adamson and Ayers (1979).

III. Collagen Type Transition during Chondrogenesis of Limb Bud Mesenchyme in Vivo

The extracellular matrix of precartilaginous stage 22–23 limb bud mesenchyme stains with antibodies to type I collagen (H. von der Mark et al., 1976) and fibronectin (Dessau et al., 1980). With condensation of the mesenchyme in the limb core, the intensity of the type I collagen and fibronectin reaction increases, reaching a maximum in the cartilage blastema at early stage 24 (Fig. 2a). This observation confirms earlier findings which demonstrated that chick limb bud mesenchyme prior to stage 25 primarily synthesizes type I collagen (Linsenmayer et al., 1973a).

At late stage 24, the first reaction with anti-type II collagen antibodies appears in the cartilage blastema (Fig. 2b) while type I collagen and fibronectin are still present. This is approximately the stage at which metachromasia after toluidine blue or Giemsa staining in the blastema indicated the beginning of cartilage differentiation (Searls, 1965). Biochemically, de novo synthesis of type II collagen was discovered at stage 26 in the limb core (Linsenmayer et al., 1973a). This time

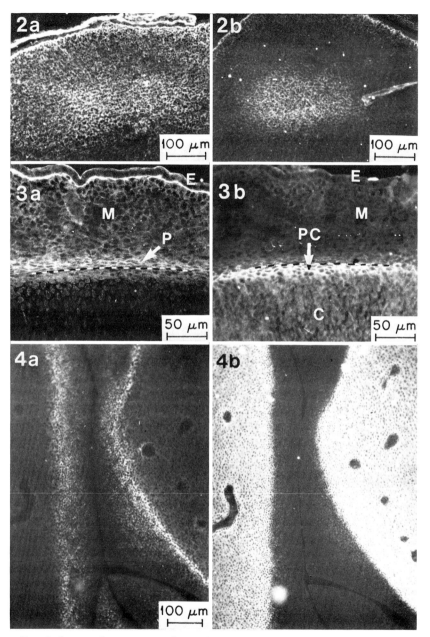

FIG. 2. Immunofluorescent study on the transition of collagen types during chondrogenesis in a stage 24 chick limb bud. Prior to overt cartilage differentiation, the cartilage blastema stains with antibodies to type I collagen (a), while the appearance of type II collagen indicates the onset of chondrogenesis (b).

FIG. 3. Transition of collagen types in the zone of appositional growth of the cartilage model of a stage 28 chick tibia. (a) Antibodies to type I collagen stain fibroblast-like cells

lag may be explained by the higher sensitivity of the immunofluorescence method.

With progress of differentiation, the intensity of the type II collagen fluorescence of the cartilage anlage increases, while type I collagen and fibronectin disappear from the core of the blastema (Dessau et al., 1980). Cells round up, retract cellular processes, and become separated by the secreted cartilage matrix at stages 26–27. From that stage on, type I collagen focuses in the perichondrium surrounding the cartilage models of femur, tibia, and fibula or the corresponding anlagen of the wing, humerus, ulna, and radius.

A biochemical analysis of the collagen type transition during chondrogenesis cannot exclude the possibility that the chondroblasts arise from a population of blastema cells that do not synthesize type I collagen, while the type I collagen-synthesizing blastema cells degenerate or sort out to form the perichondrium. The immunofluorescence results, however, demonstrate an even distribution of type I and type II collagen at stage 25 throughout the cartilage blastema, suggesting a gradual transition from type I to type II collagen synthesis in the blastema cells or their progeny. Zones of cell death which are observed during limb chondrogenesis are located mainly in the myogenic area (Thorogood and Hinchliffe, 1975).

Transition from type I to type II collagen synthesis also occurs during subsequent cartilage development. During appositional growth of the cartilage model, chondrocytes proliferate from the inner layer of the perichondrium (Bloom and Fawcett, 1975), consisting of a layer of fibroblast-like cells that produce type I collagen (Fig. 3a). At the border between perichondrium and cartilage type I collagen merges into type II collagen (Fig. 3b).

---

of the perichondrium (P), and the mesodermal–ectodermal interface. (b) Antibodies to type II collagen stain the young cartilage in the growth zone (periphery of the diaphysis) only, but not the mature cartilage (C), which stains only after treatment with testicular hyaluronidase (see Fig. 4b). The borderline between type I collagen and type II collagen indicates the zone where chondrocytes generate from the inner layer of the perichondrium. E, Ectoderm; M, mesenchyme; PC, precartilage. (From K. von der Mark et al., 1976, with the kind permission of Academic Press.)

FIG. 4. Immunofluorescence staining of a stage 43 embryonic chick knee joint, showing a transition from type I collagen synthesis by presumptive chondrocytes of the articular cartilage (a) to type II collagen synthesis by epiphyseal chondrocytes (b). Type I collagen was labeled with guinea pig antibodies to chick type I collagen, followed by fluorescein-labeled swine anti-guinea pig immunoglobulin (a); on the same section, type II collagen was stained with rabbit antibodies to type II collagen, followed by rhodamine-conjugated goat anti-rabbit immunoglobulin (b). (From K. von der Mark et al., 1976, with the kind permission of Academic Press.)

In later stages, the articular surface of the epiphyseal cartilage consists of a layer of type I collagen-synthesizing cells, the presumptive articular cartilage. In the epiphyseal cartilage chondrocytes synthesize type II collagen. Between both zones, a transition zone from type I to type II collagen was found that stains both with anti-type I and anti-type II collagen antibodies (Fig. 4a and b). This "hybrid" matrix, an overlap of types I and II collagen, persists throughout life and contains to an increasing extent type I collagen when developing into fibrous articular cartilage (Eyre *et al.*, 1978). These observations suggest that, in general, precursor cells of chondrocytes seem to synthesize type I collagen. With the onset of chondrogenic differentiation type I collagen synthesis may continue for some time while type II collagen synthesis begins, although the immunofluorescence data cannot discriminate between continued synthesis or retarded degradation of collagen.

IV. Collagen Type Transition during Chondrogenesis of Limb Bud Mesenchyme *in Vitro*

Dissociated cells of prechondrogenic limb bud mesenchyme (stages 23–24) are capable of differentiating into cartilage *in vitro* when cultured either at high cell density in monolayer culture (Caplan, 1970, 1972) or in micro mass cultures (Ahrens *et al.*, 1977), or when cultured over agar in suspension (Levitt and Dorfman, 1972; von der Mark and von der Mark, 1977a). Determination of type II collagen synthesis by biochemical and immunological methods allowed a precise description of the onset of cartilage differentiation, as well as a quantitative estimation of the extent of chondrogenesis *in vitro*.

Over agar, dissociated limb bud cells aggregate to cell clusters and synthesize type I collagen already during the first 4 hours after dissociating and plating (von der Mark and von der Mark, 1977a). This was shown by carboxymethylcellulose chromatography, as well as by immunofluorescent staining of frozen sections of these aggregates. Cyanogen bromide cleavage of the $\alpha 1$ fraction of a 24-hour culture and comparison of the peptide pattern with the peptide pattern of authentic $\alpha 1(I)$ by SDS–gel electrophoresis demonstrated that the $\alpha 1(I)$ synthesized by precartilaginous embryonic mesenchyme is in fact genetically related or identical to $\alpha 1(I)$ from adult tissues (von der Mark and Conrad, 1979).

After 48 hours in culture, a reaction with anti-type II collagen in those aggregates indicates the beginning of cartilage differentiaction. With time in culture the amount of type II collagen in the extracellular matrix increases, while type I collagen decreases. At 6–8 days in culture about 90% of the cell mass consists of translucent nodules showing characteristic features of hyaline cartilage. The cartilage matrix stains with anti-type II collagen antibodies, whereas the surrounding "perichondrium"-like cell layer, which comprises about 10% of the cell mass, contains type I and type III collagen.

This developmental pattern of collagen type transition is similar to that observed during cartilage differentiation in the limb bud *in vivo*, although it is devoid of any morphogenetic control.

The transition from type I to type II collagen can be followed quantitatively by the immunoprecipitation method: In a 24-hour culture low amounts of type I collagen can be precipitated with specific antibodies, but no type II collagen is precipitable. With time in culture increasing amounts of radioactivity precipitate with type II collagen antibodies (Fig. 5a). The increase in the ratio type II/type I collagen synthesis during *in vitro* chondrogenesis on agar is plotted in Fig. 6. After 6–8 days in culture, over 90% of the synthesized collagen is type II collagen. This indicates that more than 90% of the cells of a cluster are chondro-

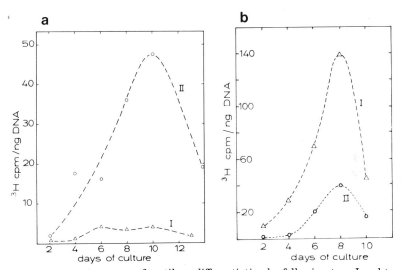

FIG. 5. Qualitative assay of cartilage differentiation by following type I and type II collagen synthesis in high-density limb bud cultures by immunoprecipitation: (a) Agar substrate; (b) tissue culture dishes. Collagen was extracted from cell cultures after 24-hour labeling periods with [³H]proline on alternate days. Aliquots of the extracts were precipitated with excess of antibodies to type I and type II collagen, followed by goat anti-rabbit immunoglobulin. With time in culture the rate of type II collagen synthesis per cell increases steeply on agar (a), while on tissue culture dishes (b) the rate of type I collagen synthesis increases more than type II collagen synthesis indicating fibrogenic differentiation. (From von der Mark and von der Mark, 1977a, with the kind permission of The Rockefeller Press, Inc.)

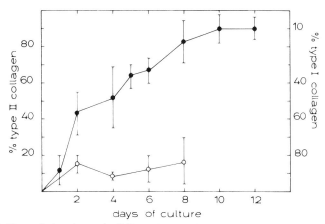

FIG. 6. Rate of chondrogenic differentiation of limb bud mesodermal cells on agar (—●—) and on tissue culture dishes (—○—), expressed as percentage of type II collagen synthesis of total collagen synthesis. (From von der Mark and von der Mark, 1977a, with the kind permission of The Rockefeller Press, Inc.)

cytes, provided that type I and type II collagen-synthesizing cells produce about equal amounts of collagen per cell. On tissue culture dishes, dissociated limb bud mesodermal cells do not form cartilage when seeded at densities below confluency (Caplan, 1970; Solursh and Reiter, 1975a). Biochemically and immunologically, only type I collagen synthesis can be observed under these conditions (von der Mark and von der Mark, 1977a). It is found intracellularly, presumably as type I procollagen, as well as extracellularly in the form of fibers (Fig. 7a).

When inoculated at densities above confluency, areas of cell condensation or "aggregates" (Ahrens et al., 1977) appear after 2 days in culture. These aggregates may correspond to the areas of cell condensation in the limb core in vivo that presage the formation of cartilage anlagen (Ede and Agerbak, 1968; Solursh et al., 1978). After 1–2 days in culture, they stain more intensely with anti-type I collagen than the surrounding mesenchyme. At the second day in culture, cells in the center of the aggregates begin to show intracellular staining with anti-type II collagen (Sasse and von der Mark, 1980). Extracellular cartilage matrix does not appear until the fourth day in culture on the basis of staining with alcian blue (Solursh and Reiter, 1975b). With the appearance of extracellular matrix an intense intra- and extracellular fluorescence with anti-type II collagen is observed (Fig. 7b). The time lag between the first intracellular appearance of type II collagen and its deposition in the extracellular matrix demonstrates the advantage of the use of an intracellular marker for the onset of chondrogenesis, as compared to classical phenotypic markers of cartilage differentiation such as the formation of a metachromatically staining extracellular matrix. The delay in the deposition of collagen in the extracellular matrix may be in part due to a delay in processing the newly synthesized type II procollagen to precipitable collagen, or to a retardation in the formation of high-molecular-weight chondroitin sulfate proteoglycan aggregates with hyaluronic acid (DeLuca et al., 1978) which are necessary to constitute cartilage matrix.

Immunofluorescence double staining allows a semiquantitative estimation of the rate of chondrogenic differentiation in such cultures. Screening through serial frozen sections of the randomly folded cell layer revealed that about 15–20% of the cells are chondrocytes. The major portion of the multicell layer, however, stains with anti-type I collagen (von der Mark and von der Mark, 1977a) and therefore consists mostly of fibroblasts or myoblasts.

Similar ratios of type I/type II collagen synthesis are obtained by biochemical methods or the immunoprecipitation method (Fig. 5b). The comparison of the percentage of type II collagen synthesis achieved in the agar and in the monolayer system reveals that suspension culture over agar favors chondrogenic differentiation, while culture on tissue culture dishes favor fibrogenic and myogenic differentiation (Fig. 6).

The different behavior of limb bud cells on agar and on culture dishes may simply be explained by the different surface properties. Tissue culture dishes allow the attachment and proliferation of fibroblast-like cells, which cannot attach to agar. In contrast, chondrogenesis is favored in suspension and in aggregates (Horwitz and Dorfman, 1970), possibly due to more intense cellular interactions and cell–matrix interactions, or due to particular nutritional conditions such as low oxygen tension (Pawelek, 1969).

The immunological data, however, do not tell us whether the almost exclusive development of cartilage on agar results from a selective survival and differentiation of presumptive chondroblasts, or from a regulative influence on undetermined mesenchymal cells. Similarly, the high extent of fibrogenic differentiation on tissue culture plastic may be due to stimulation of fibrogenic differentiation and/or inhibition of chondrogenic differentiation. The rate of cell division as indicated by the rate of thymidine uptake is about equal under both culture conditions. This problem will not be settled as long as the question is still open as to whether stage 23 limb bud cells consist of a mixed population of determined presumptive chondroblasts, myoblasts, fibroblasts, etc. (Dienstman et al., 1974; Holtzer, 1978) or of undetermined cells that are still "regulatory" (Searls, 1973). Rates of 20–40% cell death in limb bud cell cultures that cannot be avoided under presently employed culture conditions prevent an experimental analysis of this problem.

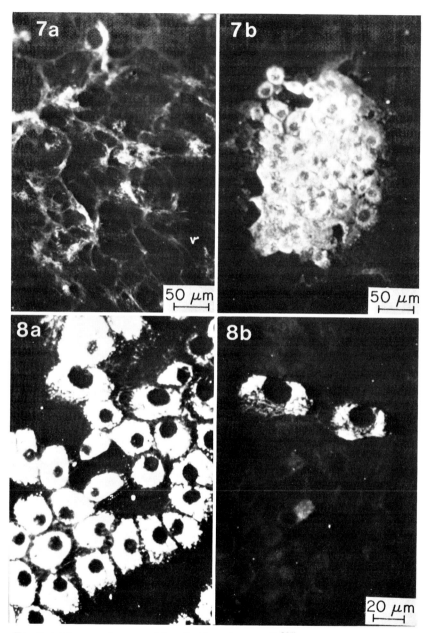

FIG. 7. (a) Immunofluorescent localization of extracellular type I collagen in high-density cell culture of stage 23 chick limb bud cells, 2 days after inoculation. Intracellular fluorescence with anti-type II collagen was first obtained after 3–4 days in culture. (Courtesy of J. Sasse.) (b) Type II collagen in a chondrocyte colony, differentiated from limb bud mesenchymal cells, 8 days after inoculation.

FIG. 8. Transition from type II to type I collagen synthesis in a clone of chick sternal

V. Transition of Collagen Types in Chondrocyte Cultures

In monolayer culture, mature chondrocytes of hyaline cartilages from different species lose several features of the cartilage phenotype (Holtzer and Abbott, 1968). When cultured at medium to high cell density and grown to confluency, polygonal chondrocytes derived from chick sternal cartilage (Coon, 1966; Abbott and Holtzer, 1966) eventually acquire fibroblast-like cell shape. They lose the ability to form cartilage colonies and to accumulate cartilage matrix after approximately 4 weeks in culture (Müller et al., 1975, 1977) or after four passages (Mayne et al., 1976a). This modulation of the cartilage phenotype is associated with a transition from type II to type I collagen synthesis (Schiltz et al., 1973; Müller et al., 1975; Mayne et al., 1976a), as determined by the appearance of $\alpha 2$ chains on CM-cellulose chromatography. It is not due to overgrowth by fibroblasts, possibly derived from the perichondrium, since this transition was also observed in cloned chondrocytes (Mayne et al., 1976b; Dessau et al., 1978). "Dedifferentiated" or modulated chondrocytes also synthesize a collagen molecule composed of three $\alpha 1(I)$ chains—the so-called $\alpha 1(I)$ trimer (Mayne et al., 1975)—and, type III collagen, as well as A and B chains (Benya et al., 1977), but no type II collagen.

"Dedifferentiation" occurs spontaneously, but is initiated and accelerated considerably by whole embryo extract (Mayne et al., 1976b) or the heavy fraction of it (Coon, 1966), by bromodeoxyuridine (Abbott and Holtzer, 1968; Schiltz et al., 1973; Mayne et al., 1975), or by the cocarcinogen phorbol-myristate-acetate (Pacifici and Holtzer, 1977; Lowe et al., 1978). The chondrocyte phenotype is stable for at least 35 cell generations, however, when the cells are cultured at clonal density in the presence of the light fraction of embryo extract (Coon, 1966).

Biochemical studies permitted a precise and quantitative description of the overall transition of collagen-type synthesis. However, they do not allow us to decide whether this transition occurred in individual cells at different times, concomitantly with the change in the cell shape, or whether the dedifferentiation is a slow process extending in all cells over the whole culture period.

Immunofluorescence double staining experiments demonstrated that the transition from type II to type I collagen occurs in individual

chondrocytes in monolayer culture (second passage). Double staining with anti-type I and anti-type II collagen antibodies reveals that two cells in the clone have begun to synthesize type I collagen (b) in addition to type II collagen (a). Later in culture, more chondrocytes will synthesize type I collagen only.

cells at different times and not necessarily concomitantly with the change in cell shape. Chick sternal chondrocytes when dissociated from cartilage matrix and plated on tissue culture dished at medium cell density $(3 \times 10^4/cm^2)$ show only intracellular type II (pro)collagen staining until 4 to 6 days in culture (von der Mark et al., 1977a). With time in culture, an increasing number of polygonal cells from the edge of epitheloid clones and fibroblast-like cells stain with antibodies to type I collagen. Few cells can be observed that stain with both antibodies simultaneously (Fig. 8) suggesting that the switch in collagen type synthesis must occur rather rapidly. Furthermore it proves that the biochemically observed transition from type II to type I collagen synthesis is not due to an overgrowth of fibroblasts, but is in fact due to a switch in gene expression in chondroblasts.

Later in culture, most of the type I collagen-synthesizing cells are of fibroblast-like or amoeboid cell shape; however, principally no conclusion can be drawn from the cell morphology of a chondrocyte as to the collagen type it is producing. Some fibroblast-like as well as giant cells continue to produce type II collagen (von der Mark et al., 1977a; Dessau et al., 1978). Chondrocytes that synthesize type II collagen fail to deposit this collagen in the extracellular space for some time in culture. Type I collagen-synthesizing cells, however, are covered by a dense network of type I collagen fibers (Dessau et al., 1978). After 8–10 days in culture, in epitheloid chondrocyte clones which have not dedifferentiated, extracellular cartilage matrix accumulates which stains with anti-type II collagen. This delay in the deposition of extracellular collagen may have causes similar to those discussed for the matrix deposition by limb bud cells (Section IV).

The fact that, in the progeny of a single chondrocyte, cells do not switch to type I collagen simultaneously suggests that the time when a chondrocyte "dedifferentiates" in culture is determined by microenvironmental factors, e.g., the location in a clone or the degree of intercellular associations, rather than by cellular origin and history.

The collagen pattern of dedifferentiated chondrocytes, types I, III, A, and B collagen, seems to be characteristic of the "degenerated" status of connective tissues cells in vitro. It is shared by smooth muscle cells, tendon fibroblasts (Herrmann et al., 1980), corneal fibroblasts (Conrad et al., 1980), and other fibroblast lines. The maintenance of the differentiated state in chondrocytes and other specialized fibroblasts, characterized by the synthesis of large quantities of one collagen type, apparently requires the presence of the complete extracellular matrix.

VI. Collagen Type Transition during Cartilage–Bone Metamorphosis

A transition from type II to type I collagen can also be observed *in vivo* in the growth plate of the developing bone. Replacement of cartilage by bone begins with the resorption of cartilage in the diaphyseal shaft by blood vessels, invading from the periosteum through the bone cylinder. Marrow cavities develop in the cartilage and protrude toward the epiphysis. On the surface of eroded cartilage an irregular osteoid seam is deposited by bone marrow-derived osteoprogenitor cells (Fig. 9). This osteoid seam consists of type I collagen, while the underlying cartilage contains type II collagen even when calcified (K. von der Mark *et al.*, 1976; von der Mark and von der Mark, 1977b). In the mammalian bone, endochondral osteoid becomes mineralized with the beginning of cartilage resorption while in the fowl long bone ossification of the endochondral osteoid occurs first when bone marrow cavities have reached the epiphysis (von der Mark and von der Mark, 1977b). It has been suggested that endochondral osteoid may be partially synthesized and deposited by hypertrophic chondrocytes at the cartilage–marrow interface. In fact, by immunofluorescence staining type I collagen was detected in the inner lacunar walls of hypertrophic chondrocytes, several cell layers away from the cartilage–marrow interface (Gay *et al.*, 1976; K. von der Mark *et al.*, 1976, 1977a,b). Also in spicules of spongy bone in the growth plate of freshly hatched chicken, chondrocyte lacunae were observed in the core of calcified cartilage that stained with antitype I collagen antibodies (Fig. 10).

The *in vitro* experiments on chondrocyte dedifferentiation have clearly shown that chondrocytes have the potential to reinitiate type I collagen synthesis in response to changes of the cellular environment. However, it cannot be excluded that those lacunae of hypertrophic chondrocytes had been invaded be osteoprogenitor cells through capillary sprouts, or by cell processes of osteoclasts (Schenk *et al.*, 1967) which secrete type I collagen.

VII. Immunological Studies on Ectopic Cartilage Formation

A. Bone Matrix-Induced Chondrogenesis in Muscle

Muscle contains a population of undifferentiated stem cells that can be triggered to undergo chondrogenic and finally osteogenic differentiation by demineralized bone matrix from rat long bones. This matrix, also called "bone matrix gelatin," induces the formation of cartilage when implanted subcutaneously or into muscle pouches of allogeneic recipients, or when used as a substrate for muscle explants in tissue

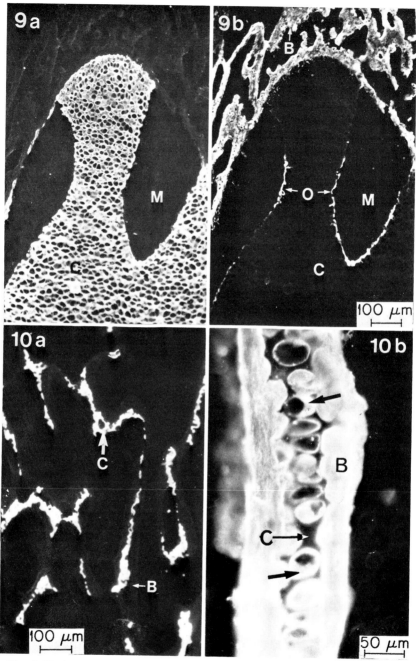

FIG. 9. Replacement of type II by type I collagen during cartilage–bone metamorphosis. In the epiphysis of a stage 43 tibia, bone marrow processes (M) degrade cartilage matrix (C), and on the surface of eroded cartilage an osteoid seam (O) is deposited, which

culture experiments (Urist and Nogami, 1970; Reddi and Huggins, 1972; Nogami and Urist, 1974). The histological details of the cellular differentiation events and the morphological changes have been described in several places (Reddi and Anderson, 1976; Anderson and Griner, 1977). Bone matrix implants initially cause an inflammatory process, as indicated by the appearance of polymorphonuclear leukocytes and lymphocytes in the vicinity of the explants. Approximately 3 days after implantation, fibroblast-like cells immigrate, proliferate, and turn into chondrocytes after contact with the matrix 6 to 7 days after implantation.

The deposition of cartilage matrix was determined histologically and by morphological criteria. Recently, the appearance of chondrocytes in these implantates was confirmed immunologically with antibodies to types I, II, and III collagen (Reddi et al., 1977). In the inflammatory tissue around the immigrating fibroblast-like cells, type III collagen was located. Surprisingly, type I collagen was not found in this area.

The appearance of ectopic cartilage adjacent to bone implants was demonstrated by the positive reaction with antibodies to type II collagen, while the surrounding soft connective tissue continued to stain with anti-type III collagen antibodies only. In this study, type I collagen first appeared with the formation of endochondral osteoid and bone 11 days after of implantation. It is preceded by hypertrophy and calcification of the ectopic cartilage.

The nature of the inducing factor in demineralized bone and the nature of cells in muscle tissue responding to bone matrix are still unknown. It seems to be clear that collagen which constitutes 95% of the dry weight of the demineralized bone matrix is not responsible for cartilage induction. More likely, it is a diffusible glycoprotein (Nakagana and Urist, 1977; Butler et al., 1977) which is present in bone and dentin.

In vitro studies in which clones of muscle connective tissue fibroblasts as well as cloned myoblasts were cultured on demineralized bone matrix suggested that both cell types may be precursor cells of chon-

stains with type I collagen-specific antibodies (arrows). Double staining with antibodies to type II (a) and to type I collagen (b), as in Fig. 4. B, Periosteal bone trabeculae.

Fig. 10. Bone spicules in the epiphyseal growth plate of a hatched chicken, containing a core of calcified cartilage. The matrix of the cartilage stains with antibodies to type II collagen (a), whereas the inner lacunar walls show a coating with type I collagen (b, arrows) which may be produced either by hypertrophic chondrocytes or by invading osteoprogenitor cells. B, Bone; C, cartilage.

drocytes (Nathanson *et al.*, 1978). However, both cell types have been shown to synthesize type I collagen (Mayne and Strahs, 1974; Sasse and von der Mark, 1978) which is not consistent with the immunofluorescence demonstration of the absence of type I collagen in the prechondrogenic inflammatory tissue (Reddi *et al.*, 1977).

The transition from type II to type I collagen observed in ectopic bone formation (Reddi *et al.*, 1977) is due to the differentiation of bone cells from osteoprogenitor cells similar to the endochondral bone formation *in vivo*.

B. INDUCTION OF CHONDROGENESIS BY EPITHELIAL–MESENCHYMAL INTERACTIONS

In embryonic development, epithelial–mesenchymal interactions (Grobstein, 1967) are of importance for the differentiation of cartilage in three cases: Vertebral cartilage develops from somitic mesenchyme adjacent to the notochord sheath (for review see Hall, 1978); pigmented epithelium seems to stimulate chondrogenesis of adjacent head mesenchyme to scleral cartilage (Newsome, 1972); and mandibular cartilage formation from neural crest-derived mesenchyme is induced by maxillary ectoderm (Balinsky, 1975). The role of the epithelia is still unclear as it was demonstrated that the somitic mesenchyme is also capable of undergoing chondrogenic differentiation in the absence of epithelia when cultured under appropriate conditions. It is possible that in some cases the epithelium implies only a morphogenetic control function on the differentiating cartilage rather than providing the "inducer" molecule for chondrogenic differentiation. Some epithelia, however, may play a more than permissive role in epithelial–mesenchymal interactions. This has become evident from experiments in which it was shown that epithelial tissues such as urinary bladder epithelium (Huggins, 1931), HeLa cells (Anderson, 1976), or established epithelial cell lines (Wlodarski, 1969) are capable of inducing chondrogenesis in tissues that would normally not form cartilage *in vivo*. Embryonic mouse tooth germ mesenchyme that normally gives rise to odontoblasts synthesizing type I collagen (dentin) develops cartilage when recombined with avian limb bud ectoderm (Hata and Slavkin, 1978). The active role of the limb bud ectoderm is stressed by the observation that removal of the apical ridge prior to the recombination of the tooth bud with the limb bud mesenchyme destroys the activity of the ectoderm. In limb chondrogenesis, the apical ridge is responsible for the development of cartilage models of the digits.

The appearance of cartilage in recombination cultures of mouse tooth germ mesenchyme with avian limb bud ectoderm was unequivocally demonstrated by biochemical and immunological identification of type II collagen synthesis (Hata and Slavkin, 1978). Development of hyaline cartilage nodules staining intensely with antibodies to type II collagen was also observed in organ cultures of avian neural crest cells, recombined with cranial or maxillary ectoderm (Bee and Thorogood, 1980), as well as in chick somites cultured with notochord (K. von der Mark, unpublished).

VIII. Conclusions

During cartilage differentiation not only the amount of collagen synthesis per cell, but also the type of collagen changes from type I to type II collagen.

Therefore, the immunological identification of collagen types I and II permits a specific qualitative and quantitative description of the onset of chondrogenic differentiation in embryonic development and in tissue culture. Besides collagen, also the chondroitin sulfate proteoglycan synthesized by a differentiated chondrocyte is different from the type of chondroitin sulfate proteoglycan synthesized by prechondrogenic cells. Analysis of the proteoglycans under gentle, dissociative conditions by density gradient centrifugation and gel chromatography revealed that the chondroitin sulfate proteoglycans of precartilage and cartilage differ in size (Okayama et al., 1976), in the ability to form high-molecular-weight aggregates with hyaluronic acid (Hascall et al., 1976; Goetinck et al., 1974; Vasan and Lash, 1977), and in the nature of the protein core (Ho et al., 1977).

Both macromolecules represent biochemical markers for cartilage that are more specific than those assays based on the incorporation of [^{35}S]sulfate into acidic glycosaminoglycans, or on metachromatic staining dyes, since it has been shown that also precartilaginous or noncartilaginous tissues produce sulfated glycosaminoglycans (Searls, 1973; Conrad et al., 1977). The immunofluorescence localization of type II collagen is also a more sensitive assay for the onset of chondrogenesis, as the beginning of the synthesis of cartilage-specific gene products can be detected intracellularly 1 day before the appearance of extracellular cartilage matrix. Although the immunofluorescence technique is not quantitative and cannot describe the rate of synthesis and turnover of collagen, it offers advantages over the biochemical collagen assays as it is able to describe changes in the gene activity at the level of a single cell. Thus it was possible to demonstrate that a single chondrocyte can produce type I and type II collagen (Fig. 8) which supports the interpretation that the transition of collagen types in chondrocyte cultures results from changes in the gene activity in each cell, rather than from overgrowth by fibroblast-like cells.

Similarly, the simultaneous staining of the cartilage blastema in the limb bud at stage 24 with antibodies to type I and II collagen suggests a transition in the collagen types synthesized during chondrogenic differentiation, rather than a cell selection and overgrowth of the blastema cells by chondrocytes.

Two general limitations of the immunofluorescence technique that are also relevant when using collagen-type-specific antibodies should be kept in mind. First, even when using absorbed and carefully tested antibodies to a distinct collagen type, a cross-reaction with another yet unknown collagen type or a collagen-like molecule cannot be excluded. This is also true when using monoclonal antibodies, since several collagen types may (and do) carry identical antigenic sites in addition to type-specific antigenic determinants. Second, lack of positive fluorescence does not necessarily mean absence of antigen, since the antigens may have been lost or destroyed during fixation or staining. The latter possibility has been particularly observed in tissue sections (H. von der Mark et al., 1976). Therefore, the immunohistological identification of collagen types should be complemented with biochemical data if available.

The transition of collagen types during embryonic development occurs rather rapidly according to a highly complex schedule. The replacement of type I collagen by type II collagen during chondrogenesis of embryonic mesenchyme, and the reappearance of type I collagen during cartilage degradation and osteogenesis suggests a specific function for type II collagen that cannot be exerted by type I collagen or another collagen type. That each collagen type seems to have a particular function is also suggested by the complex pattern of different collagen types interwoven or adjacent to each other in organs like the eye (von der Mark et al., 1977b), the vessel wall (Gay et al., 1976), or the liver (Nowack et al., 1976).

From ultrastructural investigations it is well known that collagen occurs in a variety of macromolecular organizations in different connective tissues. Comparison of collagen fibrils in hyaline cartilage, containing almost exclusively type II collagen, with the collagen of bone and tendon, containing mostly type I collagen, led to the conclusion that functional differences of the collagen types may result from differences in diameter and structural organization of their fibrils. Thus type I collagen, occurring mostly in fibrils of 40 to 100 nm diameter that are parallel-oriented, seems to be preferentially employed in tissues exposed to high mechanical tension or pressure, such as bone, tendon, skin, and dentin. Type II collagen, however, occurring mostly in irregular-oriented 5- to 15-nm fibers, is found in tissues that are highly hydrated such as hyaline cartilage or vitreous humor.

How the macromolecular organization of genetically distinct collagens is controlled by the primary structure and other chemical features of the collagen molecules such as the degree of hydroxylation, glycosylation, and cross-linking, is still unclear. *In vitro* studies on the fibril formation of collagen types I and III have shown that the purified collagen types are able to aggregate to the same type of fibril, exhibiting a cross-striation of 68 nm (Wiedemann *et al.*, 1975). This suggests that *in vivo* the fibril size as well as the structural organization are controlled by specific interactions with other constituents of the extracellular matrix such as glycoproteins or proteoglycans. For example, type II collagen forms thin, unbanded fibrils in embryonic epiphyseal cartilage, however, up to 80 nm thick but cross-banded fibrils in calcified cartilage indistinguishable from type I collagen (Anderson and Parker, 1968).

The importance of noncollagenous tissue glycoproteins and proteoglycans in collagen assembly was shown in several studies (Öbrink, 1973; Toole and Lowther, 1968). For instance, a tendon glycoprotein of approximately 30,000 molecular weight was shown to influence the fibril formation of type I collagen (Anderson, 1976). Other studies on the interaction of chondroitin sulfate proteoglycans with different types of collagen, however, did not reveal any type-specific differences (Toole, 1976).

In addition to its role as a mechanical support and framework of connective tissues, collagen plays a central role in embryonic development in providing the major substrate for cell attachment (Klebe, 1975), cell migration, and perhaps cell differentiation (Reddi, 1976). Cell attachment to collagen seems to be mediated by a cell surface glycoprotein called fibronectin (Vaheri and Mosher, 1978) or LETS-protein (Hynes, 1976). The migration of fibroblasts along collagen fibrils can be demonstrated *in vitro* on reconstituted collagen fibrils (Elsdale and Bard, 1972). Collagen also acts as a promoter and stabilizer of myoblast fusion (Hauschka and Königsberg, 1966), and stimulates the collagen synthesis of corneal epithelium (Meier and Hay, 1974).

However, collagen types I–IV apparently are equally effective in promoting muscle differentiation (Ketley *et al.*, 1976) and cornea differentiation (Meier and Hay, 1974).

A specific role for type II collagen was reported in chondrogenesis of stage 17 chick somites *in vitro*. Type II collagen, which is also synthesized by the notochord (H. von der Mark *et al.*, 1976), the "inducer" of somite chondrogenesis *in vivo* (Holtzer and Detwiler, 1953; Strudel, 1953), stimulates the formation of cartilage nodules and type II collagen synthesis in somite cultures more than type I collagen or noncollagenous substrates (Minor *et al.,* 1975; von der Mark, 1977). It also stimulates the synthesis of the cartilage-specific chondroitin sulfate proteoglycan (Lash and Vasan, 1978) more than collagen types I, III, and IV. The mechanism of this *in vitro* interaction of type II collagen substrates with embryonic cells is still unknown.

ACKNOWLEDGMENTS

I wish to thank Mrs. Lieselotte Sieweck and Miss Magdalena Grujic for their skillful technical assistance, which has enabled the presentation of this work, and Dr. Waltraud Dessau and my wife for providing antibodies to type I and type II collagen. I am also grateful to the generous support by Dr. Klaus Kühn, and to the support of the Deutsche Forschungsgemeinschaft (Ma 534/1-4).

REFERENCES

Abbott, J., and Holtzer, H. (1966). *J. Cell Biol.* **28,** 473–487.
Abbott, J., and Holtzer, H. (1968). *Proc. Natl. Acad. Sci. U.S.A.* **59,** 1144–1151.
Adamson, E. D., and Ayers, S. E. (1979). *Cell* **16,** 953–965.
Adelmann, B. C., Gentner, G. J., and Hopper, K. (1973). *J. Immunol. Methods* **3,** 319–336.
Ahrens, P. B., Solursh, M., and Reiter, R. S. (1977). *Dev. Biol.* **60,** 69–82.
Anderson, C. E., and Parker, J. (1968). *Clin. Orthop. Relat. Res.* **58,** 225–241.
Anderson, H. C. (1976) *Clin. Orthop. Relat. Res.* **119,** 211–224.
Anderson, H. C., and Griner, S. A. (1977). *Dev. Biol.* **60,** 351–358.
Anderson, J. C. (1976). *Int. Rev. Connect. Tissue Res.* **7,** 251–322.
Balinsky, B. I. (1975). "An Introduction to Embryology." Saunders, Philadelphia, Pennsylvania.
Bee, J., and Thorogood, P. (1980). In preparation.
Beil, W., Furthmayr, H., and Timpl, R. (1972). *Immunochemistry* **9,** 779–788.
Bentz, H., Bächinger, H. P., Glanville, R., and Kühn, K. (1978). *Eur. J. Biochem.* **92,** 563–567.
Benya, P. D., Padilla, S. R., and Nimni, M. E. (1977). *Biochemistry* **16,** 865–872.
Bloom, W., and Fawcett, D. W. (1975). "A Textbook of Histology," pp. 233–243. Saunders, Philadelphia, Pennsylvania.
Bornstein, P. (1974). *Annu. Rev. Biochem.* **43,** 567–603.
Burgeson, R. E., Al Adli, F. A., Kaitila, I. I., and Hollister, D. W. (1976). *Proc. Natl. Acad. Sci. U.S.A.* **73,** 2579–2583.
Burgeson, R. E., and Hollister, D. W. (1979). *Biochem. Biophys. Res. Commun.* **87,** 1124–1131.
Butler, W. T., Miller, E. J., and Finch, J. E. (1974). *Biochem. Biophys. Res. Commun.* **57,** 190–195.
Butler, W. T., Mikulski, A., and Urist, M. R. (1977). *J. Dent. Res.* **56,** 228–232.
Byers, P. H., McKenney, K. H., Lichtenstein, J. R., and Martin, G. R. (1974). *Biochemistry* **13,** 5243–5248.
Caplan, A. I. (1970). *Exp. Cell Res.* **62,** 341–355.
Caplan, A. I. (1972). *J. Exp. Zool.* **180,** 351–362.
Chung, E., and Miller, E. J. (1974). *Science,* **183,** 1200–1201.
Chung, E., Rhodes, R. K., and Miller, E. J. (1976). *Biochem. Biophys. Res. Commun.* **71,** 1167–1174.

Conrad, G. W., Hamilton, C., and Haynes, E. (1977). *J. Biol. Chem.* **252**, 6861–6870.
Conrad, G. W., Dessau, W., and von der Mark, K. (1980). *J. Cell Biol.* (in press).
Coon, H. G. (1966). *Proc. Natl. Acad. Sci. U.S.A.* **55**, 66–73.
Dehm, P., and Prockop, D. J. (1973). *Eur. J. Biochem.* **35**, 159–166.
DeLuca, S., Caplan, A. I.,and Hascall, V. C. (1978). *J. Biol. Chem.* **253**, 4713–4720.
Dessau, W., Sasse, J., Timpl, R., Jilek, F., and von der Mark, K. (1978). *J. Cell Biol.* **79**, 342–355.
Dessau, W., von der Mark, H., von der Mark, K., and Fischer, S. (1980). *J. Embryol. Exp. Morphol.* (in press).
Dienstman, S. R., Biehl, J., Holtzer, S., and Holtzer, H. (1974). *Dev. Biol.* **39**, 83–95.
Ede, D. A., and Agerbak, G. S. (1968). *J. Embryol. Exp. Morphol.* **20**, 81–100.
Elsdale, T. R., and Bard, J. B. L. (1972). *J. Cell Biol.* **54**, 626–637.
Epstein, E. H., Jr. (1974). *J. Biol. Chem.* **249**, 3225–3231.
Eyre, D. R., Brickley, D. M., and Glimcher, M. J. (1978). *FEBS Lett.* **85**, 259–263.
Fessler, J., and Fessler, L. (1978). *Annu. Rev. Biochem.* **47**, 129–162.
Fietzek, P. P., and Kühn, K. (1976). *Int. Rev. Connect. Tissue Res.* **7**, 1–59.
Fietzek, P. P., Allmann, H., Rauterberg, J., and Wachter, E. (1977).*Proc. Natl. Acad. Sci. U.S.A.* **74**, 84–86.
Furthmayr, H., and Timpl, R. (1976). *Int. Rev. Connect. Tissue Res.* **7**, 61–99.
Furthmayr, H., Timpl, R., Stark, M., Lapiere, C. M., and Kühn, K. (1972).*FEBS Lett.* **28**, 247–250.
Gay, S., Balleisen, L., Remberger, K., Fietzek, P. P., Adelmann, B. C., and Kühn, K. (1975). *Klin. Wochenschr.* **53**, 899–904.
Gay, S., Müller, P. K., Lemmen, C., Remberger, K., Matzen, K., and Kühn, K. (1976). *Klin. Wochenschr.* **54**, 969–976.
Goetinck, P. F., Pennypacker, J. P., and Royal, P. D. (1974). *Exp. Cell Res.* **87**, 241–248.
Grant, M. E., and Jackson, D. S. (1976). *Essays Biochem.* **12**, 77–113.
Grobstein, C. (1976). *Natl. Cancer Inst., Monogr.* **26**, 279–299.
Hahn, E., Timpl, R., and Miller, E. J. (1974). *J. Immunol.* **113**, 421–423.
Hahn, E., Timpl, R., and Miller, E. J. (1975). *Immunology* **28**, 561–568.
Hall, B. K. (1978). *Ergeb. Anat. Entwicklungsgesch.* **53**, 5–49.
Hascall, V. C., Oegama, T. R., Brown, M., and Caplan, A. I. (1976). *J. Biol. Chem.* **251**, 3511–3519.
Hata, R. I., and Slavkin, H. C. (1978). *Proc. Natl. Acad. Sci. U.S.A.* **75**, 2790–2794.
Hauschka, S., and Königsberg, I. R. (1966) *Proc. Natl. Acad. Sci. U.S.A.* **55**, 119–126.
Herrmann, H., Dessau, W., Fessler, L., and von der Mark, K. (1980). *Eur. J. Biochem.* (in press).
Ho, P. L., Levitt, D., and Dorfman, A. (1977) *Dev. Biol.* **55**, 233–243.
Holtzer, H. (1978). *In* "Stem. Cells and Tissue Homeostasis" (B. I. Lord, G. S. Potten, and R. J. Cole, eds.), pp. 1–27. Cambridge Univ. Press, London and New York.
Holtzer, H., and Abbott, J. (1968). *Results Problems Cell. Differ.* **1**, 1–16.
Holtzer, H., and Detwiler, S. R. (1953). *J. Exp. Zool.* **123**, 335–366.
Horwitz, A. L., and Dorfman, A. (1970). *J. Cell Biol.* **45**, 434–438.
Huggins, C. B. (1931) *Arch. Surg. (Chicago)* **22**, 377–392.
Hynes, (1976). *Biochim. Biophys. Acta* **458**, 73–107.
Kefalides, N. A. (1973). *Int. Rev. Connect. Tissue Res.* **6**, 63–104.
Kessler, S. W. (1975). *J. Immunol.* **115**, 1617–1624.
Ketley, J. M., Orkin, R. W., and Martin, G. R. (1976). *Exp. Cell Res.* **99**, 261–268.
Klebe, R. J. (1975). *Nature (London)* **250**, 248–251.
Lash, J. W., and Vasan, N. S. (1978) *Dev. Biol.* **66**, 151–171.

Levitt, D., and Dorfman, A. (1972) *Proc. Natl. Acad. Sci. U.S.A.* **69**, 1253–1257.

Levitt, D., and Dorfman, A. (1974). *Curr. Top. Dev. Biol.* **8**, 103–149.

Linsenmayer, T. F., and Hendrix, M. J. C. (1980). *Biochem. Biophys. Res. Commun.* **92**, 440–446.

Linsenmayer, T. F., Toole, B. P., and Trelstad, R. L. (1973a). *Dev. Biol.* **35**, 232–239.

Linsenmayer, T. F., Trelstad, R. L., and Gross, J. (1973b). *Biochem. Biophys. Res. Commun.* **53**, 39–45.

Linsenmayer, T. F., Smith, G. N., and Hay, E. D. (1977). *Proc. Natl. Acad. Sci. U.S.A.* **74**, 39–43.

Linsenmayer, T. F., Hendrix, M. J. C., and Little, C. D. (1979). *Proc. Natl. Acad. Sci. U.S.A.* **76**, 3703–3707.

Lowe, M. E., Pacific, M., and Holtzer, H. (1978). *Cancer Res.* **38**, 2350–2356.

Mayne, R., and Strahs, K. R. (1974). *J. Cell Biol.* **63**, 212a.

Mayne, R., Vail, M. S., and Miller, E. J. (1975). *Proc. Natl. Acad. Sci. U.S.A.* **72**, 4511.

Mayne, R., Vail, M. S., Mayne, R. M., and Miller, E. J. (1976a). *Proc. Natl. Acad. Sci. U.S.A.* **73**, 1674–1678.

Mayne, R., Vail, M. S., and Miller, E. J. (1976b). *Dev. Biol.* **54**, 230–240.

Meier, S., and Hay, E. D. (1974). *Dev. Biol.* **38**, 249–270.

Miller, E. J. (1971a). *Biochemistry* **10**, 1652–1659.

Miller, E. J. (1971b). *Biochemistry* **10**, 3030–3035.

Miller, E. J. (1976). *Mol. Cell. Biochem.* **13**, 165–191.

Miller, E. J., and Matthews, H. (1974). *Biochem. Biophys. Res. Commun.* **60**, 424–430.

Miller, E. J., and Matukas, V. A. (1969) *Proc. Natl. Acad. Sci. U.S.A.* **64**, 1264–1268.

Minor, R. P., Rosenbloom, J., Lash, J. W., and von der Mark, K. (1975). *In* "Extracellular Matrix Influences on Gene Expression" (H. C. Slavkin and R. G. Greulich, eds.), pp. 169–174. Academic Press, New York.

Müller, P. K., Lemmen, C., Gay, S., von der Mark, K., and Kühn, K. (1975). *In* "Extracellular Matrix Influences on Gene Expression" (H. C. Slavkin and R. G. Greulich, eds.), pp. 292–302. Academic Press, New York.

Müller, P. K., Lemmen, C., Gay, S., Gauss, V., and Kühn, K. (1977). *Exp. Cell Res.* **108**, 47–55.

Nakagawa, M., and Urist, M. R. (1977). *Proc. Soc. Exp. Biol. Med.* **154**, 568–572.

Nathanson, M. A., Hilfer, S. R., and Searls, R. (1978). *Dev. Biol.* **64**, 99–117.

Newsome, D. A. (1972). *Dev. Biol.* **27**, 575–579.

Newsome, D. A., Linsenmayer, T. F., and Trelstad, R. L. (1976). *J. Cell Biol.* **71**, 59–67.

Nist, C., von der Mark, K., Hay, E. D., Olsen, B. R., Bornstein, P., Ross, R., and Dehm, P. (1975). *J. Cell Biol.* **65**, 75–87.

Nogami, H., and Urist, M. R. (1974). *J. Cell Biol.* **62**, 510–519.

Nowack, H. S., Gay, S., Wick, G., Becker, U., and Timpl, R. (1976). *J. Immunol. Methods* **12**, 117–124.

Öbrink, B. (1973). *Eur. J. Biochem.* **33**, 387–400.

Okayama, M., Pacifici, M., and Holtzer, H. (1976). *Proc. Natl. Acid. Sci. U.S.A.* **73**, 3224–3228.

Olsen, B. R., and Prockop, D. J. (1974). *Proc. Natl. Acad. Sci. U.S.A.* **71**, 2033–2037.

Pacifici, M., and Holtzer, H. (1977). *Am. J. Anat.* **150**, 207–212.

Pawelek, J. M. (1969). *Dev. Biol.* **19**, 52–72.

Reddi, A. H. (1976). *In* "Biochemistry of Collagen" (G. N. Ramachandran and A. H. Reddi, eds.), pp. 449–478. Plenum, New York.

Reddi, A. H., and Anderson, W. A. (1976). *J. Cell Biol.* **69**, 557–572.

Reddi, A. H., and Huggins, C. B. (1972). *Proc. Natl. Acad. Sci. U.S.A.* **69**, 1601–1605.

Reddi, A. H., Gay, R., Gay, S., and Miller, E. J. (1977). *Proc. Natl. Acad. Sci. U.S.A.* **74,** 5589–5592.

Rhodes, R. K., and Miller, E. J. (1978). *Biochemistry* **17,** 3442–3448.

Sasse, J., and von der Mark, K. (1978). *J. Cell Biol.* **79,** 323a.

Sasse, J., and von der Mark, K. (1980). In preparation.

Schenk, R. K., Spiro, D., and Wiener, J. (1967). *J. Cell Biol.* **35,** 115.

Schiltz, J. R., Mayne, R., and Holtzer, H. (1973). *Differentiation* **1,** 97–108.

Searls, R. L. (1965). *Dev. Biol.* **11,** 155–168.

Searls, R. L. (1973) *In* "Developmental Regulation" (S. J. Coward, ed.), pp. 219–521. Academic Press, New York.

Smith, G. N., Linsenmayer, T. F., and Newsome, D. A. (1976). *Proc. Natl. Acad. Sci. U.S.A.* **73,** 4420–4423.

Solursh, M., and Reiter, R. S. (1975a). *Cell Differ.* **4,** 131–137.

Solursh, M., and Reiter, R. S. (1975b). *Dev. Biol.* **44,** 278–287.

Solursh, M., Ahrens, P. B., and Reiter, R. S. (1978). *In Vitro* **14,** 51–61.

Strudel, G. (1953). *C. R. Seances Soc. Biol. Ses Fil.* **147,** 132–133.

Thorogood, P. V., and Hinchliffe, J. R. (1975). *J. Embryol. Exp. Morphol.* **33,** 581–606.

Timpl, R. (1976). *In* "Biochemistry of Collagen" (G. N. Ramachandran and A. H. Reddi, eds.), pp. 319–375. Plenum, New York.

Timpl, R., Wick, G., and Gay, S. (1977). *J. Immunol. Methods* **18,** 165–182.

Toole, B. P. (1976). *J. Biol. Chem.* **251,** 895–897.

Toole, B. P., and Lowther, D. A. (1968). *Biochem. J.* **109,** 857–866.

Trelstad, R. L., Kang, A. H., Igarashi, S., and Gross, J. (1970). *Biochemistry* **9,** 4993–4998.

Trelstad, R. L., Kang, A. H., Toole, B. R., and Gross, J. (1972). *J. Biol. Chem.* **247,** 6469–6473.

Uitto, J. (1977). *Biochemistry* **16,** 3421–3429.

Urist, M. R., and Nogami, H. (1970). *Nature (London)* **225,** 1051–1053.

Vaheri, A., and Mosher, J. (1978). *Biochim. Biophys. Acta* **516,** 1–25.

Vasan, N. S., and Lash, J. W. (1977). *Biochem. J.* **164,** 179–183.

von der Mark, H., von der Mark, K., and Gay, S. (1976). *Dev. Biol.* **48,** 237–249.

von der Mark, K. (1977). *Fed. Eur. Biochem. Soc. Meet., 11th, 1977,* Vol. 48, pp. 35–44.

von der Mark, K., and Conrad, G. (1979). *Clin. Orthop. Relat. Res.* **139,** 185–205.

von der Mark, K., and von der Mark, H. (1977a). *J. Cell Biol.* **73,** 736–747.

von der Mark, K., and von der Mark, H. (1977b). *J. Bone Joint Surg., Br. Vol.* **59,** 458–463.

von der Mark, K., Click, E. M., and Bornstein, P. (1973) *Arch. Biochem. Biophys.* **156,** 356–364.

von der Mark, K., von der Mark, H., and Gay, S. (1976) *Dev. Biol.* **53,** 153–170.

von der Mark, K., Gauss, V., von der Mark, H., and Müller, P. (1977a). *Nature (London)* **267,** 531–532.

von der Mark, K., von der Mark, H., Timpl, R., and Trelstad, R. (1977b). *Dev. Biol.* **59,** 75–85.

Wiedemann, H., Chung, F., Fujii, T., Miller, E. J., and Kühn, K. (1975). *Eur. J. Biochem.* **51,** 363–368.

Wlodarski, K. (1969). *Exp. Cell Res.* **57,** 446–448.

CHAPTER 10

THE APPLICATION OF LABELED LECTINS AND ANTIBODIES TO SDS GELS AND THEIR USE IN STUDYING GLYCOPROTEINS AND CELL SURFACE ANTIGENS DURING DEVELOPMENT

Keith Burridge and Lois Jordan

COLD SPRING HARBOR LABORATORY
COLD SPRING HARBOR, NEW YORK

I. Introduction

Being the primary site of cellular interactions, the cell surface has a critical role in the development of multicellular, differentiated organisms. In spite of this importance the cell surface is a region about which surprisingly little is known. This may be due largely to the limitations of conventional biochemical techniques when applied to the analysis of surface proteins and glycoproteins, which often have difficult properties because of their close relationship to the plasma membrane (spanning it or being embedded in it), and because surface components are usually present in small amounts. Special techniques have been developed to study proteins and glycoproteins exposed at the cell surface. One approach has been to use reagents that will selectively label the components on the outside of cells, but being impermeable to the plasma membrane will not label internal proteins or glycoproteins. Such techniques have provided new information about the surfaces of cells and how they change with development, but this form of analysis is limited by the subset of the proteins or glycoproteins that are labeled by any particular reagent. A different approach has been developed recently by several laboratories for detecting in sodium dodecyl sulfate (SDS) polyacrylamide gels both glycoproteins (Robinson *et al.*, 1975; Tanner and Anstee, 1976; Burridge, 1976; West and McMahon, 1977) and antigens (Stumph *et al.*, 1974; Burridge, 1976; Olden

227

and Yamada, 1977) by the direct binding of lectins or antibodies, respectively. The binding is detected by labeling the lectin or antibody with an enzymatic, fluorescent, or radioactive marker. Since a characteristic of developing systems is the expression of new surface antigens, many of which will also be glycoproteins, both techniques should be of particular value in analyzing surface changes during differentiation. We wish to illustrate this approach with some of our own results using lectins applied to gels to analyze glycoproteins in two differentiating systems: the development of the cellular slime mold, *Dictyostelium discoideum,* and the differentiation of a muscle cell line in tissue culture.

II. Principles of the Technique

Detailed technical procedures for both lectin and antibody staining of gels are described elsewhere (Burridge, 1978). Here we shall describe only the principle of the approach. After electrophoresis of proteins in a conventional SDS polyacrylamide slab gel (Laemmli and Favre, 1973) the proteins are fixed within the gel and the SDS is removed (for example, in a methanol:acetic acid:water mixture). The gel is then brought back into a buffered, physiological saline solution to permit antibody or lectin interaction. Gel slices can be totally immersed in a solution of lectin or antibody or the gel slices can be placed flat and overlayed with a solution. We have found the overlay method is more convenient and uses less reagent. Diffusion of proteins into the gel is slow and most of the reaction between lectin and glycoprotein or antibody and antigen occurs close to the gel surface. After reacting the gels for several hours, the slices are washed extensively in buffer to allow unbound lectin or antibody to diffuse out. For detecting the reactive gel bands we prefer radioiodinated probes over those coupled with fluorescein or peroxidase. The sensitivity of autoradiography is considerable and different exposures of the same gel can be made easily.

When the technique is used with antibodies the detection is usually indirect using a second iodinated antibody directed against the first or using iodinated Staphylococcal A protein (which binds the Fc portion of the IgG molecule of many species). Indirect detection has the advantage of amplification and it avoids iodinating the first antibody, which is frequently a limited and precious commodity. Protein A has the advantage that a single labeled reagent can be used with antibodies from different species, but in general we have found greater sensitivity with a second, specific antibody directed against the first one. Protein A has been used with a variety of antigens (Bigelis and Burridge, 1978; Burridge, 1978). For iodination of either the second antibody or the protein A, we now prefer the use of the Bolton–Hunter reagent (Bolton and Hunter, 1973). Although more expensive, it gives considerably higher specific activities and appears to cause less damage to these proteins.

It is perhaps surprising that any antigens retain or regain their antigenicity after boiling in reducing agent and electrophoresis in SDS detergent. Certainly, it should be recognized that a few antigens are irreversibly destroyed, but the large majority of antibodies so far tested on gels have proved successful (Burridge, 1978). The survival of an antigenic site after gel electrophoresis must depend on the nature of the particular antigen, the extent to which the antigenic site is affected by the denaturing agents, and on how much it is restored upon removal of the SDS and a return to more gentle ionic conditions. Our results with a wide variety of antibodies suggest that there is a complete spectrum of antigens ranging from those that are destroyed in gels to those that are readily detected even in the nanogram range of protein concentration.

In principle, macromolecules other than lectins and antibodies might be used on gels to detect their corresponding ligands. For example, it might be possible to detect the binding of repressors and similar molecules to specific DNA restriction fragments within gels. Alternatively, the receptors for toxins or hormones might be directly visualized by the binding of a labeled toxin or hormone to the receptor resolved within a gel. Whether interactions such as these are possible in gels will depend on the stability of the particular molecules to denaturation, but where such interactions are possible they should provide direct means of identifying receptor molecules of special interest.

III. Changes in the Glycoproteins of *Dictyostelium discoideum* during Its Life Cycle

The vegetative amoebae of *D. discoideum* multiply as single cells. With the exhaustion of nutrients their developmental cycle is initiated. The cells become increasingly cohesive and are stimulated to aggregate in response to chemotactic signals. Within the resulting pseudoplasmodium two cell types differentiate, the prestalk and prespore cells. With further development these give rise to the stalk and spore cells of the mature sorocarp or fruiting body (Bonner, 1967). The life cycle is completed by the germination of the spores to give rise to the free-living, vegetative amoebae. In our work we have used the axenic strain Ax-2, developed by Watts and Ashworth (1970). After plating on Millipore filters the cells of the various stages in the developmental cycle can be easily harvested for gel analysis by dissolving the whole cells in gel sample buffer. Analyzing the glycoproteins from whole cells as opposed to from purified plasma membranes has been a convenient

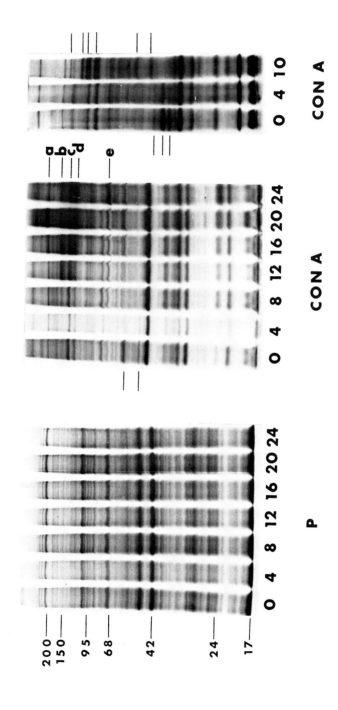

approach. It avoids problems of proteolysis encountered during membrane preparation and permits working with small quantities of cells without the need for large batches that are required for membrane preparations. However, in analyzing the glycoproteins from whole cells, both the surface glycoproteins as well as the internal ones will be included in the sample. For any particular glycoprotein further work is necessary to determine whether it is a component of the plasma membrane and exposed on the surface.

Figure 1 (P) shows a slab gel stained with Coomassie blue and analyzing the total protein of cells harvested every 4 hours during the developmental cycle. Development was complete by 24 hours after the initial plating. When the pattern of proteins is compared on this gel, surprisingly few changes are revealed at this level of resolution. Increasing the resolution, for example by using two-dimensional gels, has shown that a considerable number of proteins do change with development (Alton and Lodish, 1977). This is particularly noticeable when rates of synthesis of various proteins are compared rather than their absolute quantity. A parallel slab gel of the same samples is shown in Fig. 1 after reaction with radioiodinated concanavalin A (Con A). A great many glycoproteins can be seen to bind Con A. This binding is inhibited by specific sugars, such as α-methyl-mannoside (data not

---

Fig. 1. SDS gel analysis of the proteins and Con A-binding glycoproteins of successive stages in the development of *D. discoideum*. Cells of the Ax-2 strain of *D. discoideum* were grown axenically. Washed cells were plated on Millipore filters and allowed to progress through their life cycle. Cells were harvested at 4-hour intervals by washing off the filters, spinning down the cells, and directly dissolving the cell pellets in gel sample buffer. After protein determination, 50 μg of protein for each time point during development was electrophoresed on SDS polyacrylamide gels using the buffer system of Laemmli and Favre (1973). It should be noted that there was a miscalculation of the protein concentration for the cells harvested at 4 hours on the first two gels displayed and that approximately 30 μg was electrophoresed and not 50 μg. The intensity of bands in these slots is consequently decreased uniformly. The first gel (P) is a photograph of a dried down 10% polyacrylamide gel stained with Coomassie brilliant blue. The time of harvesting the cells is given in hours beneath all the samples in this figure and in Fig. 2. On the left of the gel the molecular weight ($\times$ 10^{-3}) of standard proteins is indicated. Protein standards used were rabbit skeletal muscle myosin, the 150,000-dalton polypeptide of RNA polymerase, phosphorylase B, bovine serum albumin, actin, trypsin, and hemoglobin. The second panel (Con A) shows an autoradiograph of a parallel 10% polyacrylamide gel which was reacted with ^{125}I-labeled Con A and then washed extensively. Two bands which can be seen to decrease or disappear during development are indicated on the left side of the gel, whereas five bands that increase with development have been marked on the right side of the gel (a–e). The third panel shows an autoradiograph of a 7.5% polyacrylamide gel also reacted with ^{125}I-labeled Con A but on which samples from 0, 4, and 10 hours of development only were analyzed. The different percentage acrylamide gives some enhanced resolution and reactive gel bands which change with development have again been indicated.

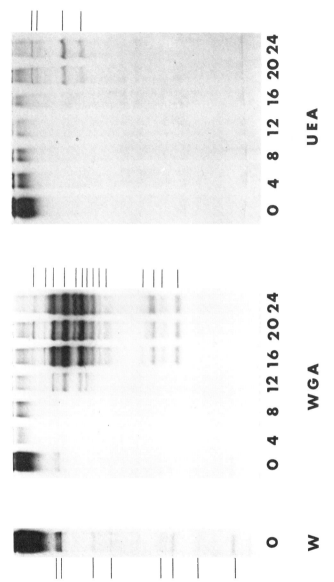

FIG. 2. SDS gel analysis of the glycoproteins binding wheat germ agglutinin and the *Ulex europeus* agglutinin (UEA) during *D. discoideum* development. The first panel (W) is the same as the first slot of the second panel, but it shows a longer autoradiographic exposure so that the faint gel bands that react with WGA can be seen in this sample of vegetative cells (time = 0 hours). The second panel (WGA) shows an autoradiograph of a 10% polyacrylamide gel on which 50-μg samples were electrophoresed after cells were harvested at 4-hour intervals as described for Fig. 1. The gel was reacted with ^{125}I-labeled WGA. At least 14 gel bands can be seen to appear and to accumulate from about 12 hours of development onward, whereas most of the bands in the vegetative cells are lost. The

shown). Several general points should be noted concerning the pattern of bands reacting with Con A. First, the large number of bands should be emphasized. Con A exerts multiple effects on the live cells of *D. discoideum*, and these multiple effects have been often considered as if Con A bound to a single or a few receptors. Clearly in *D. discoideum* (and in most other cells too) there is no such thing as a single glycoprotein receptor for Con A. Second, the majority of Con A-reactive bands are unaltered in intensity during the cycle of differentiation. Such components probably represent membrane molecules whose function is essential to all cells. Third, some of the bands in this gel do change, appearing or disappearing with time. In the vegetative cells two prominent bands with molecular weights of about 55,000 and 48,000 can be seen to decrease with development and have been indicated in Fig. 1. On the other hand, at least five bands (a, b, c, d, e) can be seen to increase or to appear during development. These have molecular weights of approximately 200,000, 160,000, 145,000, 135,000, and 70,000. When Smart and Hynes (1974) used surface iodination to analyze the surface of *Dictyostelium*, they found a band of about 130,000 daltons which appeared after 12 hours of development. This may correspond to band d described here or to one of the bands that binds wheat germ agglutinin (WGA) revealed in Fig. 2. Geltosky *et al.* (1976) found a band at about 150,000 that was surface labeled, bound to Con A affinity columns, and which accumulated between 6 and 18 hours of development. This probably corresponds to band c in our analysis. The very large number of bands present tends to obscure some of the changes that occur, and a two-dimensional gel will probably be more effective in this analysis. In some experiments changes have been more clearly demonstrated by using gels of different percentage acrylamide and by running the gels for a longer time. A gel of different percentage acrylamide is also illustrated in Fig. 1 which was used to analyze cells during early time points in the developmental sequence. Some of the changing glycoproteins can be seen more clearly and have been indicated in this gel.

When the WGA is reacted with similar gels of cells taken at succes-

---

pronounced reduction in the intensity of the material at the top of the first slot (vegetative cells) should be noted. The third panel (UEA) shows an autoradiograph of a parallel gel that was reacted with the fucose-binding lectin from *Ulex europeus*. Note the intense staining at the top of the initial slot (vegetative cells) which decreases sharply as development continues. Otherwise, there is an absence of reactive gel bands until the two final time points analyzed (20 to 24 hours of development) when four reactive gel bands can be seen.

sive time points through the life cycle of *D. discoideum,* a different
pattern of bands is revealed (Fig. 2). First, the number of bands reacting is considerably less. Second, there is a striking change in the pattern with almost no bands remaining unaltered during this differentiation. The bands revealed in vegetative cells are lost and a whole series
of new glycoproteins are expressed beginning at the time of pseudoplasmodium formation. The sample of the vegetative cells shows a relatively few bands reacting weakly with WGA. A longer exposure of the
first gel sample (vegetative cells) is shown in Fig. 2 (W) so that the
weakly reactive gel bands can be seen. The most prominent labeling of
the vegative cell is at the very top of the separating gel where consistently WGA labels most intensely. The nature of this material has not
been resolved, but its failure to yield a discrete gel band and its poor
entry into the gel may suggest material other than glycoprotein, such
as a mucopolysaccharide or a form of cellulose. A marked decrease in
this material seems to be one of the first detectable changes in the
sequence of *Dictyostelium* development. During the course of the first 8
to 12 hours of development, the initial bands labeled by WGA disappear and at least 14 new bands appear and accumulate between 12 and
20 hours of development. Four of these high-molecular-weight bands
comigrate with bands a, b, c, and d (Fig. 1) that react with Con A. It
seems likely that the same glycoproteins bind both lectins. It is of
interest that one of the enzymes that has been shown to vary in activity
during *D. discoideum* development is β-*N*-acetylglucosaminidase
(Loomis, 1969). In the axenic strain used here the activity has been
found to be sinusoidal (Quance and Ashworth, 1972) with an initial
increase in activity after plating, possibly correlating with the disappearance of the initial bands reacting with WGA. The activity then
falls off before rising again during spore formation. It will be interesting to establish whether any of the gel bands reacting with WGA are
natural substrates for this enzyme.

  Lectins which bind fucose, for example that from *Lotus tetragono-
lobus* or that from *Ulex europeus,* have given interesting results when
applied to gels of developing *D. discoideum.* Results with the lectin
from *U. europeus* are shown in Fig. 2. Vegetative cells and the stages
up to the final two time points show no reactive gel bands, with the one
exception of intense staining at the very top of the gel track containing
the vegetative cells. The reaction in this region is similar to the labeling with WGA, and it seems likely that this is the same material and
very possibly not glycoprotein as discussed above. Otherwise, no reactive areas or bands are revealed on the gel until the final developmental stages of culmination and the final maturation of the spores and

stalks. At this point at least four reactive gel bands can be detected (see final two gel slots). This late expression of a set of glycoproteins containing fucose is of particular interest in relation to the data of Gregg and Karp (1978) who have studied the direct incorporation of [³H]fucose into the various stages and visualized this by microscopy of autoradiographs of embedded sections of the specific stages. They found that most cells throughout the life cycle were capable of limited incorporation of fucose, but there was markedly enhanced incorporation by the prespore and mature spore cells. Furthermore, most of this incorporated label was localized at the edge of the cells in the region of the developing spore cell walls. The incorporation they have observed correlates in time with the appearance of these fucose-containing gel bands. If further work confirms that these glycoproteins are components of the spore wall, then these could be useful biochemical markers for this stage of differentiation. Markers for specific stages in differentiation would be valuable when studying development under perturbed *in vitro* conditions or in various mutants in which the normal pattern of differentiation is upset.

Some lectins do not react at all with gels of the various stages of *D. discoideum* development. We have found this both for phytohemagglutinin (PHA, from the red kidney bean) which has a specificity for N-acetylgalactosamine and also for the lectin RCA$_{120}$ (*Ricinus communis* agglutinin, MW 120,000) which has a specificity for terminal galactose. This result has been consistent with similar lectin analysis by West *et al.* (1978) and with the sugar analysis of *Dictyostelium* plasma membranes performed by Gilkes and Weeks (1977) and Hoffman and McMahon (1977) which showed minimal levels of these sugars. These results, however, are somewhat surprising since *D. discoideum* produces two lectins (carbohydrate binding proteins) during its aggregation which have a specificity for galactose and N-acetylgalactosamine. These intrinsic lectins are of particular interest, and they have been implicated in the increased cellular cohesion that occurs in *Dictyostelium* during the aggregation phase of its development (Rosen *et al.*, 1973). It would be important to identify the receptors for these intrinsic lectins. Accordingly, we have applied these purified, labeled intrinsic lectins to gels of *Dictyostelium;* but, as with PHA and RCA$_{120}$, we were unable to detect any bands reacting with these lectins. It could be that the receptors are not present in sufficient quantity to detect, but it seems more likely that they are glycolipids or similar molecules which do not migrate in the gel or which are not fixed after electrophoresis. Further work will be required to test this.

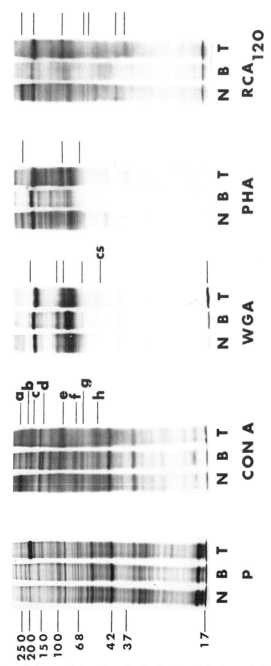

FIG. 3. Protein and glycoprotein gel analysis of rat myoblast–myotube differentiation in culture. Three cell types have been compared in these parallel 10% polyacrylamide gels: 7 day cultures of the NF2 nonfusing clone of myoblasts (N), 4 day cultures of G22N

IV. Glycoprotein Changes during Myogenesis

The cell surface is a critical region in muscle cell differentiation. Some of the stages of muscle cell development can be conveniently studied in tissue culture using either primary cultures or myoblast cell lines. These cell lines have the advantages that they are free from other contaminating cell types and that they can be kept in the precursor myoblast form indefinitely, with differentiation being triggered by manipulation of the growth conditions (Yaffe, 1968). When this occurs the myoblasts first align and then fuse to form multinucleated syncitia (myotubes). Within these the characteristic muscle proteins are synthesized, myofibrils are assembled, and the specialized membrane systems develop. On the surface nicotinic acetylcholine receptors appear (Fambrough and Rash, 1971; Patrick et al., 1972) and the plasma membrane becomes electrically excitable (Fischbach et al., 1971; Kidokoro, 1973). A number of recent reviews have described many of these aspects of myogenesis in detail (see, for example, Yaffe, 1969; Fischman, 1970; Merlie et al., 1977).

The clonal rat myoblast line (G22N) is a derivative of Yaffe's L8 line. Under appropriate conditions of culture medium as many as 95% of the cells will fuse in a culture during a period of about 24 hours. The glycoproteins of the prefused myoblasts and the postfused myotubes have been compared by lectin-binding analysis to SDS polyacrylamide gels of whole cells. They have also been compared with the glycoproteins of a related nonfusing myoblast clone NF2. Typical results are shown in Fig. 3.

When the proteins of the nonfusing, the prefused, and fused cells are compared few differences are seen in these one-dimensional gels with the exception of the very large increase in the amount of myosin heavy chain in the myotubes. Surprisingly, perhaps, the amount of

---

prefused myoblasts (B), and 7 day cultures of the same G22N myoblasts by which time over 90% of the cells have fused to become myotubes (T). Approximately 40 μg of protein for each cell type was compared. The first panel (P) shows a Coomassie blue-stained gel of these samples. The molecular weight ($\times$ 10^{-3}) of standard proteins is shown adjacent to this gel. The proteins used were LETS protein, rabbit skeletal muscle myosin, the 150,000-dalton polypeptide of RNA polymerase, α-actinin, bovine serum albumin, muscle actin, muscle tropomyosin, and hemoglobin. Note the increase in the myosin heavy chain in the fused myotube sample. The four remaining panels were reacted with the iodinated lectins Con A, WGA, PHA, and RCA$_{120}$, respectively. Prominent changes in the glycoproteins have been indicated. For reference in the text, changes revealed in the Con A-reacted gel have been labeled a–h. The position of one weak band that appears in the myotube sample has been tentatively marked cs since it may represent calsequestrin, a glycoprotein of the sarcoplasmic reticulum of about this molecular weight and which is known to contain glucosamine (Ostwald and Maclennan, 1974).

actin appears unaltered although from other work it is known that the types of actin synthesized are changed (Whalen *et al.*, 1976; Garrels and Gibson, 1976). Just as in the gels of the *Dictyostelium* samples, a great many bands over the complete molecular weight range can be seen to react with iodinated Con A. With the three other lectins illustrated here, fewer bands are seen and most are above 80,000 in molecular weight. The gel reacted with Con A reveals some interesting glycoprotein changes, although some are difficult to see and many may not be detected on account of the large number of overlapping bands. Some glycoprotein changes are very prominent. For example, band d is a major band reacting with Con A in the unfused myoblasts, but it is absent or much reduced in cultures of the fused myotubes. Since it is also absent or much reduced in the parallel culture of nonfusing myoblasts, it would seem that the decrease in this band does not relate to myoblast fusion, but rather that this is a glycoprotein which correlates with actively growing cultures. On the other hand, band e (and possibly h) appears to increase specifically in myotubes but not in parallel cultures of the nonfusing clone. These bands may thus represent either glycoproteins involved in the fusion event or specialized glycoproteins of the differentiated myotube. Certainly, the mature muscle does have specialized membranes and membrane functions not present in myoblasts. For example, there is the sarcoplasmic reticulum and the transverse tubular system. In the sarcoplasmic reticulum there is a set of distinctive proteins associated with calcium transport, storage, and release such as the Ca^{2+}, Mg^{2+}-ATPase, the high-affinity Ca^{2+} binding protein and calsequestrin. Band e has a molecular weight close to 100,000 which is the value for the ATPase of the sarcoplasmic reticulum (Maclennan and Holland, 1976), but there is no evidence that this enzyme is a glycoprotein. It has been shown, however, that calsequestrin is a glycoprotein containing glucosamine (Ostwald and Maclennan, 1974). The apparent molecular weight has been found to vary between 63,000 and 44,000 according to the gel system used (Maclennan and Holland, 1976). A faint gel band reacting with WGA specifically in the fused myotubes can be distinguished (particularly in longer autoradiographic exposures) with a molecular weight of about 55,000 (tentatively marked CS in Fig. 3). The use of specific antibodies against calsequestrin and their reaction on similar gels could indicate whether this glycoprotein band is indeed calsequestrin. Bands f and g appear to be decreased in the myotubes compared with the myoblast and nonfusing myoblast samples. The decrease in these bands could relate to fusion or to the maturation of the myotube membrane.

Of particular interest is band a which is coincident with the large, external, transformation-sensitive protein (LETS) also known as fibronectin. This we have established using specific antisera which react with this band on parallel gels (K. Burridge and L. Jordan, unpublished results). In the myoblast sample this area clearly contains a doublet of bands, whereas in the myotubes only a single band (the lower one) can be identified. The situation in the nonfusing cells is uncertain because of the increased staining in this region, but it looks as if the doublet may be present. By antibody staining on gels an increase in total LETS protein in both myotubes and the nonfusing cells has been found. Hynes *et al.* (1976) have also found by surface iodination that there is an increase in LETS during myogenesis. Whereas Chen (1977) found using indirect immunofluorescence that after myoblast fusion there was a major redistribution of LETS protein on the myotube surface with the fibrillar network giving way to condensed foci of LETS protein. The identity of the upper band in the band a doublet is intriguing. If it is a component of LETS protein or relates to it, then does its loss from the myotubes relate to the redistribution of LETS protein on the surface of myotubes as described by Chen (1977)?

Another feature of band a that is interesting is that it is more heavily labeled by Con A in the nonfusing cells than in either the myoblasts or myotubes. It is also intensely labeled in gels of these NF2 cells by PHA and RCA_{120}. Since antibody studies have suggested that the amount is not significantly increased in these cells over that found with the myotubes, this increase in lectin binding suggests that the carbohydrate portion of this glycoprotein is different. Either there has been increased glycosylation or a decreased incorporation of sialic acid, resulting in the availability of more lectin-binding sites. It would be interesting to know whether such changes in the carbohydrate on the surface of these cells might affect their ability to fuse.

The three lectins, RCA_{120}, WGA, and PHA all label intensely a band (possibly a doublet, see the RCA gel) with a molecular weight of 200,000. In these gels it appears coincident with the myosin heavy chain band. Because of the increased size of the myosin band after fusion, it appears somewhat distorted in the gels of the myotube samples. In gels of different percentage acrylamide we have found it to run so as to be distinguishable from the myosin heavy chain, which clearly it is not. Certain other glycoprotein changes are revealed by these lectins. They all label a band at about 95,000 which is present in the myotubes but absent or much lower in the myoblasts and NF2 cells. In contrast, WGA labels a band at about 110,000 in the NF2 cells and myoblasts but not in the myotubes. These bands could relate to the fusion process, or alternatively the appearance of the new band at 95,000 may represent the appearance of a new differentiated function associated with myotube membranes.

V. Concluding Remarks

Lectin binding to SDS gels provides a sensitive technique for analyzing glycoproteins according to both their apparent molecular weight and their carbohydrate content. The resolution of the technique is essentially equal to the resolution of the gel system used. As a result, more detailed information will be achieved when the analysis described here is extended to a second dimension. When lectin binding is used to analyze glycoproteins it also suggests a way of purifying any glycoproteins of interest since lectins can be used for affinity chromatography. For example, it should be relatively easy to purify the fucose-containing glycoproteins that are revealed in Fig. 2 by using the same fucose-binding lectin immobilized on a matrix such as agarose or polyacrylamide. The purified glycoproteins could then be studied biochemically or they could be used as antigens to raise specific antisera. In turn, such antisera could be used in a wide variety of ways. Similarly, it should be possible to use lectin columns to isolate the glycoproteins of interest in myogenesis. Here also, antibodies against specific glycoproteins will be powerful reagents. It would be interesting, for example, to find one which blocked myoblast fusion or which affected any other parameter in the myogenic sequence of events.

Immunological methods are popular in the study of the cell surface. A common strategy has been to raise antisera against whole cells or plasma membranes and then to use selective adsorption against mutant cells or cells from a different developmental stage to produce antisera that are specific for the starting cell used as an antigen. This approach has been applied, for example, by Gerisch's group in their analysis of aggregation in *Dictyostelium discoideum* (Beug *et al.*, 1973). In many studies of this kind the nature of the reactive antigen has not been determined. In such cases the direct detection of surface antigens within gels should be useful. It seems probable that monoclonal antibody techniques will be used increasingly in the dissection of the cell surface during development, especially since by cloning the antibody-producing cells pure antibodies can be obtained even after immunization with crude antigenic mixtures such as plasma membranes or whole cells. The identification of reactive antigens will be necessary in many of these studies and toward this end the direct detection of antigens within SDS gels should provide a sensitive and valuable technique.

ACKNOWLEDGMENTS

Part of this work was done when one of us (KB) held an Anna Fuller Fund Postdoctoral Fellowship. The authors also gratefully acknowledge the support of a grant from the Muscular Dystrophy Association, Inc. and from the NCI Cancer Center grant (CA13106) to Cold Spring Harbor Laboratory.

REFERENCES

Alton, T. H., and Lodish, H. F. (1977). *Dev. Biol.* **60**, 180.

Beug, H., Katz, F. E., and Gerisch, G. (1973). *J. Cell Biol.* **56**, 647.

Bigelis, R., and Burridge, K. (1978). *Biochem. Biophys. Res. Commun.* **82**, 322.

Bolton, A. E., and Hunter, W. M. (1973). *Biochem. J.* **133**, 529.

Bonner, J. T. (1967). "The Cellular Slime Molds," 2nd ed. Princeton Univ. Press, Princeton, New Jersey.

Burridge, K. (1976). *Proc. Natl. Acad. Sci. U.S.A.* **73**, 4457.

Burridge, K. (1978). *In* "Methods in Enzymology" (V. Ginsburg, ed.), Vol. 50, p. 54. Academic Press, New York.

Chen, L. B. (1977). *Cell* **10**, 393.

Fambrough, D., and Rash, J. E. (1971). *Dev. Biol.* **26**, 55.

Fischbach, G. D., Nameroff, M., and Nelson, P. G. (1971). *J. Cell. Physiol.* **78**, 289.

Fischman, D. A. (1970). *Curr. Top. Dev. Biol.* **5**, 235.

Garrels, J. I., and Gibson, W. (1976). *Cell* **9**, 793.

Geltosky, J. E., Siu, C.-H., and Lerner, R. A. (1976). *Cell* **8**, 391.

Gilkes, N. R., and Weeks, G. (1977). *Biochim. Biophys Acta* **464**, 142.

Gregg, J. H., and Karp, G. C. (1978). *Exp. Cell Res.* **112**, 31.

Hoffman, S., and McMahon, D. (1977). *Biochim. Biophys. Acta* **465**, 242.

Hynes, R. O., Martin, G. S., Shearer, M., Critchley, D. R., and Epstein, C. J. (1976). *Dev. Biol.* **48**, 35.

Kidokoro, Y. (1973). *Nature (London) New Biol.* **241**, 158.

Laemmli, U. K., and Favre, M. (1973). *J. Mol. Biol.* **80**, 575.

Loomis, W. F. (1969). *J. Bacteriol.* **97**, 1149.

Maclennan, D. H., and Holland, P. C. (1976). *In* The Enzymes of Biological Membranes" (A. Martonosi, ed.), Vol. 3, p. 221. Plenum, New York.

Merlie, J. P., Buckingham, M. E., and Whalen, R. G. (1977). *Curr. Top. Dev. Biol.* **11**, 61.

Olden, K., and Yamada, K. M. (1977). *Anal. Biochem.* **78**, 483.

Ostwald, T. J., and Maclennan, D. H. (1974). *J. Biol. Chem.* **249**, 974.

Patrick, J., Heinemann, S., Lindstrom, J., Schubert, D., and Steinbach, J. H. (1972). *Proc. Natl. Acad. Sci. U.S.A.* **69**, 2762.

Quance, J., and Ashworth, J. M. (1972). *Biochem. J.* **126**, 609.

Robinson, P. J., Bull, F. G., Anderton, B. H., and Roitt, I. M. (1975). *FEBS Lett.* **58**, 330.

Rosen, S. D., Kafka, J. A., Simpson, D. L., and Barondes, S. H. (1973). *Proc. Natl. Acad. Sci. U.S.A.* **70**, 2554.

Smart, J. E., and Hynes, R. O. (1974). *Nature (London)* **251**, 319.

Stumph, W. E., Elgin, S. C. R., and Hood, L. (1974). *J. Immunol.* **113**, 1752.

Tanner, M. J. A., and Anstee, D. J. (1976). *Biochem. J.* **153**, 265.

Watts, D. J., and Ashworth, J. M. (1970). *Biochem. J.* **119**, 171.

West, C. M., and McMahon, D. (1977). *J. Cell Biol.* **74**, 264.

West, C. M., McMahon, D., and Molday, R. S. (1978). *J. Biol. Chem.* **253**, 1716.

Whalen, R. G., Butler-Browne, G. S., and Gros, F. (1976). *Proc. Natl. Acad. Sci. U.S.A.* **73**, 2018.

Yaffe, D. (1968). *Proc. Natl. Acad. Sci. U.S.A.* **61**, 477.

Yaffe, D. (1969). *Curr. Top. Dev. Bio.* **4**, 37.

CHAPTER 11

UNIVALENT ANTIBODY FRAGMENTS AS TOOLS FOR THE ANALYSIS OF CELL INTERACTIONS IN *DICTYOSTELIUM*

Günther Gerisch

MAX-PLANCK-INSTITUT FÜR BIOCHEMIE
MARTINSRIED, FEDERAL REPUBLIC OF GERMANY

I. Introduction

Labeled antibodies are routinely used in developmental biology for the localization of antigens and for their quantitative determination. Antibodies can, however, also be applied as probes that inhibit or stimulate developmental processes by interaction with specific cell surface constituents. This chapter will focus on this aspect. Intact immunoglobulins, when applied to living cells, have the disadvantage of agglutinating cells and inducing antigen redistribution in the form of patches and caps. This can be avoided by the use of univalent antibody

243

CURRENT TOPICS IN
DEVELOPMENTAL BIOLOGY, VOL. 14

fragments. These have been introduced into developmental biology by A. Tyler and C. Metz in their pioneering studies on the inhibition of sea urchin fertilization by antibodies against sperm. In the first of these studies Tyler (1959) has produced univalent fragments by photooxidation which caused partial inactivation of antibodies. Metz and Thompson (1967) could make use already of papain digestion (Porter, 1959) which is now the standard technique for the preparation of Fab. Because the cells in *Dictyostelium discoideum* (Dd) are single at the beginning of development and aggregate thereafter, this microorganism is unusually suitable to the analysis of cell interactions by Fab. Studies on cell adhesion in the neuroretina of the chicken (Rutishauser *et al.*, 1976; Thiery *et al.*, 1977), between sea urchin blastomeres (McClay *et al.*, 1977; Noll *et al.*, 1979), and in mammalian embryos (Kemler *et al.*, 1977) have demonstrated that techniques similar to those described here for Dd can be applied to a variety of embryonic systems.

II. Membrane Changes during Development of *Dictyostelium discoideum*

A. THE DEVELOPMENTAL CYCLE

The asexual development of Dd can be divided into (*a*) spore germination, (*b*) growth phase, (*c*) the interphase between the end of growth and the beginning of aggregation, (*d*) aggregation, (*e*) the "finger" and "migrating slug" stage, and (*f*) culmination (Fig. 1). During growth the cells feed on bacteria or, in selected laboratory strains, on nutrient solutions including chemically defined media (Franke and Kessin, 1977). Differentiation of growth phase cells into aggregation competent ones is initiated by the removal of nutrients whereby amino acid depletion seems to play a major role (Marin, 1976, 1977). The interphase requires 4 to 8 hours, depending on the particular strain of Dd. In the course of aggregation the cells assemble into a tissue-like mass by cyclic AMP-mediated chemotaxis and by cell-to-cell adhesion. The cell mass develops into a polar body and becomes organized into an area of prestalk cells in the tip region of the slug, and an area of prespore cells behind. Fluorescent antisera against spores are of diagnostic value for the distinction of prespore and prestalk areas (Takeuchi, 1972; Forman and Garrod, 1977a,b). They presumably react with a mucopolysaccharide which is later secreted to form the slime that surrounds the spores. Also cells which are in an early stage of development into spores can be labeled with those antisera. Thus immunolabeling can be used as a tool to follow the transformation of prestalk into prespore

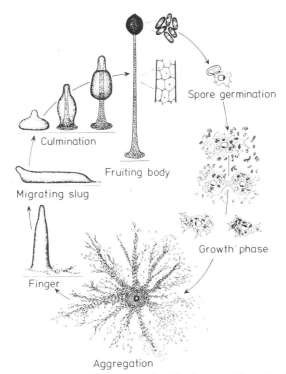

Spore germination

Culmination

Fruiting body

Migrating slug

Growth phase

Finger

Aggregation

FIG. 1. Developmental cycle of Dd as explained in the text. (From Gerisch, 1965.)

cells, and vice versa, which occurs when pieces of a slug are isolated or transplanted into another position (Raper, 1940; Bonner *et al.*, 1955; Gregg, 1965).

During the culmination phase the fruiting body acquires its definite shape. Simultaneously the cells differentiate into spores and stalk cells (including the cells of the footpad which resemble stalk cells). The cells constituting the fruiting body are covered by cell walls that consist of cellulose.

B. REGULATION OF MEMBRANE ANTIGENS

The single cells are surrounded by a plasma membrane which appears to lack a thick surface coat as is characteristic of the giant amoebae, *Chaos carolinensis* and *Amoeba proteus* (see Jeon, 1972). The major antigenic groups are the carbohydrate residues of glycosphingolipids (Wilhelms *et al.*, 1974) which stick out from the outer electron-dense layer of the membrane to a distance of probably less than 100 Å (Schwarz, 1973; Gerisch *et al.*, 1974). Also protein antigens are exposed on the cell surface, together with a great variety of glyco-proteins.

The first demonstration that membrane antigens are changing during development has been provided by agglutination studies. Gregg (1956, 1960) and Gregg and Trygstad (1958) have shown that the agglutinability of cells by certain antisera against aggregating cells increases during development from the growth phase to the aggregation stage. Sonneborn *et al.* (1963) have applied complement fixation in order to demonstrate new antigen specificities that become detectable in membrane fractions of cells which reach the aggregation stage.

Iodination of cell surface proteins followed by SDS–polyacrylamide electrophoresis has enabled Siu *et al.* (1975) to estimate the minimal number of different cell surface proteins that change during the interphase between growth and aggregation. Nine polypeptides showed changes during development, among them a major developmentally regulated protein complex (Bordier *et al.*, 1978). The relative intensity of one glycoprotein band increased strongly between 6 and 18 hours of development (Geltosky *et al.*, 1976). West and McMahon (1977) found among a total number of more than 35 concanavalin A-binding glyco-proteins in plasma membranes of Dd, 12 glycoproteins which increased, in terms of concanavalin A binding activity, between growth phase and the aggregation-competent stage. Functionally characterized cell surface constituents which are developmentally regulated include cyclic AMP receptors and cyclic AMP phosphodiesterase (see Gerisch and Malchow, 1976). The latter is a concanavalin A-binding glycoprotein (Eitle and Gerisch, 1977).

The multiplicity of membrane changes associated with the acquisition of aggregation competence makes it necessary to employ more specific methods for the identification of those cell surface constituents which are involved in cell adhesion. Two approaches have led to the purification and characterization of specific molecules: (a) The blockage of cell adhesion by Fab and the identification of the target antigen(s) of the blocking Fab molecules (Gerisch, 1977). (b) The localization of lectins at the cell surface and the search for glycoconjugates which act as receptors for these carbohydrate-binding proteins (Rosen and Barondes, 1978). In the following emphasis will be put on the first method. Its limitations will be discussed together with divergent results obtained by the second approach.

C. Changes of Adhesiveness during Development

Cells of the wild-type strain v-12 of Dd can be grown in shaken suspension cultures with washed bacteria as nutrients. After exhaustion of the bacteria the cells require several hours for development into aggregation-competent ones. Aggregation competence can be assessed by transferring the cells on a substratum where they are able to move. Noncompetent cells are of irregular shape. They either remain single or assemble into loose, cloudy masses. Aggregation competence is indicated by elongation of the cells and their aggregation into chains and streams. Aggregating cells adhere to each other most tightly at their ends. In contrast to side-to-side adhesion, the end-to-end adhesion is highly resistant against EDTA. This property has been exploited for testing aggregation competence in cell suspensions: competent cells will agglutinate in the presence of EDTA, whereas growth phase cells will virtually not agglutinate (Gerisch, 1961).

The previous statements require some modification for cells grown not on bacteria, but under axenic conditions in a medium containing yeast extract and peptone (Watts and Ashworth, 1970). As long as axenically grown cells stay in the growth medium the cells show little, if any, agglutinability. This appears to be, at least in part, due to an adhesion-inhibiting factor of low molecular weight which has been partially purified from stationary phase cultures (Swan *et al.*, 1977).

If the cells are freed from the nutrient medium during exponential growth and resuspended in nonnutrient buffer, development toward the aggregation-competent stage is initiated. When the cells are left in the growth medium until late stationary phase, they loose their ability to develop. Those cells can be induced to develop by pulses of cyclic AMP, as will be discussed in Section III, E. In the context of this chapter the term "growth phase cells" will be reserved for cells tested immediately after the depletion of bacteria and also for cells, grown in axenic culture, that have been washed free of the nutrient medium during the exponential growth phase.

III. Analysis of Cell Adhesion by Fab

A. EDTA-RESISTANT AND -SENSITIVE TYPES OF CELL ADHESION ARE BLOCKED BY DIFFERENT FAB MOLECULES

From the changes of adhesiveness during development it has been hypothesized that Dd cells have a dual adhesion system: one class of adhesion sites, being already present in growth phase cells, is responsible for irregular cell assembly. In elongated cells this is mainly a side-by-side assembly. A second class of adhesion sites appears, in this view, at the cell surface when the cells acquire aggregation competence. These sites are responsible for the EDTA stable end-to-end adhesion. The activities of both types of adhesion sites, superimposed upon

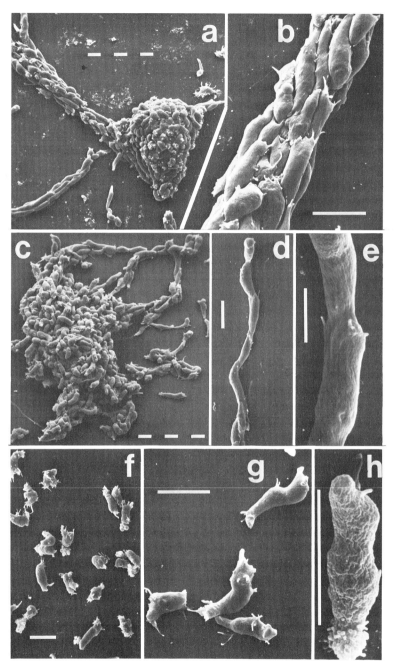

FIG. 2. Morphology of aggregating cells of Dd, strain v-12/M2, and the effects of Fab. (a, b) Untreated cells aggregating on a plastic surface. (b) In a stream the cells are associated by end-to-end and side-to-side adhesion. (c, d, e) Cells aggregating in the presence of Fab directed against membrane antigens of growth phase cells. (c) Inhibition

each other, result in the formation of streams as they are typical for aggregating cells (Beug *et al.,* 1973a) (Figs. 2b and 3a and b).

These assumptions have received support from the blockage of cell adhesion by Fab molecules of different specificities. Fab against a membrane fraction of growth phase cells inhibits adhesion of growth phase cells completely (Beug *et al.,* 1973a). In aggregating cells the same Fab inhibits the side-by-side adhesion, leaving the end-to-end adhesion unblocked (Fig. 2c–e). Fab against membranes of aggregation-competent cells completely blocks adhesion in cells of both developmental stages (Fig. 2f–h). After exhaustive absorption of the Fab with membranes of growth phase cells only adhesion in aggregation-competent cells is affected, and what is blocked is specifically end-to-end adhesion (Fig. 3c–f).

The fact that the two types of cell adhesion are independently blocked is of importance for the interpretation of the Fab effects. It shows that when Fab molecules are attached to one class of contact sites the cell surfaces can still approach each other close enough for interactions at the other sites to occur. The localized blocking effect of Fab suggests that cell adhesion depends on the interaction of discrete cell surface sites. For the target antigens of the adhesion blocking Fab molecules the term "contact sites" has been introduced (Beug *et al.,* 1973a). Fab molecules that block EDTA-stable contacts are said to bind to "contact sites A." These are the ones which are specific for aggregation-competent cells (Fig. 4). Accordingly, the target antigens of Fab molecules which block the EDTA-labile type of adhesion are called "contact sites B."

B. NOT ANY FAB THAT BINDS TO THE CELL SURFACE BLOCKS ADHESION

Specificity of the target sites of adhesion blocking Fab is further exemplified by binding to living cells Fab molecules which are directed against other surface sites. This has been accomplished with Fab from the antisera of rabbits immunized with heated cells of Dd (Gerisch *et al.,* 1969). These antisera reacted strongly with the carbohydrate

---

of contact sites B results in aggregates which are not as compact as control aggregates (a). (d) Mainly end-to-end contacts are preserved. (e) These contacts are often very tight as indicated by the absence of a clear borderline between cohering cells. (f, g, h) Cells treated with Fab against membranes of aggregating cells. These cells are unable to aggregate (f). They are, however, motile and able to elongate as is typical of aggregation-competent cells (g). Often—but not always—these Fab-treated cells show groups of microvilli at their uropods (h). Fab concentrations were 2 mg/ml, the medium was 0.017 M Soerensen phosphate buffer, pH 6.0. The scale indicates 10 μm. Scanning EM photographs by Dr. R. Guggenheim, Basel.

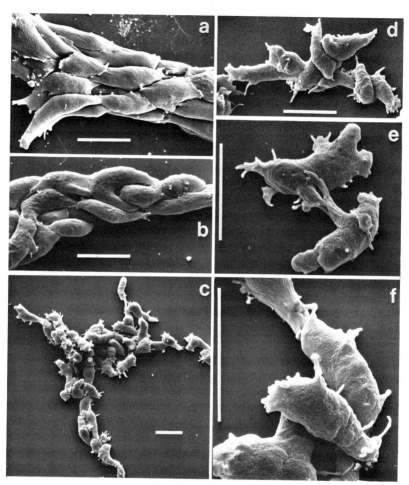

FIG. 3. Aggregation of Dd cells, strain v-12/M2, and the effects of Fab against contact sites A. Same experiment as Fig. 2. (a, b) Streams of aggregating control cells. (c–f) Cells showing rudimentary aggregation in the presence of Fab against membrane antigens of aggregating cells, which had been absorbed with growth phase cells. (c) The Fab-treated cells form loose aggregates whereby the typical end-to-end adhesion of aggregating cells is largely suppressed. (d) Adhesion occurs without preference for the ends of the cells, although the cells are often elongated. (e, f) In the presence of the Fab the cells show active pseudopod formation, and they often adhere to each other by lateral extensions. Fab concentrations 2 mg/ml. The medium was $0.017 M$ Soerensen phosphate buffer, pH 6.0. The scale indicates 10 μm. Photographs by Dr. R. Guggenheim.

moieties of glycosphingolipids and of one glycoprotein (Beug *et al.*, 1970; Wilhelms *et al.*, 1974). According to indirect immunolabeling with peroxidase, IgG from these sera bound to the surface of single cells in a dense, uniform layer (see Gerisch *et al.*, 1974). Fab from the same sera, called anticarbohydrate Fab, did not block contact sites A (Beug

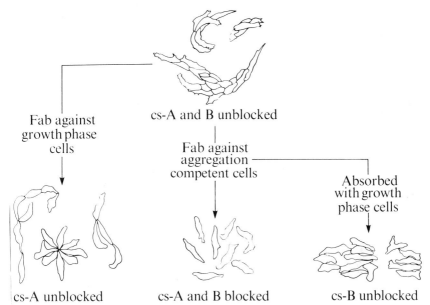

Fab against
growth phase
cells

cs-A and B unblocked

Fab against
aggregation
competent cells

Absorbed
with growth
phase cells

cs-A unblocked   cs-A and B blocked   cs-B unblocked

Fɪɢ. 4. Diagram of Fab effects on aggregating cells of Dd, based on data of Beug *et al.* (1973a). (From Müller and Gerisch, 1978.)

et al., 1973b). It partially blocked contact sites B only at high concentrations. One explanation for the lack of contact site A inhibition would be the absence of the target antigens of anticarbohydrate Fab from the ends of the cells, where contact sites A are actually active. This has been excluded by incubating cells shortly before aggregation with fluorescent anticarbohydrate Fab. The Fab remained bound to the whole cell surface after aggregation, including the areas of intimate contact at the ends of the cells (Beug *et al.*, 1973b).

The three-dimensional topography of the target antigens of adhesion blocking and nonblocking Fab has been examined by Schwarz (1973) who studied the distribution of ferritin-conjugated antibodies. There was a layer of rather uniform thickness on the cell surface formed by the antigens of the nonblocking anticarbohydrate Fab. An IgG preparation of the same specificity as contact site A blocking Fab bound to surface sites which were interspersed between the carbohydrate antigens and extended about 40 Å beyond them into the extracellular space (Gerisch *et al.*, 1974). These sites probably extend up to the middle of the intercellular space where they can interact with molecules extending from an adjacent membrane. They were found at discrete, separate loci, quite in contrast to the target antigens of anticarbohydrate Fab.

The contact site A blocking Fab was prepared from antibodies against the membranes of aggregation-competent cells by absorption with membranes from growth phase cells, and so was the IgG used for cell surface labeling. Therefore, the IgG might label not only contact sites A, but also other antigens that are specific for aggregation-competent cells. It is necessary, therefore, to repeat these studies with Fab that is monospecific for contact sites A, before the results can be taken as evidence that contact sites A, although present on the whole cell surface, are specifically activated at the actual ends of a cell. Independent evidence is provided, however, by experiments in which cells were locally stimulated by cyclic AMP (Gerisch *et al.*, 1975a). When an elongated cell, which adhered at both its ends to other ones, was stimulated at its side, a new tip was induced, and the previous ends lost their strong adhesiveness.

C. QUANTITATION OF CELL ADHESION AND OF ITS BLOCKAGE BY FAB

Two ways of quantitating cell adhesiveness are: (*a*) the determination of the rate of cell association; and (*b*) the measurement of aggregate size under equilibrium conditions. An example of the rate method is the aggregate collection assay developed by Roth and Weston (1967): single, labeled cells are incubated with aggregates, and the attachment of the labeled cells to the aggregates is measured at intervals. An equilibrium method has been used by us for quantitating the adhesion-blocking activity of Fab (Beug *et al.*, 1973a). Cell suspensions are rotated with constant speed in cuvettes with elongated cavities in order to expose the cells to standard shear (Beug and Gerisch, 1972). The size of the aggregates developed under these conditions is a function of the strength of adhesion, provided that aggregation remains reversible throughout the experiment. The average aggregate size is reflected in the intensity of light scattering which can be determined in the aggregometer of Born (1962; Born and Garrod, 1968) or in the apparatus shown in Fig. 5. This has been developed for the simultaneous measurement of 20 samples. Although the apparatus enables one to measure both the rate of aggregation and the size of aggregates under equilibrium conditions, the latter has been used throughout in our experiments.

Cell dissociation as a function of the concentration of Fab is shown in Fig. 6. Absorption with either intact cells or plasma membrane fractions decreases the adhesion-blocking activity of the Fab solution. This effect indicates the presence of either contact sites A or B, or of both. The presence of other membrane antigens proved to be irrelevant and the use of monospecific Fab unnecessary for the detection of contact

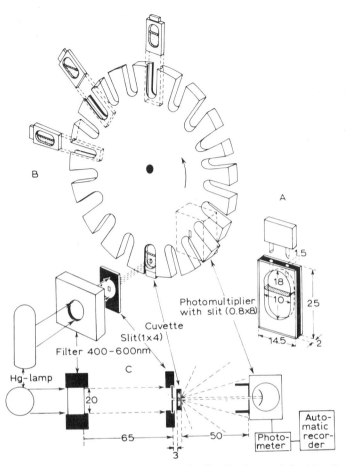

FIG. 5. Apparatus used for quantitation of cell adhesion, and for titration of the adhesion-blocking effect of Fab. Cell suspensions are filled into elongated cuvettes (A), which are rotated on a carrier with constant speed in order to apply standardized shear forces (B). Cell agglutination is determined by recording nonscattered light in each of the 20 cuvettes which can be rotated under identical conditions. Units in millimeters. (From Beug and Gerisch, 1972.)

sites by Fab absorption. The test can be made specific for contact sites B by the use of growth phase cells as test cells for retitration of the absorbed Fab. Contact sites A can be assayed with Fab against membranes of aggregation-competent cells. The Fab is titrated with aggregation-competent cells in the presence of EDTA in order to block contact sites B. The specificity for the A sites can be improved by preabsorption of the Fab with membranes of growth phase cells. Details of these procedures are given by Beug *et al.* (1973a).

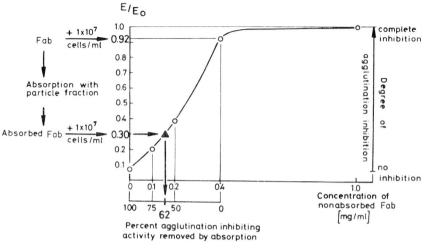

Fig. 6. Inhibition of cell adhesion by Fab, and determination of contact sites by Fab absorption. Cell agglutination is measured using the equipment shown in Fig. 5. Ordinate: Light scattering is expressed as apparent absorption (E) in the test sample, divided by apparent absorption in a completely dissociated but otherwise identical cell suspension (E_0). Thus $E/E_0 = 1$ indicates complete dissociation of the test sample into single cells. Assay for contact sites is performed by absorption of Fab with particle fractions (or with living cells, or solubilized membrane components). The absorbed Fab is retitrated with living cells. The difference in adhesion inhibition before and after absorption is taken as a measure for the presence of contact sites in the antigen preparation tested.

D. Quantitation of Fab Binding Sites

The electron microscopic data previously discussed which indicated that cell adhesion is blocked by binding of Fab to discrete, spatially separated loci on the cell surface have been substantiated by estimating the number of radiolabeled Fab molecules bound per cell. For quantitative binding studies it is essential that the labeled and unlabeled antibody molecules have the same affinity. [³H]Dinitrofluorobenzene (DNFB) as a label for Fab fulfills this requirement. Fab could be loaded with more than one DNFB residue per molecule without detectably reducing its adhesion-blocking activity (Beug et al., 1973b).

The adhesion-blocking activity of different Fab species was compared with the numbers of Fab molecules bound per cell. As previously, contact site A blocking Fab was obtained by immunization of rabbits with membranes of aggregation-competent cells, and by absorption of the Fab with membranes from growth phase cells. Nonblocking anticarbohydrate Fab was also the same as previously. Contact sites A were completely blocked when not more than 3×10^5 Fab molecules were bound per cell (Beug *et al.*, 1973b). This was the number obtained with saturating concentrations of the blocking Fab. The Fab molecules bound under these conditions covered less than 2% of the total surface area. Nonblocking Fab could be bound up to a number of 2 to 3×10^6 molecules per cell (Fig. 7). This shows clearly that blockage of adhesion does not depend on the number of Fab molecules bound per surface area; rather it depends on their specificity.

E. DEVELOPMENTAL REGULATION OF CONTACT SITES A: THE EFFECT OF CYCLIC AMP PULSES

The possibility of specifically assaying contact sites by their ability to reduce the blocking titer of Fab allowed us to study their developmental regulation (Beug *et al.*, 1973a). Contact sites A became detectable as membrane antigens at the time when cells acquired the ability to form EDTA-stable contacts. Simultaneously, cells moving on a substratum started to aggregate into streams of elongated cells. In the streams the cells adhered to each other preferentially at their ends. In contrast to contact sites A, the number of B sites showed no significant

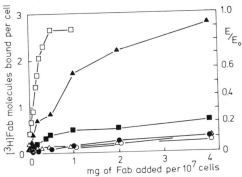

FIG. 7. Blockage of contact sites A (open symbols) related to the numbers of Fab molecules bound per cell (closed symbols). In order to demonstrate that blockage depends on antibody specificity rather than on the total number of molecules bound, Fab from two different types of antisera are compared. (▲, △) Fab from anticarbohydrate serum showing extensive binding but no inhibition. (■,□) Fab from antiserum against membranes of aggregation-competent cells which had been absorbed with membranes of growth phase cells. This Fab showed about 8-fold less binding but almost complete inhibition of adhesion in aggregation-competent cells. B-site contacts had been suppressed in those cells by EDTA. Nonimmune Fab showed no inhibition of cell adhesion (○), and little binding (●). Right ordinate: Inhibition of cell adhesion was measured as shown in Fig. 6; left ordinate: binding was determined with Fab labeled by [³H]1-fluoro-2,4-dinitrobenzene; numbers indicate $n \times 10^6$ molecules. Data from Beug *et al.* (1973b).

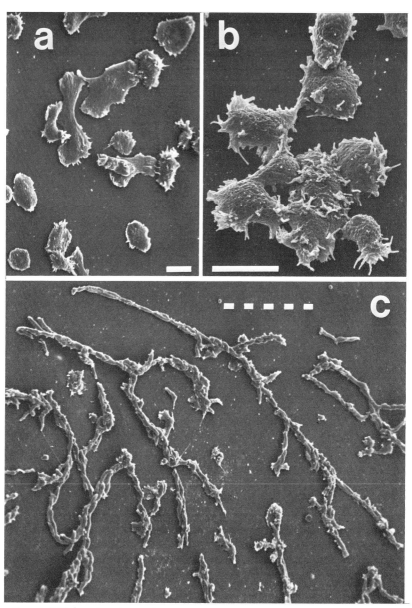

FIG. 8. Effects of cyclic AMP pulses on differentiation of Dd, strain Ax-2, into aggregation-competent cells. The cells were harvested during the exponential growth phase and washed free of nutrient medium in 0.017 M phosphate buffer, pH 6.0. (a) Cells moving on a glass surface, photographed shortly after the removal of growth medium. (b, c) After 4 hours of development in the phosphate buffer on a shaker. (b) Unstimulated cells, showing intense pseudopodial activity but no elongation. (c) The same but stimulated every 6–8 minutes with cyclic AMP pulses of 100 μm amplitude. The suspended

change during cell development from the growth phase to the aggregation-competent stage.

In a certain Dd strain, NC-4, as well as in its axenically growing derivative, Ax-2, the expression of contact sites A is regulated through cyclic AMP receptors on the cell surface. In these strains cyclic AMP acts not only as a chemotactic agent (Konijn, 1972) but also as a stimulant of cell development (Fig. 8). During the second half of the interphase between the growth phase and the aggregation-competent stage, adenylate cyclase undergoes periodic changes of its activity which lead to the rhythmic, pulsatile release of cyclic AMP (Gerisch and Wick, 1975; Roos et al., 1977a). Those pulses are much more efficient in stimulating cell development than a continuous increase of the cyclic AMP concentration, apparently because the receptor and signal-processing system that mediates this effect undergoes rapid adaptation (see Gerisch, 1979). The effect of cyclic AMP pulses on the expression of contact sites A can be clearly demonstrated in cells harvested from nutrient medium during the late stationary phase. In contrast to cells depleted from nutrients during the exponential growth phase, these late stationary phase cells do not develop into aggregation-competent ones. They do so, however, when stimulated by cyclic AMP pulses. Simultaneously, the ability to form EDTA-stable contacts and the number of contact sites A is substantially increased (Gerisch et al., 1975b) (Fig. 9). The effect of cyclic AMP pulses can also be demonstrated by the use of nonaggregating mutants. A certain class of those mutants becomes aggregation competent and forms EDTA-stable contacts in response to cyclic AMP pulses (Darmon et al., 1975).

F. PURIFICATION OF CONTACT SITES A

The Fab absorption assay has been used for purification of the developmental regulated contact sites. Membranes of aggregation-competent cells were solubilized by detergents, chromatographed on Sephadex and DEAE-cellulose columns, and, after removal of the detergent, used for the absorption of Fab. Its adhesion-blocking activity was then retitrated with living cells (Huesgen and Gerisch, 1975). Advantage has been taken of the possibility to test 20 samples simultaneously in the apparatus shown in Fig. 5.

---

cells were washed again and plated without any added cyclic AMP on a glass surface. Elongation of the cells, end-to-end adhesion, and chemotactic orientation indicates the aquisition of full aggregation competence after a time substantially shorter than is required for spontaneous development. Fine surface structure of the aggregating cells is similar to those shown in Figs. 2b and 3a and b. The scale indicates 10 μm. Scanning EM photographs taken by Dr. R. Guggenheim.

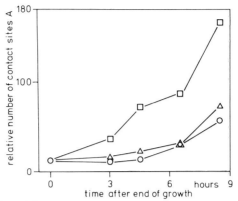

FIG. 9. Regulation of the number of contact sites A by pulses of cyclic AMP. Cells of Dd, strain Ax-2, were harvested from nutrient medium during the stationary phase in order to suppress spontaneous acquisition of aggregation competence. Contact sites A were measured in living cells by Fab absorption according to Fig. 6. Fab absorbing activity of 100 corresponds to the activity of bacteria grown, aggregation-competent wild-type cells. ○, Untreated control cells; □, cells stimulated every 6 to 7 minutes by cyclic AMP pulses of 5 nM amplitude; △, cells treated with the same average influx of cyclic AMP per unit time, applied as a continuous flow in order to maintain a nonfluctuating cyclic AMP level in the extracellular medium. Data from Gerisch et al. (1975b).

Contact sites A proved to be concanavalin A-binding glycoproteins (Eitle and Gerisch, 1977). Butan-1-ol was most efficient in extracting contact sites A together with other glycoproteins. Removal of the accompanying glycoproteins by conventional chromatographic procedures and sucrose gradient centrifugation yielded a glycoprotein that formed a single band after SDS–polyacrylamide electrophoresis (Fig. 10). This single glycoprotein completely absorbed the Fab molecules that blocked contact sites A (Müller and Gerisch, 1978). This means the glycoprotein contains the complete set of antigenic determinants to which these Fab molecules bind. This conclusion is drawn under the assumption that Fab molecules against any possible cell surface antigen of aggregating Dd cells was present in the preparation used. In order to make the Fab as polyspecific as possible it was prepared from a pool of 22 antisera against membranes of aggregating cells.

As predicted from immunoelectron microscopy and labeling of the cell surface with [³H]DNFB-Fab, the glycoprotein with the antigenic properties of contact sites A is quantitatively a minor constituent of the plasma membrane. It is only one among many concanavalin A-binding glycoproteins in the membrane of Dd cells (West and McMahon, 1977) and can be easily separated from another with known function, cAMP-phosphodiesterase (Eitle and Gerisch, 1977).

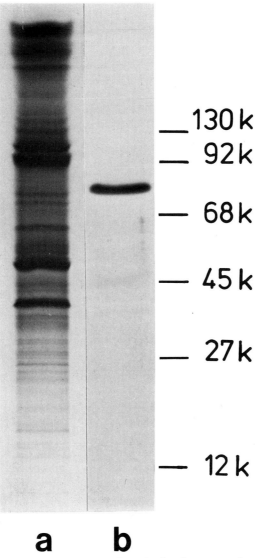

FIG. 10. SDS–polyacrylamide electrophoresis of a plasma membrane preparation (a) and of purified contact sites A (b). The gels were stained with Coomassie blue. Molecular weights are indicated. (From Müller and Gerisch, 1978.)

G. Contact Sites A in Mutants

Another application of the Fab absorption assay is its use in the screening for and in the characterization of mutants deficient in contact sites. Mutants deficient in contact site A activity can be divided into three categories: (a) those which lack contact sites A as a Fab-binding antigen, (b) those which lack only certain immunodeterminants such that they absorb a specific fraction of contact site A blocking Fab, and (c) mutants which, although forming no EDTA-stable contacts, have the full Fab-absorbing activity (Huesgen, 1975; Gerisch et al., 1974). In category (a) mutants are known which are blocked in an early stage of cell differentiation, before contact sites A are expressed. These mutants are pleiotropic. They also show low activities of developmentally regulated constituents of the cyclic AMP signal system: cyclic AMP receptors, cell surface phosphodiesterase, and adenylate cyclase (Roos et al., 1977b). Category (b) is represented by one known mutant which leaves, after exhaustive absorption, about 30% of the contact site A blocking Fab in an unbound state. This unabsorbed Fab fraction, applied in sufficiently high concentrations, still completely blocks EDTA-stable cell adhesion in wild-type cells. This indicates that the contact site A system can be inactivated by Fab binding to more than one immunodeterminant, and that complete inactivation is accomplished when only part of these determinants is covered by Fab. In category (c) two mutants are known. In both of them the cells do not elongate as it is typical of aggregating cells. Another characteristic of these mutants is that cells cannot control their pseudopodial activity. These cells often change the direction of their movement because competing pseudopods are simultaneously extended into different directions, thus competing with each other. This class of mutants suggests an activation mechanism for contact sites A which is linked to cell elongation. The activation results in the high adhesiveness of elongated wild-type cells at their ends.

H. Species Specificity of Contact Sites and Sorting Out of Cells

In mixed cultures of Dd with certain related species the cells sort out during aggregation on agar plates (Raper and Thom, 1941; Bonner and Adams, 1958). If cell suspensions of Dd and *Polysphondylium pallidum* are mixed and gently shaken such that chemotaxis as a mechanism of aggregation is eliminated, the two species will form common agglutinates. However, they eventually sort out into separate areas within the agglutinates (Bozzaro and Gerisch, 1978; Nicol and Garrod, 1978). These areas may eventually detach from each other such that complete separation of the two species is achieved. Since the two species respond to different chemotactic factors—cyclic AMP in one case and in the other a factor which is probably an oligopeptide (Wurster *et al.*, 1976)—sorting out appears to be partly due to chemotaxis.

The contact sites of Dd and *P. pallidum* are different with regard to serological specificity (Bozzaro and Gerisch, 1978). There is virtually no cross-reactivity of adhesion-blocking Fab (Fig. 11). Functional specificity has been investigated by the use of Fab. As in Dd, the contact site system in *P. pallidum* consists of two classes of antigenic sites: one is present already in growth phase cells and the other is characteristic of aggregation-competent cells. Mixed growth phase cells of Dd and *P. pallidum* do not sort out. This occurs only later when the developmentally regulated contact sites have been formed. This suggests that the sites responsible for sorting out are contact sites A in Dd and their developmentally regulated counterparts in *P. pallidum*. This is substantiated by the result of Fab action. Anti-Dd and anti-*P. pallidum* Fab has been made specific for developmentally regulated cell surface antigens by absorption with growth phase cells. These Fab species do not block the mixed agglutination but they inhibit sorting out in the aggregates (Gerisch *et al.*, 1980). In conclusion, the B-type contact active in growth phase cells of Dd and *P. pallidum* does not appear to be

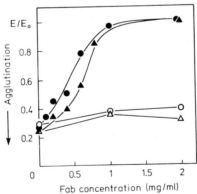

FIG. 11. Antigenic specificity of contact sites from *D. discoideum* and *P. pallidum*. Aggregation-competent cells were tested with Fab (as explained in Fig. 6) in order to demonstrate inhibition of cell adhesion by homologous Fab (closed symbols), and absence of inhibition by heterologous Fab (open symbols). ●, *P. pallidum* cells incubated with anti-*P. pallidum* Fab; ○, the same cells incubated with anti-*D. discoideum* Fab; ▲, *D. discoideum* cells incubated with anti-*D. discoideum* Fab; △, the same cells incubated with anti-*P. pallidum* Fab. EDTA (10 mM) was added for blockage of contact sites B. Data from Bozzaro and Gerisch (1978).

species specific, whereas the A-type contact probably involves a specific recognition mechanism.

Specificity of cell adhesion has been established by eliminating chemotaxis as a mechanism of sorting out. Cells of Dd and *D. purpureum* attach preferentially to monolayers of homologous cells under conditions where it is unlikely that chemotaxis plays a role in cell association (Springer and Barondes, 1978). Furthermore, cells can be immobilized and rounded up by 2,4-dinitrophenol. These cells still sort out during agglutination (Gerisch *et al.*, 1980).

I. CONTACT SITES AND CELL SURFACE LECTINS: ARE THEY RELATED?

From Dd and related species developmentally regulated, erythrocyte-agglutinating factors have been isolated (Barondes and Haywood, 1979). These lectins, called discoidin in Dd and pallidin in *P. pallidum*, constitute 1% or more of the soluble cytoplasmic proteins (Simpson *et al.*, 1975; Siu *et al.*, 1976), but they are also expressed on the cell surface (Chang *et al.*, 1975, 1977; West and McMahon, 1977). This has led to the suggestion that the lectins participate in intercellular adhesion by interaction with carbohydrate residues, possibly of glycolipids, on adjacent cell surfaces (Reitherman *et al.*, 1975; Rosen *et al.*, 1975; Chang *et al.*, 1977).

Discoidin shows the highest affinities to N-acetylgalactosamine and L-fucose (Rosen *et al.*, 1973). Purified contact sites A from Dd are free of discoidin. As sugars they contain mannose, N-acetylglucosamine, fucose, and probably glucose (Müller *et al.*, 1979). Fucose could be a receptor site for discoidin. However, attempts to demonstrate an activity of contact sites A as discoidin receptors have as yet been unsuccessful.

The effect of antipallidin Fab on cell adhesion has been studied in detail (Rosen *et al.*, 1976; Bozzaro and Gerisch, 1978). The interpretation of the results is controversial, although there is agreement that in strongly adhesive cells the dissociating effect of antipallidin Fab is weak. Rosen *et al.* (1977) have therefore used conditions called permissive under which adhesiveness was tempered. This made detection of the inhibiting effect of antipallidin Fab possible. Agents used for lowering adhesiveness were $0.4 M$ glucose or 2.5 mM 2,4-dinitrophenol. Even under permissive conditions inhibition of adhesion by antipallidin Fab was incomplete, and an elevation of the Fab concentration by four orders of magnitude was required in order to increase the percentage of single cells from about 30 to about 80% (Rosen *et al.*, 1976). These kinetics suggest that a minor fraction of the Fab exerts the major inhibitory effect and renders it questionable if pallidin is the only target of the adhesion-blocking Fab.

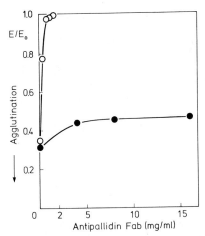

FIG. 12. Effects of antipallidin Fab on the agglutination of rabbit erythrocytes (○) and of aggregation-competent cells of *P. pallidum* (●). Data represent the means of two to three experiments, one performed with Fab against pallidin I, the others against a second lectin of *P. pallidum* cells, pallidin II. The actions of both Fab preparations were similar enough to compile the results. For original data, see Bozzaro and Gerisch (1978).

Since the apparatus shown in Fig. 5 is also suitable for the precise quantitation of erythrocyte agglutination by lectins (Beug and Gerisch, 1972), we have used it to compare the inhibitory effects of antipallidin Fab on pallidin-mediated erythrocyte agglutination and on adhesion of *P. pallidum* cells (Bozzaro and Gerisch, 1978). Fab which completely blocked the carbohydrate-binding activity of pallidin, as tested with erythrocytes, affected cell adhesion in *P. pallidum* only weakly (Fig. 12). Under the same conditions anticontact site Fab inhibited adhesion completely.

J. SHORTCOMINGS OF THE USE OF FAB FOR THE ANALYSIS OF CELL ADHESION

The results discussed in the previous sections can be summarized as follows. Cell adhesion is blocked only by Fab that binds to specific antigens on the cell surface. These antigens are not major constituents of the plasma membrane. One antigen, a specific glycoprotein, is developmentally regulated. Its expression on the cell surface is correlated with the ability of the cells to form EDTA-stable contacts. These results can be interpreted to mean that the target sites of the blocking Fab are identical with those involved in cell adhesion. This does not specify, however, the function of a target site of adhesion blocking Fab in cell adhesion. The molecule can interact with a counterpart on an adjacent cell surface, thus being directly involved in adhesion, or it can participate in cell adhesion in a more indirect way (Fig. 13); e.g., it might activate those sites which interact with a complementary site on another cell. From the absence of a blocking effect of Fab the involvement of a cell surface constituent in cell adhesion cannot be ruled out. Even Fab directed against a cell surface site that interacts with a complementary structure on an adjacent surface would not invariably inhibit adhesion. One requirement is that the affinity of Fab to its target antigen is high compared with the affinity of this site to its natural receptor structure. Alternatively, a high excess of Fab would be necessary, at a concentration which might not be tolerated by the cells. Our results on antipallidin Fab could be explained in this way. The affinity

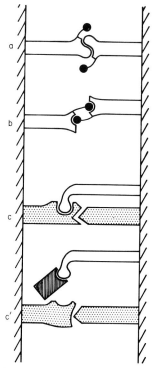

FIG. 13. Target sites of adhesion-blocking Fab might be directly or indirectly involved in cell adhesion. Open symbols represent the protein part of the target antigens of blocking Fab, closed circles their carbohydrate moieties. (a, b) These assume that cells are held together by transmembrane dimer formation between contact sites. Adhesion might be based on protein–protein interaction (a) or on mutual protein–carbohydrate interaction (b). (c, c′) These illustrate the possibility that Fab (shaded) interacts with regulatory molecules which, when unblocked, activate other surface sites (dotted) which promote tight cell adhesion. (From Müller and Gerisch, 1978.)

of pallidin to the foreign receptor—a carbohydrate on the erythrocyte surface—might be low enough for Fab to interfere with agglutination, whereas the affinity to the natural receptor on *P. pallidum* cells might be too high.

In any case it has to be ascertained that Fab blocks by a local effect at the site to which it binds. Overall effects, caused by the prevention of adjacent surfaces to come in close contact with each other, have to be excluded. In Dd the following results argue against this possibility. Contact sites A and B are independently blocked by Fab molecules of different specificities. Second, anticarbohydrate Fab, although it extensively binds to the cell surface, does not block adhesion.

In conclusion, when additional information is available the Fab blocking assay provides a valuable clue to the analysis of cell adhesion at the molecular level. But there is no guarantee that this method leads to the discovery of the complete ensemble of cell surface components that are involved in adhesion.

IV. General Outlook on the Applicability of Univalent Antibodies in Developmental Biology

A straightforward application of Fab as an adhesion-inhibiting agent is its use for the dissociation of embryonal tissues. Pieces of slug tissue of Dd can be dissociated into single cells by incubation with Fab (Beug *et al.*, 1971). Early mouse embryos fall apart into blastomeres in response to Fab directed against surface sites possibly identical with the F9 antigen (Kemler *et al.*, 1977).

Cell surface constituents play a role in the development of Dd and other multicellular organisms not only as adhesion sites but also as receptors of intercellular signals. Fab may be valuable also for blocking these signal receptors. By comparing the effects of Fab and IgG it can be tested whether aggregation of receptors in the plasma membrane is accompanied by their activation. This has in fact been shown for insulin receptors (Kahn *et al.*, 1978).

An intriguing possibility is that binding of Fab might change the conformation of a receptor molecule in a manner similar to that of the natural ligand. If this were the case, Fab could be used to simulate natural inducers of developmental processes. This might be of particular importance where induction occurs by direct membrane–membrane interaction, i.e., in cases where not only the receptor but also the inductor is membrane bound. It would be of great advantage if the intercellular signal could be replaced by Fab and single cells induced to develop.

In Dd an effect has been observed which might be due to the re-

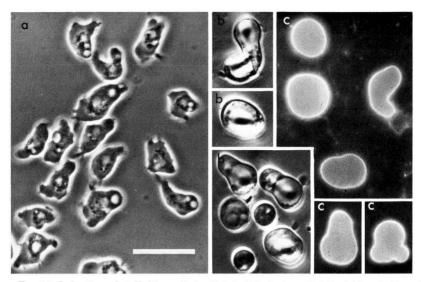

FIG. 14. Induction of stalk-like cells by Fab in Dd strain v-12/M2. (a) Incubation of aggregation-competent cells with Fab against membranes of similar cells completely inhibits adhesion, without affecting motility. (b) Within 1 day these amoebae differentiate into vacuolated cells surrounded by a wall. (c) Staining with the fluorescence brightener Calcofluor White ST indicates the presence of cellulose in the walls of stalk-like cells. (Motile amoebae like those shown in (a) will not be stained.) Conditions: 23°; barbital buffer with calcium and magnesium according to Beug *et al.* (1973a). Effective Fab concentrations: 4 to 8 mg/ml. Cell concentration: 5×10^6 per ml. The cells had contact with the water/air interphase. The scale is 20 μm.

placement of a natural signal by Fab fragments. Normally, differentiation into spores and stalk cells proceeds during and after the slug stage. This occurs within a multicellular body in which the individual cells are in contact with each other over their entire surface. Single cells can be induced by cyclic AMP in the presence of dialyzable cofactors to differentiate to stalk cells (Bonner, 1970; Town *et al.*, 1976). A similar effect is obtained by incubation of nonaggregated cells of strain v-12/M2 with Fab directed against membrane antigens of aggregating cells. The Fab inhibits aggregation and induces differentiation into stalk-like cells (Fig. 14). Sometimes single spore-like cells have also been observed in populations of Fab-treated cells. It is not known whether these effects are due to the reaction of Fab molecules with cell surface receptors for cyclic AMP. Examination of this possibility would depend on the availability of monospecific Fab against cyclic AMP receptors.

For the production of monospecific Fab the monoclonal antibody technique is the method of choice (Köhler et al., 1976; Köhler and Milstein, 1976; Williams, 1977; Milstein and Lennox, this volume). This technique makes the preparation of monospecific antibodies from impure antigens possible. A refined analysis of cell adhesion may also be possible by using monoclonal Fab against different determinants of the same antigen. This will permit the examination of the importance for intercellular adhesion of different regions of a molecule, e.g., of the carbohydrate and polypeptide moieties of a glycoprotein, and will hopefully lead to the identification of the combining sites of interacting molecules.

V. Concluding Remarks

The main conclusion from the use of Fab as an adhesion blocking agent is that processes essential for cell-to-cell adhesion are linked to specific loci on the cell surface. The antigenic material present at these loci covers only a small fraction of the surface area rather than forming a continuous surface coat. Fab molecules can bind to other surface sites in comparatively large numbers without blocking adhesion.

Another conclusion is that a cell can interact with other, identical cells by more than one type of adhesion. Specific Fab blocks each type independent of the other. Thus intercellular adhesion results from the superimposed, independent activities of different cell surface sites. The different types of adhesion may have substantially different degrees of specificity, as is in fact the case with *Dictyostelium*. Here one cannot speak of a unique specificity of adhesion between a particular pair of cells, but must separate overall adhesion into its elements in order to answer the question of specificity for each elementary type of adhesion.

Blockage of cell adhesion by Fab, in conjunction with preabsorption of Fab by solubilized antigens, has proved to be a way of purifying the target sites of Fab that blocks cell adhesion. These target sites have been called "contact sites." The developmentally regulated contact sites in *Dictyostelium discoideum* have turned out to be a specific glycoprotein. The availability of this material in a purified state makes it possible to investigate its specific function in intercellular adhesion.

ACKNOWLEDGMENTS

Work from our laboratory was supported by the Deutsche Forschungsgemeinschaft and the Schweizerischer Nationalfonds. I thank Dr. R. Guggenheim for his expert cooperation in scanning EM work, and Mr. H. P. Giuliani and J. Beltzer for able assistance.

REFERENCES

Barondes, S. H., and Haywood, P. L. (1979). *Biochim. Biophys. Acta* **550**, 297.
Beug, H., and Gerisch, G. (1972). *J. Immunol. Methods* **2**, 49.
Beug, H., Gerisch, G., Kempff, S., Riedel, V., and Cremer, R. (1970). *Exp. Cell Res.* **63**, 147.
Beug, H., Gerisch, G., and Müller, E. (1971). *Science* **173**, 742.
Beug, H., Katz, F. E., and Gerisch, G. (1973a). *J. Cell Biol.* **56**, 647.
Beug, H., Katz, F. E., Stein, A., and Gerisch, G. (1973b). *Proc. Natl. Acad. Sci. U.S.A.* **70**, 3150.
Bonner, J. T. (1970). *Proc. Natl. Acad. Sci. U.S.A.* **65**, 110.
Bonner, J. T., and Adams, M. S. (1958). *J. Embryol. Exp. Morphol.* **6**, 346.
Bonner, J. T., Chiquoine, A. D., and Kolderie, M. J. (1955). *J. Exp. Zool.* **130**, 133.
Bordier, C., Loomis, W. F., Elder, J., and Lerner, R. (1978). *J. Biol. Chem.* **253**, 5133.
Born, G. V. R. (1962). *Nature (London)* **194**, 927.
Born, G. V. R., and Garrod, D. (1968). *Nature (London)* **220**, 616.
Bozzaro, S., and Gerisch, G. (1978). *J. Mol. Biol.* **120**, 265.
Chang, C.-M., Reitherman, R. W., Rosen, S. D., and Barondes, S. H. (1975). *Exp. Cell Res.* **95**, 136.
Chang, C.-M., Rosen, S. D., and Barondes, S. H. (1977). *Exp. Cell Res.* **104**, 101.
Darmon, M., Brachet, P., and Pereira da Silva, L. H. (1975). *Proc. Natl. Acad. Sci. U.S.A.* **72**, 3163.
Eitle, E., and Gerisch, G. (1977). *Cell Differ.* **6**, 339.
Forman, D., and Garrod, D. R. (1977a). *J. Embryol. Exp. Morphol.* **40**, 215.
Forman, D., and Garrold, D. R. (1977b). *J. Embryol. Exp. Morphol.* **40**, 229.
Franke, J., and Kessin, R. (1977). *Proc. Natl. Acad. Sci. U.S.A.* **74**, 2157.
Geltosky, J. E., Siu, C. H., and Lerner, R. A. (1976). *Cell* **8**, 391.
Gerisch, G. (1961). *Exp. Cell Res.* **25**, 535.
Gerisch, G. (1965). *Publ. Wiss. Filmen* **IA**, 237.
Gerisch, G. (1977). *In* "International Cell Biology 1976–1977" (B. R. Brinkley and K. R. Porter, eds.), p. 36. Rockefeller Univ. Press, New York.
Gerisch, G. (1979). *In* "Mechanisms of Cell Change" (J. D. Ebert and T. S. Okada, eds.), p. 225. Wiley, New York.
Gerisch, G., and Malchow, D. (1976). *Adv. Cyclic Nucleotide Res.* **7**, 49.
Gerisch, G., and Wick, U. (1975). *Biochem. Biophys. Res. Commun.* **65**, 364.
Gerisch, G., Malchow, D., Wilhelm, H., and Lüderitz, O. (1969). *Eur. J. Biochem.* **9**, 229.
Gerisch, G., Beug, H., Malchow, D., Schwarz, H., and von Stein, A. (1974). *In* "Biology and Chemistry of Eucaryotic Cell Surfaces" (E. Y. C. Lee and E. E. Smith, eds.), Miami Winter Symp. No. 7, p. 49. Academic Press, New York.
Gerisch, G., Hülser, D., Malchow, D., and Wick, U. (1975a). *Philos. Trans. R. Soc. London, Ser. B* **272**, 181.
Gerisch, G., Fromm, H., Huesgen, A., and Wick, U. (1975b). *Nature (London)* **255**, 547.
Gerisch, G., Krelle, H., Bozzaro, S., Eitle, E., and Guggenheim, R. (1980). *In* "Cell Adhesion and Motility" (A. Curtis and J. Pitts, eds.). Cambridge Univ. Press, Cambridge.
Gregg, J. H. (1956). *J. Gen. Physiol.* **39**, 813.
Gregg, J. H. (1960). *Biol. Bull. (Woods Hole, Mass.)* **118**, 70.
Gregg, J. H. (1965). *Dev. Biol.* **12**, 377.
Gregg, J. H., and Trygstad, C. W. (1958). *Exp. Cell Res.* **15**, 358.
Huesgen, A. (1975). Thesis, Universität Tübingen.
Huesgen, A., and Gerisch, G. (1975). *FEBS Lett.* **56**, 46.

Jeon, K. W., ed. (1972). "The Biology of Amoeba." Academic Press, New York.

Kahn, C. R., Baird, K. L., Jarrett, D. B., and Jeffrey, S. F. (1978). *Proc. Natl. Acad. Sci. U.S.A.* **75**, 4209.

Kemler, R., Babinet, C., Eisen, H., and Jacob, F. (1977). *Proc. Natl. Acad. Sci. U.S.A.* **74**, 4449.

Köhler, G., and Milstein, C. (1976). *Eur. J. Immunol.* **6**, 511.

Köhler, G., Howe, S. C., and Milstein, C. (1976). *Eur. J. Immunol.* **6**, 292.

Konijn, T. M. (1972). *Adv. Cyclic Nucleotide Res.* **1**, 17.

McClay, D. R., Chambers, A. F., and Warren, R. H. (1977). *Dev. Biol.* **56**, 343.

Marin, F. T. (1976). *Dev. Biol.* **48**, 110.

Marin, F. T. (1977). *Dev. Biol.* **60**, 389.

Metz, C. B., and Thompson, P. H. (1967). *Exp. Cell Res.* **45**, 433.

Müller, K., and Gerisch, G. (1978). *Nature (London)* **274**, 445.

Müller, K., Gerisch, G., Fromme, I., Mayer, H., and Tsugita, A. (1979). *Eur. J. Biochem.* **99**, 419.

Nicol, A., and Garrod, D. R. (1978). *J. Cell Sci.* **32**, 377.

Noll, H., Matranga, V., Cascino, D., and Vittorelli, L. (1979). *Proc. Natl. Acad. Sci. U.S.A.* **76**, 288.

Porter, R. R. (1959). *Biochem. J.* **73**, 119.

Raper, K. B. (1940). *J. Elisha Mitchell Sci. Soc.* **56**, 241.

Raper, K. B., and Thom, C. (1941). *Am. J. Bot.* **28**, 69.

Reitherman, R. W., Rosen, S. D., Frazier, W. A., and Barondes, S. H. (1975). *Proc. Natl. Acad. Sci. U.S.A.* **72**, 3541.

Roos, W., Scheidegger, C., and Gerisch, G. (1977a). *Nature (London)* **266**, 259.

Roos, W., Malchow, D., and Gerisch, G. (1977b). *Cell Differ.* **6**, 229.

Rosen, S. D., and Barondes, S. H. (1978). *In* "Receptors and Recognition" (D. R. Garrod, ed.), p. 235. Chapman & Hall, London.

Rosen, S. D., Kafka, J. A., Simpson, D. L., and Barondes, S. H. (1973). *Proc. Natl. Acad. Sci. U.S.A.* **70**, 2554.

Rosen, S. D., Reitherman, R. W., and Barondes, S. H. (1975). *Exp. Cell Res.* **95**, 159.

Rosen, S. D., Haywood, P. L., and Barondes, S. H. (1976). *Nature (London)* **263**, 425.

Rosen, S. D., Chang, C.-M., and Barondes, S. H. (1977). *Dev. Biol.* **61**, 202.

Roth, S. A., and Weston, J. A. (1967). *Proc. Natl. Acad. Sci. U.S.A.* **58**, 974.

Rutishauser, U., Thiery, J.-P., Brackenbury, R., Sela, B.-A., and Edelman, G. M. (1976). *Proc. Natl. Acad. Sci. U.S.A.* **73**, 577.

Schwarz, H. (1973). Thesis, Universität Tübingen.

Simpson, D. L., Rosen, S. D., and Barondes, S. H. (1975). *Biochim. Biophys. Acta* **412**, 109.

Siu, C. H., Lerner, R. A., Firtel, R. A., and Loomis, W. F. (1975). *ICN-UCLA Symp. Mol. Cell. Biol.* Vol. 2, p. 129.

Siu, C. H., Lerner, R. A., Ma, G., Firtel, R. A., and Loomis, W. F. (1976). *J. Mol. Biol.* **100**, 157.

Sonneborn, D. R., White, G. J., and Sussman, M. (1963). *Dev. Biol.* **7**, 79.

Springer, W. R., and Barondes, S. H. (1978). *J. Cell Biol.* **78**, 937.

Swan, A. P., Garrod, D. R., and Morris, D. (1977). *J. Cell Sci.* **28**, 107.

Takeuchi, I. (1972). *Annu. Rep. Biol. Works, Fac. Sci., Osaka Univ.* **19**, 217.

Thiery, J. P., Brackenbury, R., Rutishauser, U., and Edelman, G. M. (1977). *J. Biol. Chem.* **252**, 6841.

Town, C. D., Gross, J. D., and Kay, R. R. (1976). *Nature (London)* **262**, 717.

Tyler, A. (1959). *Exp. Cell Res., Suppl.* **7**, 183.

Watts, D. J., and Ashworth, J. M. (1970). *Biochem. J.* **119**, 171.

West, C. M., and McMahon, D. (1977). *J. Cell Biol.* **74,** 264.

Wilhelms, O.-H., Lüderitz, O., Westphal, O., and Gerisch, G. (1974). *Eur. J. Biochem.* **48,** 89.

Williams, A. F. (1977). *Cell* **12,** 663.

Wurster, B., Pan, P., Tyan, G.-G., and Bonner, J. T. (1976). *Proc. Natl. Acad. Sci. U.S.A.* **73,** 795.

CHAPTER 12

TECHNIQUES FOR LOCALIZING CONTRACTILE PROTEINS WITH FLUORESCENT ANTIBODIES

Keigi Fujiwara

DEPARTMENT OF ANATOMY
HARVARD MEDICAL SCHOOL
BOSTON, MASSACHUSETTS

Thomas D. Pollard

DEPARTMENT OF CELL BIOLOGY AND ANATOMY
THE JOHNS HOPKINS UNIVERSITY SCHOOL OF MEDICINE
BALTIMORE, MARYLAND

I. Introduction

About 50 years ago several investigators were interested in visualizing antigen–antibody reaction and began making specific antibodies labeled with various dyes including azo-dyes (Reiner, 1930; Marrack, 1934) and fluorescent dyes (Hopkins and Wormall, 1933, 1934; Coons *et al.*, 1941). The first attempt to use labeled antibody for histochemical purposes was made by Coons and his collaborators (1942). Unfortunately, however, they faced two serious problems: (*a*) high background or nonspecific staining and (*b*) considerable loss of serological specificity of the labeled antibody. It took Coons and his associates about 10 years to partially overcome these problems (Coons and Kaplan, 1950; Coons *et al.*, 1950, 1951, 1955). Subsequently, progress was made in the fluorescent labeling of antibodies (Riggs *et al.*, 1958; Goldstein *et al.*, 1961; Wood *et al.*, 1965; Cebra and Goldstein, 1965) and in the design of microscopes and filters (Ploem, 1967, 1971; Page Faulk and Hijmans, 1972).

In the past few years there has been a sudden rise in the popularity

271

of the antibody-staining technique, especially in the field of cell biology. Several features of the fluorescent antibody technique contribute to its success in cell and developmental biology. (a) Specific antibodies to virtually any macromolecule can be produced experimentally. (b) The technique is very sensitive. (c) The fluorescent images allow one to map out the molecular anatomy of the cell to a resolution of about 0.5 μm.

Our use of fluorescent antibodies to localize cytoplasmic myosin in tissue culture cells will serve as an example to illustrate these points. Although biochemical studies established the presence of myosin in a variety of nonmuscle cells (Pollard and Weihing, 1974), little was known prior to 1976 about the localization of myosin inside cells. This was due to the fact that there are no histochemical dyes specific to myosin and that myosin aggregates in the cytoplasm are difficult to identify in electron micrographs due to their low concentration and small size. To visualize and identify myosin molecules within tissue culture cells we made antibodies against human platelet myosin, labeled them with fluorescent dyes, and used them to stain tissue culture cells grown on a microscope coverglass (Fujiwara and Pollard, 1976).

In this chapter we present our views on the technique of antibody staining. We have no doubt that each investigator who employs this technique must have thought about similar problems and concerns. Nevertheless, we feel that it might be useful to those who are planning to use this technique to describe some of the major technical problems and to give our personal views on them, especially with regard to specificity of antisera and the use of staining controls.

To make the task easier we have limited our discussion to the staining of monolayers of fixed cells with fluorescent antibodies. We do not discuss antibody-staining methods using peroxidase (Nakane and Pierce, 1966, 1967; Avrameas, 1969; Mason *et al.*, 1969; Sternberger and Cuculis, 1969; Sternberger, 1979), ferritin (Singer, 1959; Singer and Schick, 1961; McLean and Singer, 1970; Olsen *et al.*, 1973; Sternberger, 1979), or radioisotopes (Schneck *et al.*, 1966; Ghose *et al.*, 1967; Ostrowski *et al.*, 1970) to visualize antibody or the staining of sectioned materials. However, we believe that the general approach we have outlined here can also apply to these methods.

II. Preparation of Antisera

Antigen preparation is the most crucial step in conventional antibody production. Ideally an antigen should consist of a homogeneous macromolecule. In cases in which a given antigen is difficult to purify by conventional methods, it is sometimes possible to achieve purity by preparative polyacrylamide gel electrophoresis (Stumph *et al.*, 1974; Lazarides and Weber, 1974: Lazarides, 1977; Piperno and Luck, 1977; Bennett *et al.*, 1978; Sherline and Schiavone, 1978). The purity of protein antigens can be assessed by polyacrylamide gel electrophoretic techniques although it must be realized that minor protein contamination and even major nonprotein contaminants may be missed.

There is no standard immunization procedure and every investigator has his favorite method. Regardless of the immunization procedure it is important to give an animal the smallest amount of antigen that elicits a strong immune response. Since most preparations of macromolecules purified from biological materials contain a low level of contaminating macromolecules, administering the minimal amount of antigen reduces the chance of raising antibodies to these contaminants.

We have immunized more than 30 rabbits using a wide variety of antigens including muscle and nonmuscle myosins, actin, tropomyosin, α-actinin, and tubulin. In every case we used the same immunization procedure (Fujiwara and Pollard, 1976) and obtained antisera specific to these antigens. A large (5–7 kg) white New Zealand rabbit is injected with 200–300 μg protein in 2 ml of emulsion made by vigorously mixing or sonicating 1 ml of antigen solution with 1 ml Freund's complete adjuvant. We make 10 to 20 subcutaneous injections in a line along each side of the vertebral column in addition to injections of each foot pad. After 4 to 6 weeks we administer a boost subcutaneously into multiple sites consisting of the same amount of the antigen emulsified with Freund's incomplete adjuvant. Antiserum is collected three times during the second week after the boost. We have boosted some rabbits more than once and continued to obtain antisera specific only to the original antigen. However, we have an example in which contaminating antibodies appeared in the serum after multiple boosts (Fig. 1). Presumably this is due to the fact that the antigen used had a small amount of contaminant and that this contaminating antigen elicited antibody production only after prolonged stimulation.

III. Characterization of Antisera

The specificity of an antiserum can be assessed by a variety of tests. Regardless of the methods used, it is crucial to examine the reaction of the antiserum with unpurified antigen, such as an extract of the cell or tissue from which the purified antigen is isolated, because the purified antigen may contain enough impurity to elicit an immune response, but not enough impurity to form a detectable antigen–antibody reaction product. Impure antigen is used to test the antiserum, because the

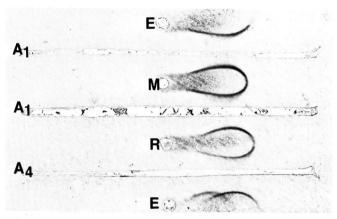

FIG. 1. Immunoelectrophoretic analysis of antimyosin antisera obtained after one boost (A₁) and four boosts (A₄). Purified antigens, human platelet myosin (M), and human platelet myosin rod (R) form a single precipitin line with both antisera. A crude antigen, human platelet extract (E), forms a single precipitin line with A₁ and two precipitin lines with A₄. The contaminating antibody in A₄ is detectable only when the antiserum is tested against an impure antigen, and is immunologically different from myosin since the two precipitin lines do not fuse. Stained with Coomassie brilliant blue.

concentrations of impurities are higher. The reaction of an antiserum with a single component in such a crude extract is a good indication that the antiserum is specific for the original antigen. The importance of using crude antigen to test the antiserum is illustrated in Fig. 1. Here two rabbit antisera against human platelet myosin are tested by immunoelectrophoresis against crude human platelet extract (impure antigen) and human platelet myosin (pure antigen). One antiserum was obtained after one boost while the other antiserum was obtained from the same animal after four boosts. After this repeated immunization the rabbit made a second antibody which does not react with myosin. This second antibody can be detected only if the serum is tested against impure antigen.

    Both immunodiffusion and immunoelectrophoresis (Ouchterloney, 1968; Axelsen et al., 1973) are commonly used to characterize an antiserum. Since these tests are based on the detection of antigen–antibody precipitates, nonprecipitating antibodies are not detected. This is frequently the case with actin antibodies (Herman and Pollard, 1979). It is bad enough if the specific antibody is missed, but if nonprecipitating contaminating antibody goes undetected, the consequence is more serious because antisera may unjustifiably be defined as specific.

Other antigen–antibody tests such as passive hemagglutination (Williams and Chase, 1977), enzyme-linked immunosorbent assay (ELISA) (Engvall et al., 1971; Butler et al., 1978; Kurki, 1978), and solid-phase (Catt, 1970; Holberton and Goldspink 1973; Rehfeld and Stadil, 1973; Minta et al., 1973; Lessard et al., 1979) or double antibody (Kowit and Fulton, 1974; Hiller and Weber, 1978; Parker, 1976) radioimmunoassay detect both precipitating and nonprecipitating antibodies. However, these tests are not particularly good for determining how many antibodies are in the antiserum.

One may use immunohistochemical methods to characterize an antiserum since these methods can reveal both precipitating and nonprecipitating antibodies. For example, staining in the mitotic spindle and the I band of the skeletal muscle are often used to demonstrate the existence of antitubulin and antiactin, respectively. Although the immunohistochemical methods are very sensitive and can provide strong supporting evidence for specificity, the staining pattern alone cannot establish the specificity of an antiserum. This is due to the fact that no biological structure is known to consist of a single species of macromolecule.

Several methods are available to characterize an antiserum by reaction with SDS denatured polypeptides separated on polyacrylamide or agarose electrophoresis gels. Components in impure antigens, such as cell extracts, are separated and often identified by their molecular weights on SDS gels. The reactivity of each band with the antiserum can be assayed. While some methods demonstrate only precipitating antibodies (Converse and Papermaster, 1975; Mabuchi and Okuno, 1977; Piperno and Luck, 1977; Kirkpatrick and Rose, 1978), other methods can detect both precipitating and nonprecipitating antibodies. These latter methods involve reacting an SDS gel with antiserum and detecting bound antibody with fluorescent (Stumph et al., 1974) or radiolabeled (Burridge, 1976) antibody against the primary antibody or with radiolabeled protein A[1] (Adair et al., 1978). Figure 2 demonstrates the specificity and the cross-reactivity of an antiserum against chicken gizzard α-actinin using the protein A method. This method has proved to be far more sensitive than double immunodiffusion for detecting both antibodies of low titer and antigens of low concentration (Adair et al., 1978). The sensitivity of this procedure permits its use to visualize a band in SDS gels which is barely detectable with

---

[1] Protein A is a component in the cell wall of Staphylococcus aureus and binds specifically to the Fc portion of most IgG subclasses, as well as IgM and IgA in some species (Kronvall et al., 1970; Kessler 1975; Peterson et al., 1975).

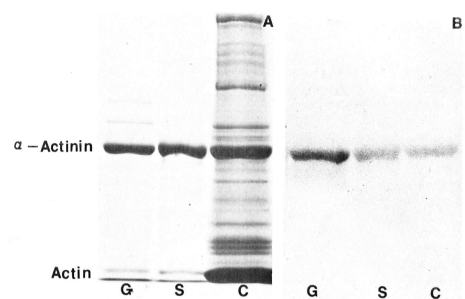

FIG. 2. Partially purified α-actinin preparations were subjected to polyacrylamide gel electrophoresis in SDS. Samples were loaded in duplicated sets so that one was stained with Coomassie brilliant blue (A) while the other was treated with anti-chicken gizzard α-actinin and then with ^{125}I-labeled protein A according to the method of Adair *et al.* (1978). (A) shows that α-actinin preparations from chicken gizzard (G) and chicken skeletal muscle (S) contain little contamination, but that the chicken cardiac muscle α-actinin preparation (C) is enriched only in α-actinin. The autoradiogram of the duplicate gel (B) shows that only α-actinin bands are radioactively labeled. It also shows that the homologous antigen, chicken gizzard α-actinin (G), reacts stronger than other heterologous antigens although the cross-reactivity of this anti-chicken gizzard α-actinin with chicken skeletal (S) and cardiac (C) muscle α-actinin is quite evident. (Courtesy of M. Mooseker.)

Coomassie blue staining (M. Mooseker, personal communication; Burridge, this volume).

Although these gel-staining methods have been applied successfully to the analysis of several antisera, further studies are required to determine whether the approach is generally useful or whether some antibodies will either fail to bind to denatured antigens or will bind nonspecifically to random proteins. If the technique is applicable to a wide variety of antigens, it may become the method of choice to determine the specificity of antiserum.

IV. Specimen Preparation

The success of fluorescent antibody localization of cytoplasmic antigens depends on adequate specimen preparation. Usually this includes fixation to immobilize antigens *in situ* followed by some treatment to make the plasma membrane permeable to antibody molecules.

The ideal fixative would retain the normal antigen distribution without altering antigenicity or inhibiting the availability of the antigen. It has never been proved that any fixative fulfills these requirements.

In our own localization studies of cytoplasmic contractile proteins, we fix cells with 1–10% formalin[2] in buffered saline for 10 minutes at room temperature. It was found that 10% formalin (a) caused the shrinkage of both astral and spindle fibers and (b) changed the distribution of spindle birefringence (Sato *et al.*, 1975). They found that these morphological alterations were minimized when 1–1.5% formalin was used. Similar information on other cytoplasmic structures is not available, however.

Glutaraldehyde is an excellent fixative for ultrastructural studies, but in the past it generally has not been recommended as a fixative for antibody staining at the light microscope level because it reduces specific binding of antibodies (Nakane, 1975; Cande *et al.*, 1977). However, there are reports of successful application of this fixative (DeBrabander *et al.*, 1977; Eckert and Snyder, 1978; Weber *et al.*, 1978). Because of the superior nature of tissue preservation (Hundgen *et al.*, 1971), more consideration should be given to the use of glutaraldehyde.

Although fixation is intended to immobilize antigens, we have evidence that an appreciable amount of protein is still extractable with physiological salt solution after various fixation and other procedures (Table I). If cells are treated with acetone only without fixation, as much as 50% of the total protein in the cell can be extracted by physiological saline. Polypeptides with electrophoretic mobility identical to actin and tubulin are present in the extract. However, we found no detectable myosin in the extract under the same conditions. After formalin fixation, less protein is extracted by saline. High concentrations of formalin are more effective in fixing proteins than low concentrations. However, a high concentration of formaldehyde (10%) introduces morphological alteration (Sato *et al.*, 1975) and also reduces the intensity of fluorescence (Fujiwara and Pollard, 1976). Thus, a compromise must be made so as to minimize these deleterious effects of fixation.

Several methods are available to make the plasma membrane permeable so that the antibody molecules become available to the cytoplasmic antigens. Most commonly fixed cells are treated with cold acetone or methanol. Occasionally, however, they are treated with detergent or simply frozen and thawed. There is no systematic study on

---

[2] Formalin is a commercially available solution of about 37% formaldehyde. This solution contains 10–15% of methyl alcohol as a preservative.

TABLE I

The Effect of Different Fixation Methods on Protein Loss during Antibody Staining[a,b]

	Experiment 1 (%)	Experiment 2 (%)	Experiment 3 (%)	Experiment 4 (%)	Experiment 5 (%)	Average (%)
Acetone (0°C, 5 minutes)[c]	0	0	0	0	0	0
PBS (20°C, 30 minutes)	48	37	49	53	66	51
Remaining	52	63	51	47	34	49
Methanol (0°C, 5 minutes)	3	0	0			1
PBS (20°C, 30 minutes)	2	9	21			11
Remaining	95	91	79			88
10% formalin (20°C, 10 minutes)	6	11	9			9
Acetone (0°C, 5 minutes)[c]	0	0	0			0
PBS (20°, 30 minutes)[c]	11	9	4			8
Remaining	83	80	87			83
2% formalin (20°C, 10 minutes)	6	8				7
Acetone (0°C, 5 minutes)[c]	0	0				0
PBS (20°C, 30 minutes)	21	19				20
Remaining	73	73				73
10% formalin (20°C, 10 minutes)	10	5				8
Methanol (0°C, 5 minutes)	0	0				0
PBS (20°C, 30 minutes)	0	4				2
Remaining	90	91				90

[a] The numbers represent the percentage of the total protein used in each experiment.

[b] Experimental procedure: HeLa cells were harvested by washing confluent tissue culture flasks with Ca^{2+}–Mg^{2+}-free Hank's solution with 1 mM EDTA. Each experiment was done in a test tube using enough cells to give a total of 500–900 μg protein. Cells were suspended in 2–3 ml of designated solutions and incubated under the conditions specified in the table and centrifuged at about 1000 g for 5 minutes. Each supernatant was carefully removed and its protein concentration was determined (Hartree, 1972). A portion of the same supernatant was also analyzed by SDS polyacrylamide gel electrophoresis.

[c] Acetone alone gave a positive reaction in the protein determination. We assumed that no protein is extracted by acetone since no detectable band can be found in SDS polyacrylamide gels of the acetone supernatant.

the effect of this treatment on the cell morphology and on the loss of cellular antigens. Table I shows that methanol-treated cells retain a much higher percentage of total protein in the cell than the cells treated with acetone. We have no information on cells treated with detergent or cells after freezing and thawing although these studies are now in progress.

V. Staining Methods

There are two methods to stain cells with antibodies: the so-called direct and indirect (or sandwich) methods. In the case of the direct method, specific antibody preparation labeled with a fluorescent dye is reacted with the cellular antigen, while in the case of the indirect method, fixed cells are first reacted with unlabeled specific antibody and then with fluorescently labeled antibody against the first antibody. Each method has both advantages and disadvantages, and they are summarized in Table II.

For direct staining, a relatively large amount of serum (at least 20 ml) is required for production of the labeled antibody. In this sense, the direct staining method is expensive. However, as we will discuss in Section VI, direct staining allows one to do more controls than the indirect method, hence the staining pattern obtained by the direct method may be more reliable. Because of this we believe that direct staining is the method of choice.

Procedures for coupling antibodies to fluorescent dyes are described in detail elsewhere (Wood et al., 1965; Cebra and Goldstein, 1965;

TABLE II

COMPARISON OF FLUORESCENT ANTIBODY-STAINING METHODS

	Direct antibody staining	Indirect antibody staining
Advantages	Minimal nonspecific staining More staining controls possible Double staining easy	Requires small amounts of antiserum Fluorescent reagent available commercially Intense fluorescence Labeling of each antibody unnecessary
Disadvantages	Requires large amounts of antiserum Necessary to label each antibody Low fluorescence	Limited number of controls possible Nonspecific staining Double staining difficult

Fujiwara and Pollard, 1976) so we will comment only on what we feel are the most important steps in the procedure. The immunoglobulin G (IgG) is chromatographed on DEAE-cellulose before conjugating it with dyes. This chromatographic step separates the charge heterodisperse IgG into two pools. The two pools contain IgG with different isoelectric points, but within each pool the isoelectric points are relatively similar. These two pools are conjugated and rechromatographed separately although these procedures are identical. This first ion exchange chromatography step is important because after reaction with the fluorochrome the labeled IgG is chromatographed on a second DEAE-cellulose column to separate favorably labeled IgG from over- and underconjugated IgG on the basis of charge carried by the conjugate. An ideal conjugate carries two to five dye molecules per IgG molecule. IgG with less fluorochrome stains weakly or not at all, while IgG with more than five dyes/IgG causes nonspecific staining (Goldstein et al., 1961; Fujiwara and Pollard, 1976). Isothiocyanate derivatives of the fluorescent dyes, fluorescein and tetramethylrhodamine, are commonly used to label IgG. Since the isothiocyanate reacts with unionized amino groups of the IgG molecule to couple the dye to the protein through a thiocarbamide bond (Fig. 3), it is important to maintain an alkaline pH (about 9.5) during the reaction.

The labeled IgG can be stored at 4°C in phosphate-buffered saline with 0.02% sodium azide almost indefinitely. In fact, we have used a preparation of tetramethylrhodamine-labeled antimyosin for over 4 years with consistent results.

Fluorescently labeled specific antibodies can be obtained from the labeled immune IgG by affinity chromatography. Purified antigans are covalently bound to chromatographic beads made of agarose, cellulose, or polyacrylamide. We made antimyosin affinity columns (Fujiwara and Pollard, 1976) with polyacrylamide beads using glutaraldehyde as a cosss-linker (Ternynck and Avrameas, 1972) and anti-α-actinin (Fujiwara et al., 1978) and antiactin (Herman and Pollard, 1979) affinity columns with CNBr-activated Sepharose 4B (Parikh et al., 1974). The labeled immune IgG is run into an affinity column and the IgG fraction which was passed through the column was used as absorbed IgG. After an extensive wash with phosphate-buffered saline, the

$$\text{Dye-N=C} \; + \; \text{H}_2\text{N-protein} \longrightarrow \text{Dye-N}-\overset{\overset{\textstyle |}{\text{C}}}{\underset{\underset{\textstyle \text{S}}{\text{||}}{}}-\text{N-protein}$$

FIG. 3. The coupling reaction of isothiocyanate derivatized fluorescent dyes to IgG. The isothiocyanate group reacts with an un-ionized amino group (mainly the ε-amino group of lysine) of IgG and forms the thiocarbamide bond under a mild alkaline pH.

bound IgG is eluted with 0.1–0.2 M glycine–HCl buffer at pH 2.75. The fractions containing pure antibodies are immediately neutralized with 1 M sodium phosphate buffer at pH 7.5 and then dialyzed against phosphate-buffered saline with 0.02% sodium azide. Other methods to elute bound antibodies from the affinity column are available (Williams and Chase, 1967), but are less commonly used.

VI. Staining Controls

Although the binding of an antibody to an antigen is extremely specific, the staining observed in cells with fluorescent antibodies does not necessarily represent a true antibody–antigen reaction. Nonspecific staining can be due to (a) antibody trapped among cellular organelles and (b) interaction of fluorescent dyes with cellular components, especially when heavily labeled antibodies are used. The trapping of antibody can be reduced or eliminated by decreasing the amount of antibody to stain cells and by prolonged or more efficient washing of the specimen. The nonspecific staining due to overconjugated antibodies mixed in with favorably labeled material is effectively eliminated by fractionating the mixture of labeled antibodies by ion exchange chromatography (Goldstein et al., 1961; Wood et al., 1965; Cebra and Goldstein, 1965; Fujiwara and Pollard, 1976).

Immunologically specific but unwanted staining will occur if the serum contains antibodies against cell constituents other than the antigen of interest. Such contaminating antibodies may arise if the antigen used to immunize an animal is impure or if the animal has been naturally immunized against the cellular components. When the level of the contaminating antibody is high, its presence may be detected in the immunodiffusion test against the extract of cells and tissues. However, if the concentration of unwanted antibody is low, it can go undetected. Since the antibody-staining technique is more sensitive than the immunodiffusion technique (Sternberger, 1979), one may see the staining due to this small amount of contaminating antibody mixed with the staining by the antibody of one's interest. Since these two staining patterns cannot be distinguished by the observer, erroneous conclusions about the distribution of the antigen of interest may follow. Since nonspecific staining due to contaminating antibodies is immunological in nature, it is more difficult to eliminate. Often the whole serum is absorbed with various tissue powders before using it for antibody staining. However, this procedure is really a "shot in the dark" and there is no assurance that it removes all the unwanted antibody.

Although there is no way to assign absolute confidence to the antibody-staining patterns, one can increase the probability that the staining is due to the antigen of interest by doing several controls. No single control reveals all the possible causes of nonspecific and unwanted staining, so it is desirable to do as many independent controls as possible. We recommend the following:

1. to examine an unstained, but fixed specimen
2. to stain with labeled immune IgG
3. to stain with labeled preimmune IgG
4. to stain with labeled absorbed immune IgG
5. to stain with labeled purified antibody
6. to stain with labeled immune IgG after pretreating the specimen with unlabeled specific immune serum (or IgG). Such a "blocking experiment" can also be done by staining the specimen with labeled antibodies in the presence of excess amount of unlabeled antibodies
7. to stain with labeled antibody after pretreatment with preimmune serum (or IgG).

Table III lists the results obtained with each of these treatments when the staining is due either to the specific reaction of the test antibody with its tissue antigen or to one of several different causes of nonspecific staining. It is clear that no single test is adequate for ruling out nonspecific staining, so that the reliability of the staining pattern is established by the consistency of several controls.

An example of these controls is illustrated in Fig. 4 which shows human blood smears stained in various ways with tetramethylrhodamine-labeled antimyosin. The observed staining is identical to that expected for staining by specific antibody (the fifth column in Table III). Although these controls show that the serum does not contain a high concentration of contaminating antibody, they do not rule out the possibility that some of the staining is due to a low concentration of contaminating antibody.

However, since the fluorescence intensity is proportional to the concentration of the fluorescent antibody used for staining, a low concentration of contaminating antibody is unlikely to contribute substantially to the total fluorescence. On the other hand, if the antigen for this postulated contaminating antibody were concentrated in one place in the cell, it might stain strongly enough to give the mistaken impression that the antibody of interest was localized in that place.

We have used these staining controls in our experiments with antibodies against myosin (Fujiwara and Pollard, 1976), tubulin (Fujiwara and Pollard, 1978; Wasserman and Fujiwara, 1978), α-actinin

TABLE III

RESULTANT FLUORESCENCE DUE TO VARIOUS CAUSES AFTER STAINING WITH DIFFERENT REAGENTS[a]

Staining reagents	Causes of fluorescence in the specimen					
	Auto-fluorescence	Nonspecific staining	Naturally occurring antibody	Contaminating antibody due to impure antigen	Specific antibody	Antimyosin
No IgG or unlabeled IgG	+	−	−	−	−	−
Fluorescent immune IgG	+	+	+	+	+	+
Fluorescent preimmune IgG	+	+	+	−	−	−
Fluorescent absorbed IgG	+	+	+	+(−)	−	−
Fluorescent pure antibody	+	+	−	(+)	+	+
Fluorescent immune IgG + immune IgG	+	+	−	−	−	−
Fluorescent immune IgG + preimmune IgG	+	+	−	+	+	+
Antimyosin staining is due to	No	No	No	(No)	Yes	

[a] +, Fluorescent image is detected; −, no fluorescent image is detected; (−), if the titer of the contaminating antibody is low, this result may be obtained; (+), contaminating antibody will copurify by the affinity chromatography since the purity of the adsorbed antigen is the same as the original antigen used for immunization; (No), no high titer contaminating antibody, but low titer contaminating antibody may be present. The staining due to this contamination should be negligible.

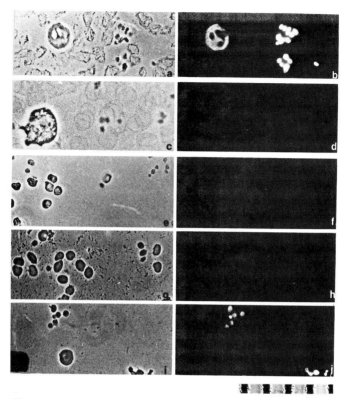

Fɪɢ. 4. Human blood smears stained with various fluorescent reagents. Each fluorescent micrograph is accompanied by a phase-contrast micrograph of the same field. (a and b) Stained with labeled antimyosin IgG (a leukocyte and platelets, but not erythrocytes, stain). (c and d) Stained with labeled preimmune IgG (no staining). (e and f) Stained with labeled antimyosin IgG absorbed with purified human platelet myosin (no staining). (g and h) Stained with labeled antimyosin IgG in the presence of unlabeled antimyosin (no staining). (i and j) Stained with labeled antimyosin IgG in the presence of unlabeled preimmune serum (platelets stain). Scale: 1 division = 10 μm. (From Fujiwara and Pollard, 1976.)

(Fujiwara et al., 1978), and actin (Herman and Pollard, 1979). In all cases we found that staining with purified antibody fulfilled all of these criteria for specificity. The fluorescent immune IgG was usually specific as well, but occasionally there is a mixture of specific and nonspecific staining, as we have found with some antisera against gizzard tropomyosin.

When the indirect method is used to stain cells, there are two independent antigen–antibody reactions. It is desirable that each antigen–antibody reaction be controlled as thoroughly as possible. Unlabeled nonimmune serum or IgG from the same animal species as the labeled anti-IgG can be mixed in during the two incubation steps with antibodies. This is similar to control 7. Unfortunately, the blocking controls cannot be done for the primary antibody with this method, because it is unlabeled. Moreover, most investigators using this method assume that the commerically available fluorescent antibodies are highly specific and omit most of the control experiments that are designed to test the specificity of the second antibody. However, as we show in Fig. 5, not all commercially available reagents are mono-specific. We have tested four commercial reagents against whole rabbit serum by immunoelectrophoresis. In all cases the major antibody is against rabbit IgG, but there are second and third precipitin lines in some products. We made no attempt to identify these contaminants, but it is clear that these contaminating antibodies can bind to some com-ponents in the rabbit serum which may bind specifically or nonspecifi-cally to cellular specimens. This will give a positive fluorescence in those areas in the cell and be interpreted as sites of specific localization of the antigen under investigation.

VII. Double Antibody Staining

Localization of two components simultaneously in the same cell is an extremely powerful approach (a) to study the organization of two cellular components relative to each other, (b) to identify sites where the two components may interact, and (c) to determine the relative

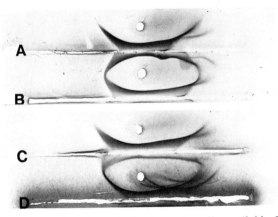

FIG. 5. Immunoelectrophoretic analysis of commercially available fluorescent anti-rabbit immunoglobulin preparations used for indirect staining. Four products from dif-ferent companies (trough A, B, C, and D) are tested against rabbit serum. Stained with Coomassie brilliant blue.

kinetics of the incorporation of two components into a cell organelle. Such studies have been done using two specific antibodies (H. von der Mark *et al.*, 1976; K. von der Mark *et al.*, 1976; Fujiwara and Pollard, 1978; Fujiwara *et al.*, 1978; Hynes and Destree, 1978; von der Mark, this volume) or using an antibody with a reagent capable of localizing another component (Heggeness *et al.*, 1977). While double antibody staining can be applied to any pair of antigens, the use of the combination of an antibody and another reagent is limited because there are only a few reagents that can localize specific molecules on or in the cell. Such reagents are heavy meromyosin (Sanger, 1975; Herman and Pollard, 1978), myosin subfragment 1 (Schloss *et al.*, 1977), and DNase I (Wang and Goldberg, 1978) for actin filament localization and various lectins and immunoglobulins for localizing specific surface receptors (DePetris, 1975; Schreiner and Unanue, 1976; Albertini *et al.*, 1977). These molecules can be labeled with fluorescent dyes and then used in combination with an antibody labeled with contrasting fluorochrome for double staining (Heggeness *et al.*, 1977; Gabiani *et al.*, 1977; Schreiner *et al.*, 1977; Braun *et al.*, 1978; Bourguignon *et al.*, 1978; Yahara and Kakimoto-Sameshima, 1978; Geiduschek and Singer, 1979; Geiger and Singer, 1979).

It is possible to do double antibody staining by both the direct and indirect methods. For indirect staining (H. von der Mark *et al.*, 1976; K. von der Mark *et al.*, 1976), two requirements must be met: (*a*) the two primary antibodies must come from two different species of animals; and (*b*) the two fluorescently labeled secondary antibodies must be cross-absorbed so that each reacts with only one of the primary antibodies. There are four sets of immunological reactions in this staining and each reaction should be thoroughly controlled. As one may imagine, this is not an easy task.

Given these difficulties with double indirect staining, we strongly recommend double staining by the direct method. In fact, no extra preparation is necessary. The two antibodies directly labeled with contrasting fluorochromes are simply mixed together and the specimen is stained in the usual way. Moreover, all of the staining controls listed in Table III are easily executed. Having done these controls it is possible to assign the same level of reliability to the double staining results as to the staining pattern of a single antibody.

We have done double staining experiments with three antibodies: antitubulin, antimyosin, and anti-α-actinin. Antitubulin and anti-α-actinin were labeled with fluorescein while tetramethylrhodamine was used to label antimyosin. Staining with antimyosin and antitubulin (Fig. 6) shows that the two antibodies bind to different cytoplasmic

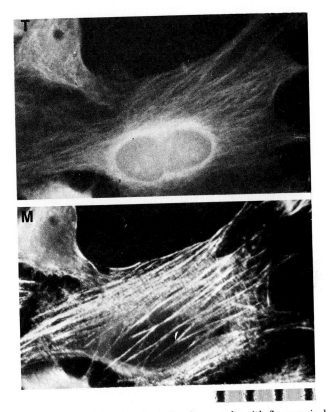

FIG. 6. An interphase HeLa cell stained simultaneously with fluorescein-labeled antitubulin (T) and tetramethylrhodamine-labeled antimyosin (M). Two different staining patterns, microtubule network (T) and stress fibers (M), are detected without interference. Scale: 1 division = 10 μm.

structures. This figure demonstrates two important points: (*a*) Microtubules (fibers stained with antitubulin) and stress fibers (fibers stained with antimyosin) are organized independently in flat tissue culture interphase cells. Thus there is little structural basis to suspect that microtubules and stress fibers interact in any specific way. (*b*) The two staining patterns are detected separately by the fluorescence microscope. There is no antimyosin signal in the antitubulin image, or vice versa. Thus, if the fluorescence from the two antibodies is found in the *same* part of a cell (Fig. 7), we can conclude that both antibodies are present. The separation of the two fluorescent signals requires high-quality, appropriately selected filter combinations in the fluorescence microscope. Fortunately, most major microscope companies manufac-

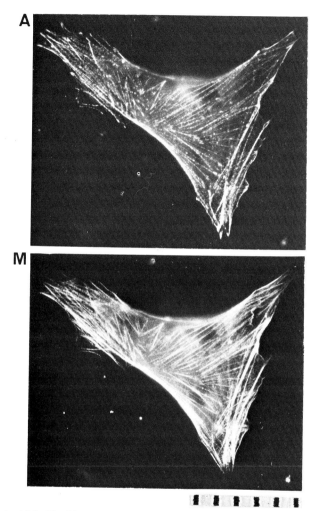

FIG. 7. A chick fibroblast stained simultaneously with fluorescein-labeled anti-α-actinin (A) and tetramethylrhodamine-labeled antimyosin (M). Most stress fibers are stained with both antibodies. Scale: 1 division = 10 μm.

ture filters for double staining, but it is still necessary to establish that the two signals are detected completely independently.

One example of the utility of double staining is our finding that some (Fig. 7), but not all (Fig. 8) stress fibers contain both myosin and α-actinin. Some stress fibers have only one of these two proteins. This observation was surprising because we had the impression from single

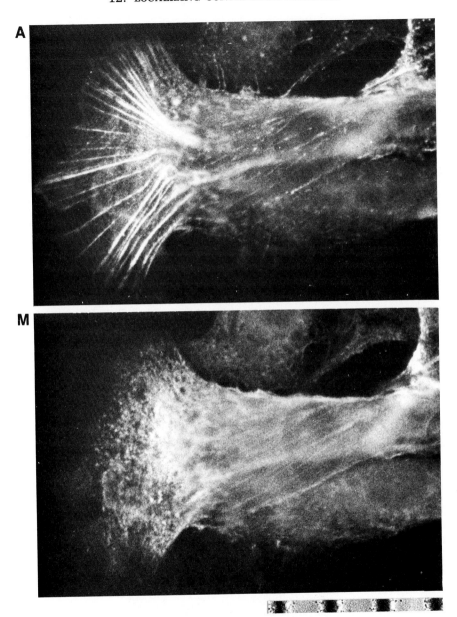

FIG. 8. A chick fibroblast stained simultaneously with fluorescein-labeled anti-α-actinin (A) and tetramethylrhodamine-labeled antimyosin (M). Many stress fibers stain only with anti-α-actinin. Scale: 1 division = 10 μm.

antibody staining that all stress fibers probably consisted of actin, myosin, tropomyosin, and α-actinin.

Double staining can also provide information on the kinetics of the assembly and disassembly of two or more components into a cell organelle. The contractile ring is one example (Fig. 9). We have shown tha both myosin and α-actinin are concentrated in the cleavage furrow region during cleavage (Fujiwara and Pollard, 1976; Fujiwara *et al.*, 1978). By double antibody staining using green anti-α-actinin and red antimyosin, we observed that (*a*) both contractile proteins concentrate simultaneously around the cell equator (the site of the cleavage furrow), but that (*b*) myosin alone disperses quickly from the furrow region once the midbody is formed, leaving α-actin behind in a contractile ring remnant (Fujiwara *et al.*, 1978). This latter observation indicates that myosin, which is thought to be the force-generating protein for the contraction of the cleavage furrow (Schroeder, 1975; Fujiwara and Pollard, 1976; Mabuchi and Okuno, 1977), disperses as soon as active contraction is over, while α-actinin and actin filaments are still present in a form of contractile ring remnant.

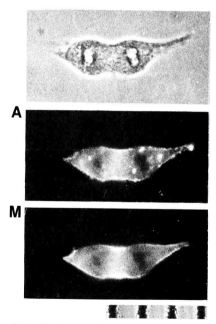

FIG. 9. A dividing chick fibroblast stained simultaneously with fluorescein-labeled anti-α-actinin (A) and tetramethylrhodamine-labeled antimyosin (M). Both antibodies stain the cleavage furrow intensely. Scale: 1 division = 10 μm.

VIII. Concluding Remarks

We have presented our views on fluorescent antibody staining, with emphasis on the caution that this technique requires. Such caution is necessary because there are many possible artifacts that can arise during the lengthy process of antigen preparation, immunization of animals, and actual staining of specimens. We offer suggestions for avoiding some of the major hazards in this work. The most important of these suggestions is to use purified directly labeled antibodies.

Many problems remain unsolved. The two major ones are characterization of the antiserum and the fixation procedure. The specificity of the antibody can be precisely defined if one uses monoclonal antibodies (Milstein and Lennox, this volume). The problem of fixation remains a big obstacle, but it is not unique to immunohistochemistry. In fact it is a problem that every morphologist faces. In the case of antibody staining, the problem becomes slightly more complicated because the antigenicity of the cell must be preserved.

ACKNOWLEDGMENTS

We are happy to acknowledge the patient and able assistance of Joan Nason and Carol McKinley. We thank Dr. Mark Mooseker for allowing us the use of his unpublished data and Randolph Byers for his suggestions during the preparation of this manuscript. The work reported here was supported by NIH research grants GM 25637 to K. F. and GM 23531 to T. D. P. and by research career development award GM 70755 to T. D. P.

REFERENCES

Adair, N. S., Jurivich, P., and Goodenough, U. W. (1978). Localization of cellular antigens in sodium dodecyl sulfate-polyacrylamide gels. *J. Cell Biol.* **79,** 281–285.

Albertini, D. F., Berlin, R. D., and Oliver, J. M. (1977). The mechanism of concanavalin A cap formation in leukocytes. *J. Cell Sci.* **26,** 57–75.

Avrameas, S. (1969). Coupling of enzymes to proteins with glutaraldehyde. Use of the conjugates for the detection of antigens and antibodies. *Immunochemistry* **6,** 43–52.

Axelsen, N. H., Krøll, J., and Weeke, B., eds. (1973). "A Manual of Quantitative Immunoelectrophoresis. Methods and Applications," Scand. J. Immunol., Vol. 2, Suppl. 1. Universitetsforlaget, Oslo.

Bennett, G. S., Fallini, S. A., Croop, J. M., Otto, J. J., Bryan, J., and Holtzer, H. (1978). Differences among 100A° filament subunits from different cell types. *Proc. Natl. Acad. Sci. U.S.A.* **75,** 4364–4368.

Bourguignon, L. Y. W., Tokuyasu, K. T., and Singer, S. J. (1978). The capping of lymphocytes and other cells, studies by an improved method for immunofluorescence staining of frozen sections. *J. Cell. Physiol.* **95,** 239–258.

Braun, J., Fujiwara, K., Pollard, T. D., and Unanue, E. R. (1978). Two distinct mechanisms for redistribution of lymphocyte surface macromolecules. I. Relationship to cytoplasmic myosin. *J. Cell Biol.* **79,** 409–418.

Burridge, K. (1976). Changes in cellular glycoproteins after transformation: Identification of specific glycoproteins and antigens in sodium dodecyl sulfate gels. *Proc. Natl. Acad. Sci. U.S.A.* **73,** 4457–4461.

Butler, J. E., Feldbush, T. L., McGivern, P. L., and Stewart, N. (1978). The enzyme-linked immunosorbent assay (ELISA): A measure of antibody concentration or affinity? *Immunochemistry* **15**, 131–136.

Cande, W. Z., Lazarides, E. L., and McIntosh, J. R. (1977). A comparison of the distribution of actin and tubulin in the mammalian mitotic spindle as seen by indirect immunofluorescence. *J. Cell Biol.* **72**, 552–567.

Catt, K. J. (1970). Radioimmunoassay with antibody-coated discs and tubes. *Acta Endocrinol. (Copenhagen)*, **142**, 222–243.

Cebra, J. J., and Goldstein, G. (1965). Chromatographic purification of tetramethyl-rhodamine-immune globulin conjugates and their use in the cellular localization of rabbit α-globulin polypeptide chains. *J. Immunol.* **95**, 230–245.

Converse, C. A., and Papermaster, D. S. (1975). Membrane protein analysis by two-dimensional immunoelectrophoresis. *Science* **189**, 469–472.

Coons, A. H., and Kaplan, M. H. (1950). Localization of antigens in tissue cells. II. Improvements in a method for the detection of antigen by means of fluorescent antibody. *J. Exp. Med.* **91**, 1–13.

Coons, A. H., Creech, H. J., and Jones, R. N. (1941). Immunological properties of an antibody containing a fluorescent group. *Proc. Soc. Exp. Biol. Med.* **47**, 200–202.

Coons, A. H., Creech, H. J., Jones, R. N., and Berliner, E. J. (1942). The demonstration of pneumococcal antigen in tissues by the use of fluorescent antibody. *J. Immunol.* **45**, 159–170.

Coons, A. H., Snyder, J. C., Cheever, F. S., and Murray, E. S. (1950). Localization of antigens in tissue cells. IV. Antigens of rickettsiae and mumps virus. *J. Exp. Med.* **91**, 31–38.

Coons, A. H., Leduc, E. H., and Kaplan, M. H. (1951). Localization of antigens in tissue cells. VI. The fate of injected foreign proteins in the mouse. *J. Exp. Med.* **93**, 173–188.

Coons, A. H., Leduc, E. H., and Connolly, J. M. (1955). Studies on antibody production. I. A method for the histochemical demonstration of specific antibody and its application to a study of the hyperimmune rabbit. *J. Exp. Med.* **102**, 49–60.

DeBrabander, M., DeMay, J., Joniau, M., and Geuens, G. (1977). Ultrastructural immunocytochemical distribution of tubulin in cultured cells treated with microtubule inhibitors. *Cell Biol. Int. Rep.* **1**, 177–183.

DePetris, S. (1975). Concanavalin A receptors, immunoglobulins, and Θ antigen of the lymphocyte surface. *J. Cell Biol.* **65**, 123–146.

Eckert, B. S., and Snyder, J. A. (1978). Combined immunofluorescence and high-voltage electron microscopy of cultured mammalian cells, using an antibody that binds to glutaraldehyde-treated tubulin. *Proc. Natl. Acad. Sci. U.S.A.* **75**, 334–338.

Engvall, E., Jonsson, K., and Perlmann, P. (1971). Enzyme-linked immunosorbent assay. II. Quantitative assay of protein antigen, immunoglobulin G, by means of enzyme-labeled antigen and antibody-coated tubes. *Biochim. Biophys. Acta* **251**, 427–434.

Fujiwara, K., and Pollard, T. D. (1976). Fluorescent antibody localization of myosin in the cytoplasm, cleavage furrow and mitotic spindle of human cells. *J. Cell Biol.* **71**, 848–875.

Fujiwara, K., and Pollard, T. D. (1978). Simultaneous localization of myosin and tubulin in human tissue culture cells by double antibody staining. *J. Cell Biol.* **77**, 182–195.

Fujiwara, K., Porter, M. E., and Pollard, T. D. (1978). Alpha-actinin localization in the cleavage furrow during cytokinesis. *J. Cell Biol.* **79**, 268–275.

Gabiani, G., Chaponnier, C., Zumbe, A., and Vassalli, P. (1977). Actin and tubulin co-cap with surface immunoglobulins in mouse B lymphocytes. *Nature (London)* **269,** 697–698.

Geiduschek, J. B., and Singer, S. J. (1979). Molecular changes in the membranes of mouse erythroid cells accompanying differentiation. *Cell* **16,** 149–163.

Geiger, B., and Singer, S. J. (1979). The participation of α-actinin in the capping of cell membrane components. *Cell* **16,** 213–222.

Ghose, T., Cerini, M., Carter, M., and Nairn, R. C. (1967). Immunoradioactive agent against cancer. *Br. Med. J.* **1,** 90–93.

Goldstein, G., SĹizys, I. S., and Chase, M. W. (1961). Studies on fluorescent antibody staining. I. Non-specific fluorescence with fluorescein-coupled sheep antirabbit globulins. *J. Exp. Med.* **114,** 89–107.

Hartree, E. F. (1972). Determination of protein. A modification of the Lowry method that gives a linear photometric response. *Anal. Biochem.* **48,** 422–427.

Heggeness, M., Wang, K., and Singer, S. J. (1977). Intracellular distributions of mechanochemical proteins in cultured fibroblasts. *Proc. Natl. Acad. Sci. U.S.A.* **74,** 3883–3887.

Herman, I. M., and Pollard, T. D. (1978). Actin localization in fixed dividing cells stained with fluorescent heavy meromyosin. *Exp. Cell Biol.* **114,** 15–25.

Herman, I. M., and Pollard, T. D. (1979). Comparison of purified anti-actin and fluorescent-heavy meromyosin staining patterns in dividing cells. *J. Cell Biol.* **80,** 509–520.

Hiller, G., and Weber, K. (1978). Radioimmunoassay for tubulin: A quantitative comparison of the tubulin content of different established tissue culture cells and tissues. *Cell* **14,** 795–804.

Holberton, E. J., and Goldspink, G. (1973). A radioimmunoassay for myosin in cultured skeletal muscle cells. *Exp. Cell Res.* **79,** 471–474.

Hopkins, S. J., and Wormall, A. (1933). Phenyl isocyanate protein compounds and their immunological reactions. *Biochem. J.* **27,** 740–753.

Hopkins, S. J., and Wormall, A. (1934). Phenyl isocyanate protein derivatives and their immunological properties. III. The amino acid derivatives and serological inhibition tests. *Biochem. J.* **28,** 228–236.

Hundgen, M., Schafer, D., and Weissenfels, N. (1971). The fixation effect of eight different aldehydes on the ultrastructure of cultured cells. II. The structural state of the cytoplasm. *Cytobiologie* **3,** 202–214.

Hynes, R. O., and Destree, A. T. (1978). Relationship between fibronectin (LETS protein) and actin. *Cell* **15,** 875–886.

Kessler, S. W. (1975). Rapid isolation of antigens from cells with a *Staphylococcal* protein A-antibody absorbent: Parameters of the interaction of antibody-antigen complexes with protein A. *J. Immunol.* **115,** 1617–1624.

Kirkpatrick, F. H., and Rose, D. J. (1978). Crossed immunoelectrophoresis from sodium dodecyl sulfate-polyacrylamide gels into antibody-containing agarose. Improved method for evaluation of a number of immunochemical determinants in polypeptides, with respect to spectrin. *Anal. Biochem.* **89,** 130–135.

Kowit, J. D., and Fulton, C. (1974). Purification and properties of flagellar outer doublet tubulin from *Naegleria gruberi* and a radioimmune assay for tubulin. *J. Biol. Chem.* **249,** 3638–3646.

Kronvall, G., Seal, U.S., Finstad, J., and Williams, R. C., Jr. (1970). Phylogenetic insight into evolution of mammalian Fc fragment of G globulin using *Staphylococcal* protein A. *J. Immunol.* **104,** 140–147.

Kurki, P. (1978). Determination of anti-actin antibodies by a solid-phase immunoenzymatic assay and by indirect immunofluorescence technique. *Clin. Immunol. Immunopathol.* **11**, 328–338.

Lazarides, E. (1977). Two general classes of cytoplasmic actin filaments in tissue culture cells: The role of tropomyosin. *J. Supramol. Struct.* **5**, 531–563.

Lazarides, E., and Weber, K. (1974). Actin antibody: The specific visualization of actin filaments in nonmuscle cells. *Proc. Natl. Acad. Sci. U.S.A.* **71**, 2268–2272.

Lessard, J. L., Carlton, D., Rein, D. C., and Akeson, R. (1979). A solid-phase assay for antiactin antibody and actin using protein A. *Anal. Biochem.* **94**, 140–149.

Mabuchi, I., and Okuno, M. (1977). The effect of myosin antibody on the division of starfish blastomeres. *J. Cell Biol.* **74**, 251–263.

McLean, J. D., and Singer, S. J. (1970). A general method for the specific staining of intracellular antigens with ferritin-antibody conjugates. *Proc. Natl. Acad. Sci. U.S.A.* **65**, 122–128.

Marrack, J. (1934). Nature of antibodies. *Nature (London)* **133**, 292–293.

Mason, T. E., Phifer, R. F., Spicer, S. S., Swallow, R. A., and Dreskin, R. B. (1969). An immunoglobulin-enzyme bridge method for localizing tissue antigens. *J. Histochem. Cytochem.* **17**, 563–569.

Minta, J. O., Goodkofsky, I., and Lepow, I. H. (1973). Solid phase radioimmunoassay of properdin. *Immunochemistry* **10**, 341–350.

Nakane, P. K. (1975). Recent progress in the peroxidase-labeled antibody method. *Ann. N.Y. Acad. Sci.* **254**, 203–210.

Nakane, P. K., and Pierce, G. B., Jr. (1966). Enzyme-labeled antibodies: Preparation and application for the localization of antigens. *J. Histochem. Cytochem.* **14**, 929–931.

Nakane, P. K., and Pierce, G. B., Jr. (1967). Enzyme-labeled antibodies for the light and electron microscope localization of tissue antigens. *J. Cell Biol.* **33**, 307–318.

Olsen, B. R., Berg, R. A., Kishida, Y., and Prockop, D. J. (1973). Collagen synthesis. *Science* **182**, 825–827.

Ostrowski, K., Barnard, E. A., Sawicki, W., Chorzelski, T., Langner, A., and Mikulski, A. (1970). Autoradiographic detection of antigens in cells using tritium-labeled antibodies. *J. Histochem. Cytochem.* **18**, 490–497.

Ouchterlony, Ö. (1968). "Handbook of Immunodiffusion and Immunoelectrophoresis." Ann Arbor Sci. Publ., Ann Arbor, Michigan.

Page Faulk, W., and Hijmans, W. (1972). Recent developments in immunofluorescence. *Prog. Allergy* **16**, 9–39.

Parikh, I., March, S., and Cuatrecacas, P. (1974). Topics in the methodology of substitution reactions with agarose. *In* "Methods in Enzymology" (W. B. Jakoby and M. Wilchek, eds.), Vol. 34, pp. 77–102. Academic Press, New York.

Parker, C. W. (1976). "Radioimmunoassay of Biologically Active Compounds." Prentice-Hall, Englewood Cliffs, New Jersey.

Peterson, P. A., Rask, L., Sege, K., Klareskog, L., Anundi, H., and Ostberg, L. (1975). Evolutionary relationship between immunoglobulins and transplantation antigens. *Proc. Natl. Acad. Sci. U.S.A.* **72**, 1612–1616.

Piperno, G., and Luck, D. J. L. (1977). Microtubular proteins of *Chlamydomonas reinhardtii*. An immunochemical study based on the use of an antibody specific for the β-tubulin subunit. *J. Biol. Chem.* **252**, 383–391.

Ploem, J. S. (1967). The use of a vertical illuminator with interchangeable dichroic mirrors for fluorescence microscopy with incident light. *Z. Wiss. Mikrosk. Mikrosk. Tech.* **68**, 129–142.

Ploem, J. S. (1971). A study of filters and light sources in immunofluorescence microscopy. *Ann. N.Y. Acad. Sci.* **177**, 414–429.

Pollard, T. D., and Weihing, R. R. (1974). Actin and myosin and cell movement. *Crit. Rev. Biochem.* **2**, 1–65.

Rehfeld, J. F., and Stadil, F. (1973). Radioimmunoassay for gastrin employing immunosorbent. *Scand. J. Clin. Lab. Invest.* **31**, 459–464.

Reiner, L. (1930). On the chemical alteration of purified antibody proteins. *Science* **72**, 483–484.

Riggs, J. L., Seiwald, R. J., Burckholter, J. H., Downs, C. M., and Metcalf, T. G. (1958). Isothiocyanate compounds as fluorescent labeling agents for immune serum. *Am. J. Clin. Pathol.* **34**, 1081–1097.

Sanger, J. W. (1975). Changing patterns of actin localization during cell division. *Proc. Natl. Acad. Sci. U.S.A.* **72**, 1913–1916.

Sato, H., Ohnuki, Y., and Fujiwara, K. (1975). Immunofluorescent antitubulin staining of spindle microtubules and critique for the technique. *In* "Cell Motility" (R. Goldman, T. Pollard, and J. Rosenbaum, eds.), pp. 419–433. Cold Spring Harbor Lab., Cold Spring Harbor, New York.

Schloss, J. A., Milsted, A., and Goldman, R. D. (1977). Myosin subfragment binding for the localization of actin-like microfilaments in cultured cells. A light and electron microscope study. *J. Cell Biol.* **74**, 794–815.

Schneck, L., Baker, R. K., and Berbonich, S. (1966). The synthesis of radioactive fluorescein isothiocyanate. *Immunology* **11**, 321–324.

Schreiner, G. F., and Unanue, E. R. (1976). Membrane and cytoplasmic changes in B lymphocytes induced by ligend-surface immunoglobulin interaction. *Adv. Immunol.* **24**, 38–165.

Schreiner, G. F., Fujiwara, K., Pollard, T. D., and Unanue, E. R. (1977). Redistribution of myosin accompanying capping of surface Ig. *J. Exp. Med.* **145**, 1393–1398.

Schroeder, T. E. (1975). Dynamics of the contractile ring. *In* "Molecules and Cell Movement" (S. Inoue and R. E. Stephens, eds.), pp. 305–332. Raven Press, New York.

Sherline, P., and Schiavone, K. (1978). High molecular weight MAPs are part of the mitotic spindle. *J. Cell Biol.* **77**, R9-R12.

Singer, S. J. (1959). Preparation of an electron dense antibody conjugate. *Nature (London)* **183**, 1523–1524.

Singer, S. J., and Schick, A. F. (1961). The properties of specific stains for electron microscopy prepared by conjugation of antibody molecules with ferritin. *J. Biophys. Biochem. Cytol.* **9**, 519–537.

Sternberger, L. A. (1979). "Immunohistochemistry," 2nd ed. Wiley, New York.

Sternberger, L. A., and Cuculis, J. J. (1969). Method for enzymatic intensification of the immunocytochemical reaction without use of labeled antibodies. *J. Histochem. Cytochem.* **17**, 190.

Stumph, W. E., Elgin, S. C. R., and Hood, L. (1974). Antibodies to proteins dissolved in sodium dodecyl sulfate. *J. Immunol.* **113**, 1752–1756.

Ternynck, T., and Avrameas, S. (1972). Polyacrylamide-protein immunoabsorbents prepared with glutaraldehyde. *FEBS Lett.* **23**, 24–28.

von der Mark, H., von der Mark, K., and Gay, S. (1976). Study of differential collagen synthesis during development of the chick embryo by immunofluorescence. I. Preparation of collagen type I and type II specific antibodies and their application to early stages of the chick embryo. *Dev. Biol.* **48**, 237–249.

von der Mark, K., von der Mark, H., and Gay, S. (1976). Study of differential collagen synthesis during development of the chick embryo by immunofluorescence. II. Localization of type I and type II collagen during long bone development. *Dev. Biol.* **53,** 153–170.

Wang, E., and Goldberg, A. R. (1978). Binding of deoxyribonuclease I to actin: A new way to visualize microfilament bundles in nonmuscle cells. *J. Histochem. Cytochem.* **26,** 745–749.

Wasserman, P., and Fujiwara, K. (1978). Immunofluorescent anti-tubulin staining of spindles during meiotic maturation of mouse oocytes *in vitro. J. Cell Sci.* **29,** 171–188.

Weber, K., Rathke, P. C., and Osborn, M. (1978). Cytoplasmic microtubular images in glutaraldehyde-fixed tissue culture cells viewed by electron microscopy and by immunofluorescence microscopy. *Proc. Natl. Acad. Aci. U.S.A.* **75,** 1820–1824.

Williams, C. A., and Chase, M. W. (1967). "Methods in Immunology and Immunochemistry," Vol. 1. Academic Press, New York.

Williams, C. A., and Chase, M. W., eds. (1977). "Methods in Immunology and Immunochemistry," Vol. 4. Academic Press, New York.

Wood, B. T., Thompson, S. H., and Goldstein, G. (1965). Fluorescent antibody staining. III. Preparation of fluorescein-isothiobyanate-labeled antibodies. *J. Immunol.* **95,** 225–229.

Yahara, I., and Kakimoto-Sameshima, F. (1978). Microtubule organization of lymphocytes and its modulation by patch and cap formation. *Cell* **15,** 251–259.

CHAPTER 13

ANTISERUM TO MYOSIN AND ITS USE IN STUDYING MYOSIN SYNTHESIS AND ACCUMULATION DURING MYOGENESIS

Richard C. Strohman, Paul S. Moss, and Julie Micou-Eastwood

DEPARTMENT OF ZOOLOGY
UNIVERSITY OF CALIFORNIA
BERKELEY, CALIFORNIA

I. Introduction

The essential regulatory events underlying terminal differentiation of skeletal muscle remain obscure. What is clear is that terminal myogenesis involves (*a*) withdrawal of myoblasts from the cell cycle, (*b*) fusion of these myoblasts to form the embryonic myotube or precursor to the cross-striated muscle fiber, and (*c*) the initiation of synthesis of the unique peptides of the myofibril. In some cases the synthesis of unique peptides may occur prior to cell fusion, but fusion remains one of the major morphological markers for terminal skeletal muscle cell differentiation in most experimental systems. Myosin is the major structural protein of skeletal muscle and measurement of its synthesis and accumulation has been used *in vivo* and *in vitro* as a biochemical marker for the transition of the myoblast or myotube to the fully differentiated state. The great fidelity displayed by tissue culture cells to normal muscle development *in vivo* and the synchrony of cell fusion and myosin synthesis achievable by tissue culture methods promise to provide answers to the primary question: what are the molecular processes by which muscle cells begin to regulate for the synthesis of the unique peptides of the myofibril?

It is, of course, the uniqueness of the myofibrillar peptides and especially myosin that emerges as a central methodological issue in

297

CURRENT TOPICS IN
DEVELOPMENTAL BIOLOGY, VOL. 14

current studies of muscle cell differentiation. The purpose of this chapter is to show that in spite of the diversity of nonmuscle cells which have recently been shown to synthesize myosin or myosin-like peptides, it remains appropriate and indeed extremely useful to focus on myosin polypeptides as unique markers for terminal myogenesis. The basis for continuing to use myosin as a marker is the immunological specificity of myosin peptides and lack of cross-reactivity of antibodies prepared to skeletal muscle myosin with myosins from other cell types.

II. Myosin Structure, Immunology, and Polymorphism

Vertebrate skeletal muscle myosin normally consists of four and perhaps five polypeptides. The biochemistry and immunology of these polypeptides and their structural interrelations have been worked out recently and most notably by Lowey and Weeds and their collaborators (Lowey *et al.*, 1969; Weeds and Lowey, 1971; Lowey and Steiner, 1972; Lowey and Holt, 1972; Weeds, 1969) and by Pepe (1966, 1967a,b; 1972) following the work of A. G. Szent-Györgyi on the enzymatic cleavage of whole myosin into functional subunits (1953). The whole molecule has a MW of approximately 510,000 and consists of two heavy chains and at least two light chains. The heavy chains are of identical MW (200,000), and each normally binds 1 mole of light chains which have different molecular weights. The light chains are released from the whole molecule by treatment with alkali and are called alkali light chains (ALC). ALC 1 and 2 have MWs of 21,000 and 17,000, respectively. There may be additional light chains (MW 18,000) which are released by treatment of myosin by thiol reagents such as DTNB [5,5-dithiobis(2-nitrobenzoic acid)]. The DTNB light chains may be removed from the myosin molecule without loss of ATPase activity whereas removal of ALCs results in complete loss of enzymatic activity.

We will discuss briefly in the following the polymorphism of myosin and its distribution within skeletal muscles, smooth muscles, cardiac muscle, and within a variety of nonmuscle cells. But while there are many distinct forms of myosin reflecting differential gene expression within different tissues, it is also true that within a particular muscle there is genetic polymorphism among light and heavy chains. For example, immunological and biochemical differences among alkali light chains within skeletal muscle are clear. It has been shown (Frank and Weeds, 1974) that ALC-1 has an N-terminal sequence of 41 amino acids not present in ALC-2. Holt and Lowey (1977) have prepared antibodies to this N-terminal peptide. In addition, an antibody has been isolated which is specific for a small sequence in ALC-2 (Silberstein and Lowey,

1978). These antibodies have been used to document the appearance of "fast" and "slow" myosin in developing muscle fibers *in vivo* in the rat diaphragm (Gauthier *et al.*, 1978).

Antibodies have also been prepared to whole myosin and to the heavy chains (Pepe, 1967a,b; Lowey and Steiner, 1972; Masaki, 1974; Masaki and Yoshizaki, 1974), and there is evidence that only the heavy chains are capable of raising antibody when the whole myosin molecule is used as antigen. Thus antibodies to adult gizzard myosin produced single bands in immunodiffusion experiments when challenged with whole myosin and heavy chains, but no bands were produced when the antimyosin was challenged with light chains (Katoh and Kubo, 1978). The heavy chains of myosin also display differences. Starr and Offer (1973) have shown that rabbit skeletal muscle heavy chain preparations show two different sequences within the N-terminal peptides when heavy chains are digested with chymotrypsin. Thus while there are still no immunological data concerning multiple forms of heavy chains within a given skeletal muscle, the biochemical evidence does suggest that heavy isoforms as well as light isoforms exist within the same muscle and perhaps within the same fiber.

The heavy chains of myosin do show, however, great immunological specificity in that heavy chains from one muscle type will not cross-react with antibody to heavy chains from any other muscle type (Masaki, 1974). Thus antibodies to skeletal muscle myosin heavy chains do not cross-react with myosin from cardiac or smooth muscle, and there is no overlap between fast and slow muscle myosin heavy chains when antibody against one is challenged with antigen from the other. Equally important, it is also apparent that skeletal muscle myosin antibody will not cross-react with myosin from fibroblasts and from a number of other nonmuscle cells (Moss and Strohman, 1976; Holtzer *et al.*, 1974, 1975; Rubinstein *et al.*, 1976). Finally, antibody to nonmuscle cell myosin does not react with skeletal muscle myosin (Ostlund *et al.*, 1974; Pollard *et al.*, 1974; Weber and Groeschel-Stewart, 1974; Willingham *et al.*, 1974; Gwynn *et al.*, 1974). On the other hand, there also appears to be a near absence of species specificity in that antibody to chick skeletal muscle myosin will cross-react with embryonic human myosin (E. Bandman and R. C. Strohman, unpublished observations, 1979) and with rat myosin (Gauthier *et al.*, 1978).

The regulation for unique myosin peptide synthesis within specific fiber types is apparently restricted to the adult state. In the chick embryo, antibody to adult breast myosin reacted with embryonic breast and cardiac muscle. After hatching, cardiac muscle evidently switches off breast muscle myosin, and at the same time adult breast muscle loses its ability to react to antibody made to cardiac myosin (Masaki and Yoshizaki, 1974). These authors have also shown that in the chicken embryo antibodies to both fast and slow myosin were localized by fluorescent staining in the developing breast muscle which in the adult is a fast muscle. Apparently in the embryo this muscle synthesizes fast, slow, and cardiac myosins and only with progressive development does a switch-off occur of the inappropriate forms.

Gauthier *et al.* (1978) used highly purified antibody to slow muscle (chick ALD) myosin and antibodies prepared against the different peptides of light chains of chick fast (pectoralis) muscle to stain frozen sections of the rat diaphragm at various stages of development. They showed that both slow red and fast white fibers of the embryonic diaphragm react with antibodies to fast muscle peptides. At the same time, both fiber types also reacted with antibody to the slow muscle myosin. As development proceeds, motor units of the diaphragm progressively shift from a pattern of multiple innervation by motor neurons to one in which the motor unit has a single neuron. With this shift in innervation pattern there is a progressive segregation of fast-type myosin into what eventually are fast-twitch fibers and a similar segregation of slow-type myosin into the slow-twitch fibers. It was concluded that fiber maturation is accompanied by a process of gene repression for the inappropriate peptides of myosin and that selective gene repression may be a response to withdrawal of multiple innervation.

Similar findings pointing to gene repression during muscle fiber differentiation have been made by Rubinstein *et al.* (1977). While disagreeing with the studies of Gauthier just cited in reporting that chick embryo pectoralis contains only fast myosin, Rubinstein *et al.* do show that embryonic ALD muscle contains both types of myosin and that in this ultimately adult slow muscle there is a progressive shutting down of fast myosin synthesis during muscle maturation. Thus the near prescient observations of Ebert (1953) concerning repression of cardiac myosin during chick development are generally confirmed and extended.

It is becoming clear from the few studies previously cited that the immunological properties of myosin will continue to provide biochemical probes for further defining changes occurring in skeletal muscle during growth and accompanying changes in neural input during maturation. Furthermore, it has been apparent for some time that fiber type (fast red, slow white, intermediate) together with the biochemical changes characterizing fiber type is under control of the nervous system (see Weeds, 1978, for brief review). The pattern of neural innervation and stimulation and the resulting speed of contraction of a particular muscle fiber is apparently able to regulate gene expression. From a developmental point of view, control of gene expression and myosin synthesis by neuronal activity and/or actual contraction by muscle fibers constitutes a continuum of control over the entire life cycle since (a) in early embryonic development continued myosin accumulation appears to be dependent upon either the spontaneous electrical activity or spontaneous contractions of the embryonic myotubes (Walker and Strohman, 1978; Bandman et al., 1978; Brevet et al., 1975), (b) the adult type of muscle fiber is established by and may be altered by the pattern of neuronal innervation (Gauthier et al., 1978) and by the pattern of impulse activity (Salmons and Sreter, 1976; Rubinstein et al., 1978), (c) finally, the rate of skeletal muscle protein accumulation continues to be profoundly affected late into the life of the organism by changes in muscle activity (Astrand and Rodahl, 1971; Goldberg et al., 1975).

Thus, the late stages of muscle growth and maturation, and the further advances of hypertrophy and hypotrophy all potentially contribute to our understanding of gene control and the expression of that control which results in terminal muscle cell differentiation. It is to this early stage of the continuum of control, the stage of terminal myogenesis, that the remainder of this chapter returns.

III. Terminal Differentiation of Skeletal Muscle *in Vitro*

It has been established that the events of terminal myogenesis involve coordinate synthesis of many myofibrillar peptides together with the synthesis and/or increased accumulation of their respective mRNAs (Paterson and Bishop, 1977; Strohman et al., 1977; Devlin and Emerson, 1978). In addition to those peptides and proteins which are exclusively associated with the myofibril there are additional proteins specific for skeletal muscle which also appear at the time of terminal differentiation. Creatine kinase-specific isozymes, for example, have been studied in the transition from presumptive myoblast to myotube (Dym and Yaffe, 1979; Turner et al., 1974), and the mRNAs for creatine kinase isozymes have been detected in myogenic cell cultures using *in vitro* translation and identification of product with antibodies specific for the particular isozyme (Perriard et al., 1978). Myosin, however, is the most abundant contributor to myofibrillar peptides and for that reason and for the reasons of immunological specificity of myosin peptides, that myosin and/or its constituent peptides have been the molecules of choice for marking terminal skeletal muscle differentiation. In what follows, this chapter will emphasize those experiments using myogenic cell cultures which have focused on myosin synthesis and on the synthesis of specific myosin heavy chain mRNA (MHC mRNA). Before proceeding to an analysis of these experiments, however, a brief review of myogenesis in cell culture will be provided.

Table I is a general description of the chick embryo primary cell culture system. Cells derived from day 10–12 embryo breast muscle are plated on collagen-coated dishes and within 7 days of culture time there is a recapitulation of the normal developmental process leading to the formation of cross-striated, functional muscle fibers (Holtzer *et al.*, 1972; Coleman and Coleman, 1968; Fischman, 1970; Paterson and Strohman, 1972). The same scheme holds roughly for clonal analysis of myogenesis in culture as developed by Konigsberg (1963; Hauschka and Konigsberg, 1966) or for myogenesis from cell lines as established by Yaffe (1968). In the various systems appropriate changes in cell density and in the medium will result in prolonged time of cell replication and delayed fusion or the reverse (O'Neill and Stockdale, 1972; Yaffe, 1971). Cell fusion and the transition from cell proliferation to cell differentiation can be arranged to occur within a 10- to 15-hour period (O'Neill and Strohman, 1969; Fluck and Strohman, 1973) for chick cells and within a similar period for primary newborn rat skeletal muscle (Yaffe, 1971). The culture system offers, therefore, the advantages of normal patterns of growth and development and, in addition, a degree of synchrony of events not obtainable from studies *in situ* or *in vivo* where various stages of myogenesis are occurring in parallel and where complex interactions between muscle and nerve and between

TABLE I

SUMMARY OF SKELETAL MUSCLE MYOGENESIS *in Vitro*

0–40 hours	40–60 hours	60 hours to day 5–7
Cells from embryonic muscle plated onto collagen-coated culture dishes. Cells are mostly presumptive myoblasts. Other cells present are fibroblasts and small percentage of myotubes that differentiated *in vivo*	Presumptive myoblasts divide for approximately the first 40 hours. Myoblasts exit cell cycle and cell fusion begins at approximately 40 hours. Fibroblasts continue to divide Myoblasts and fused cells begin to produce mRNA for muscle-specific polypeptides	Myotubes formed and muscle-specific peptides are synthesized. Cross-striated fibers appear around day 5. Spontaneous contractions occur at day 5–6

muscle and the blood vascular system serve to complicate experimental design.

There are some disadvantages of myogenic primary cell cultures and when these have not been heeded or recognized they may lead experimenters to oversimplified conclusions. One of the disadvantages or complexities of the primary myogenic cell culture system is that there are usually four distinct cell types present in the innoculum from the embryonic muscle tissue. Although the great majority of cells are presumptive myoblasts (roughly 80–90%), there is present as well a population of muscle fibroblasts (normally 10–20%) (O'Neill and Strohman, 1969; Konigsberg, 1963). Often overlooked is the fact that in addition to these two major cell types there is often present a small but significant number of myoblasts which have previously withdrawn from the mitotic population *in vivo*. In addition, it is not unusual for the culture innoculum to contain a variable number of small myotubes which escape the filtration process designed to remove the majority of preformed fibers and myotubes. These myoblasts and/or small myotubes are a source of myosin and other proteins of differentiated muscle together with their respective mRNAs. It is the failure to recognize and account for this latter contribution to myosin synthesis that may lead to difficulties in interpreting the data (vide infra). Therefore, while there is great synchrony of events such as cell fusion and the initiation of synthesis of myofibrillar proteins for the majority of cells present, it is also true that it has not been possible to eliminate from primary cell cultures a degree of asynchrony introduced by small numbers of "precocious" myoblasts and myotubes. Even for studies using cell lines it is not entirely clear that these cultures may not carry small numbers of cells in an advanced stage of differentiation.

Another source of potential error in measuring rates of myosin synthesis as a marker for terminal differentiation is the fact that fibroblasts are also synthesizing myosin (Adelstein *et al.*, 1972). There are, however, immunological differences between fibroblast myosin and skeletal muscle myosin so that it is a relatively simple matter to quantitate the amount of muscle cell myosin present even in the presence of a large overgrowth of fibroblasts which may occur in long-term cultures (vide infra).

In summary, the process of terminal differentiation of chick embryo muscle cells growing *in vitro* together with the potential analytical problems may be described as follows. For the first 40 hours or so the presumptive myoblasts undergo one or more rounds of cell division. There is usually a low rate of myosin synthesis detected within the total culture during this time. This "early" myosin is most probably associated with the few postmitotic myoblasts and small myotubes that were seeded in the primary culture. The evidence for this conclusion is that (*a*) myosin has been detected in culture in single myogenic cells, but these appear to be postmitotic (Coleman and Coleman, 1968; Emerson and Beckner, 1975; Moss and Strohman, 1976; Fambrough and Rash, 1971), (*b*) quantitative measurements on the rate of myosin heavy chain synthesis have provided calculations which account for all of the early myosin on the basis of a 1% contamination of 2-day-old cultures of quail myogenic cell cultures with small myotubes (Emerson and Beckner, 1975), and (*c*) *in situ* hybridization of labeled cDNA made to MHC mRNA showed that the great majority of single cells did not hybridize with the probe prior to the time of cell fusion although there was hybridization to a minority of cells during mitosis (John *et al.*, 1977). This latter finding is also relevant to the argument, to be discussed fully in the following, that MHC mRNAs may be present in early presumptive myoblasts but in an untranslated or masked form.

At about 40 hours cell fusion begins and is followed with a variable lag period by increasing rates of myosin synthesis (Coleman and Coleman, 1968; Paterson and Strohman, 1972; Emerson and Beckner, 1975; John *et al.*, 1977) and by the increasing rates of synthesis of myosin and other myofibrillar peptides and their respective mRNAs (Paterson and Bishop, 1977; Devlin and Emerson, 1978, 1979; Przybyla and Strohman, 1974; Strohman *et al.*, 1977). Our general working assumption is that at the time of cell fusion all of the cells which have just made the transition from presumptive myoblast to myoblast and then almost immediately to myotube begin to produce, for the first time, myosin and other peptides which are specific for the skeletal muscle myofibril and for associated differentiated functions of muscle tissue. The central question remains: Is the rate limiting control the production of new message transcripts for myofibrillar peptides or are transcripts produced during proliferative periods of myogenesis which are later activated by cytoplasmic signals? In the latter case, our attention would have to focus on cytoplasmic translational controls as well as on events of transcriptional and post-transcriptional nuclear processing. In resolving this problem the utilization of antibodies to skeletal muscle myosin has been a useful tool not only in the direct estimation of myosin accumulation by differentiating cells but in the identification of skeletal muscle myosin synthesized in cell-free systems under the direction of mRNAs prepared from myogenic cells at different progressive stages of terminal differentiation.

IV. Antimyosin Applied to Detection of Myosin Synthesis during Myogenesis *in Vitro*

Although antimyosin has been used to quantitate myosin synthesis during normal myogenesis *in vitro* and *in vivo*, one of the more valuable uses of this antibody has been in the determination of myosin synthesis in unfused myogenic cells. In these studies, the use of the fluorescent antibody technique has the distinct advantage of allowing the investigator to examine directly a large number of cells individually, an observation not possible with conventional biochemical methods. For example, Holtzer et al. (1957) used fluorescent antimyosin to demonstrate the elaboration of myosin filaments in somite myoblasts by stage 16 *in vivo*, and Okazaki and Holtzer (1965, 1966) found that at least some single cells can synthesize myosin prior to fusion *in vitro*. Similar findings were reported by Coleman and Coleman (1968) who showed that although myosin synthesis could not be detected biochemically until 18–24 hours after the majority of myogenic cells had fused, a few mononucleated cells reactive with fluorescent antimyosin could be found prior to fusion. Fambrough and Rash (1971), working with rat myoblasts, also presented evidence for myosin in single cells. These authors observed that when fusion was blocked with a low calcium medium, some of the elongated cells developed the acetylcholine sensitivity and myofibrillar striations characteristic of differentiated muscle. Other investigations (Holtzer, 1970; Sanger and Holtzer, 1970; Dawkins, 1971; Papademitriou and Dawkins, 1973; Dienstmann, 1974; Rubinstein et al., 1976; Bayne and Simpson, 1975; Chi et al., 1975; Holtzer et al., 1975; Trotter and Nameroff, 1976) have revealed similar findings, all suggesting that at least a small percentage of myogenic cells may be capable of myosin synthesis in the absence of cell fusion. None of these studies, however, dealt with the rates at which these cells synthesized or accumulated myosin in comparison to normally fused cells, nor whether they might represent a subpopulation of specialized myoblasts (Moss, 1968; Fambrough and Rash, 1971).

The discrepancies that existed in the literature about the presence of myosin in unfused cells were further complicated by two additional considerations. First, many of the previously discussed investigations relied on the use of antimyosin prepared by immunization with myosin prepared by ammonium sulfate precipitation (Holtzer et al., 1957; Coleman and Coleman, 1968; Holtzer, 1970; Dienstmann, 1974). Offer (1976), however, has shown that myosin prepared in this manner contains contaminants that are highly antigenic and may interfere with the interpretation of immunological assays. Second, as discussed previ-

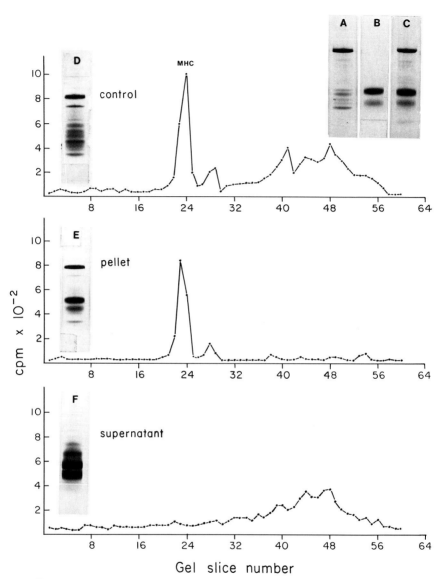

Fig. 1. Direct immunoprecipitation of MHC from the high salt extract. Three-day-old normal cultures were pulsed for 1 hour with 20 μCi/ml [4,5-³H]leucine and extracted for myosin (Paterson and Strohman, 1972). A small aliquot of the pooled high salt extract in pH 7.4 buffer was reduced and electrophoresed on 3.36% SDS–polyacrylamide gels, and the MHC region was scanned to determine the amount of MHC in the extract. Sufficient antimyosin was added to the volume of the extract containing 10 μg MHC so that the antibody was in 2- to 3-fold excess of that amount required to precipitate all of the antigen. Triton X-100 and sodium deoxycholate were added to a final concentration of 1% and the mixture was incubated for 18 hours at 4°C. After centrifugation at 7500 rpm for 30 minutes in the HB-4 rotor, the supernatant was carefully separated from the pellet. The

ously, it now has been firmly established that myosin can be extracted from a variety of nonmuscle cells (Pollard et al., 1974; Pollard and Weihling, 1974; Weber and Groeschel-Stewart, 1974; Willingham et al., 1974; Burridge and Bray, 1975; Rubinstein et al., 1976; Shibata et al., 1975; Mabuchi, 1976; Roisen et al., 1978; Stossel and Pollard, 1973) and that myosin-like peptides can be found in ordinary cell organelles (Brandon, 1975; Ohnishi et al., 1974; Berl et al., 1973; Fujiwara and Pollard, 1976). Since, as previously mentioned, muscle cell cultures contain fibroblasts and it has been demonstrated that fibroblasts synthesize myosin (Adelstein et al., 1972), it is clear that extracts from myogenic cell cultures will contain contaminating proteins similar to myofibrillar myosin.

Moss (1976) and Moss and Strohman (1976) have used an antibody to highly purified chick skeletal muscle myosin to resolve some of these discrepancies. In these studies it was shown (a) that fluorescent antibody, while staining very early myotubes, did not stain the vast majority of single cells in the culture and (b) that cells blocked from fusing by low calcium will nevertheless begin to synthesize myosin as single cells if they are maintained for long periods in primary cell culture or if they are subcultured for shorter periods. It is clear from this work and from related studies (Emerson and Beckner, 1975; Vertel and Fischman, 1976; Turner et al., 1976) that cell fusion is not an absolute requirement for terminal myogenic cell differentiation although fusion does precede myosin synthesis under normal conditions. Taken together, these studies and the studies of cDNA hybridization (John et al., 1977) previously discussed briefly also support the view that under normal culture conditions the vast majority of unfused, proliferating myogenic cells do not contain detectable levels of myosin and that at the approximate time of cell fusion these cells begin to synthesize skeletal muscle myosin for the first time.

Another example of the use of antimyosin is in the direct immunoprecipitation of myosin from cell cultures, followed by analysis of the dissolved immunoprecipitate on SDS–polyacrylamide gels and quanti-

---

twice-rinsed pellet and aliquot of the supernatant were electrophoresed on 3.36% gels. The gels were stained, sliced, and counted as previously described (Paterson and Strohman, 1972). The 3.36% gels were loaded with: (A) 10 μg of marker myosin; (B) antimyosin IgG; (C) immune precipitate from (A) and (B); (D) high salt extract (control) from fused cultures; (E) immune precipitate of (D) with antimyosin; (F) supernatant from (E). As shown in (E), 93% of the MHC counts were recovered in the immune precipitate from the high salt extract. The smaller peak at slice number 27 has a molecular weight of approximately 150,000 and is presumably the MHC degradation product investigated by Etlinger et al. (1976).

tation of optical density or cpm of the myosin heavy chain (MHC) component of the gel. This procedure, exemplified by Fig. 1, was used with 3-day-old cultures which are normally in an optimal phase of myotube growth and myosin synthesis. Cells were labeled with [H³]leucine and a crude myosin extract was prepared which contained myofibrillar myosin together with whatever fibroblast myosin is present. Antimyosin IgG was added under conditions known to cause optimal precipitation of the total myosin present and the immune precipitate was then analyzed by SDS gel electrophoresis and compared with a total myosin extract to determine the amount of myosin present. As shown in Fig. 1, approximately 93% of the total MHC counts were precipitated by the antibody. A control series showing the inability of normal rabbit serum to precipitate myosin and the lack of trapping of myosin by a BSA–anti-BSA immune precipitate is depicted in Fig. 2.

Furthermore, the problem of fibroblast myosin and the potential complexity that the synthesis of this protein introduces to the kinetic analysis of skeletal muscle myosin synthesis is completely dealt with by virtue of the immunological differences between the two myosins. We have examined the ability of our myosin antibody to precipitate

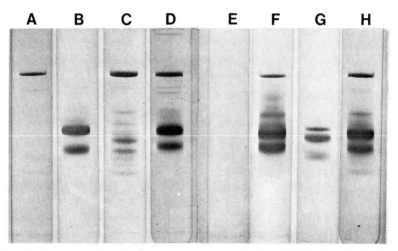

FIG. 2. Control gels for the direct immune precipitation of MHC from the high salt extract. Myosin was extracted from the cultures as described in Fig. 1. (A) Column purified myosin; (B) IgG; (C) high salt extract prepared as described in Fig. 1; (D) immune precipitate from (C) and antimyosin; (E) immune precipitate of the high salt extract and NRS; (F) 50% of the supernatant from (E); (G) immune precipitate of the high salt extract with BSA and anti-BSA; (H) 50% of the supernatant from (G). The amounts of BSA and anti-BSA added were designed to yield an immune pellet containing the same amount of protein as the myosin–antimyosin pellet.

newly synthesized myosin from fibroblast polysomes completing synthesis in a reticulocyte cell-free system. As shown in Fig. 3, while newly synthesized myosin from polysomes prepared from muscle cell cultures was precipitated by the antibody, nascent myosin from fibroblast polysomes was not. Instead, fibroblast myosin remained in the supernatant from the immune reaction and could be precipitated by adjusting the salt concentration downward following removal of the skeletal muscle myosin immune pellet. Therefore, even in the presence of large numbers of fibroblasts it is possible to carry out an analysis of kinetics of skeletal muscle myosin synthesis by precipitation of a high salt extract of the culture with specific antibody to skeletal myosin.

In summary, precipitation of myosin from cell culture extracts with skeletal muscle myosin antibody can be applied to an analysis of

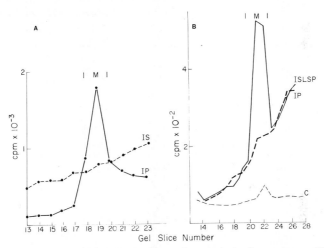

FIG. 3. Selective precipitation of skeletal muscle myosin in the presence of fibroblast myosin. (A) MHC synthesis with polysomes from myogenic cell cultures. 3.2 OD_{260} of polysomal material was added to the assay system. The assay was processed for product identification with antimyosin as described in Fig. 1. (———) Immune pellet (IP); (-----) immune supernatant (IS); M, MHC region of the gel. (B) Synthesis with polysomes from fibroblasts. 5.7 OD_{260} of polysomal material added to the lysate was isolated from confluent fibroblast cultures. After precipitation of the assay with antimyosin and 10 μg of carrier myosin, the immune supernatant was removed and diluted with 3.3 ml H_2O and then left at 0°C overnight. This preparation was then centrifuged for 30 minutes at 9500 rpm in the HB-4 rotor and the pellet from this spin was dissolved in 50 μl of 0.04 M $NaPP_i$–HCl, pH 7.4, prior to reduction and electrophoresis. (-----) Immune pellet (IP); (———) immune supernatant low salt pellet (ISLSP); (C– – –) control (no polysomes added to the lysate). Separate experiments (Strohman et al., 1977) have demonstrated that NRS and BSA–anti-BSA do not cause precipitation of MHC from stimulated reticulocyte lysates.

myosin synthesis during terminal differentiation (Moss and Strohman, 1976; Strohman *et al.*, 1977) and during normal and drug-induced relaxation and hypotrophy of muscle fibers in culture (Walker and Strohman, 1978; Bandman *et al.*, 1978; Walker *et al.*, 1979). The method of specific antibody precipitation of myosin avoids many of the difficulties presented by the complexity and polymorphism of myosin, and, in many cases, especially in the sensitive matter of assaying myosin synthesis by cell-free protein synthesizing systems, it is absolutely essential (see Section V).

V. Antimyosin in the Detection of MHC mRNA during Development

As pointed out in Section IV, it is necessary to know to what extent mRNA transcripts for MHC are present in the myogenic cell cytoplasm prior to the actual synthesis of myosin. If such transcripts are synthesized well in advance of translation and remain stored until appropriate developmental signals arrive, then clearly translational controls have special importance for terminal differentiation.

On the other hand, if the time constant describing the complete process of MHC mRNA transcription and translation is relatively short, then the rate limiting steps are most certainly nuclear and the interesting focus for terminal myogenesis will be on cytoplasmic–nuclear interactions. Given the importance of deciding between these two possibilities, it should be clear that translational controls are always present and will serve to regulate, depending on ambient cellular conditions, overall rates of protein synthesis. For example, cells entering either stationary phase of growth, or mitosis, will reversibly disassemble polysomes and, in disassembly, mRNAs previously on polysomes will appear as mRNPs. In a similar manner, L-cell polysomes will disassemble when cells are exposed to elevated temperatures (Schocketman and Perry, 1972), and cultured muscle cells will release 80% of their ribosomes from polysomes following brief periods of amino acid deprivation (Hosick and Strohman, 1971). These translational regulatory mechanisms, however, occur at all times, do not necessarily pertain to mechanisms unique to terminal differentiation, and should alert us to the fact that the presence of specific mRNAs as mRNPs rather than as polysomes may have more to do with conditions surrounding the cells at the moment than they have to do with unique processing of mRNA related to basic mechanisms of terminal differentiation and expression of complex sets of functionally related genes (Dym *et al.*, 1979).

The question of whether or not MHC mRNAs occur in myogenic cell cytoplasm for long periods as stored or masked entities as mRNPs can be approached with the use of antibodies to myosin to detect synthesis of skeletal muscle MHC when cell-free protein-synthesizing systems are challenged with RNA preparations from cells at different stages of development. Given certain limitations to this approach, it nevertheless is an important adjunct to current methods which lack the specificity of an immunoassay to distinguish between the variety of myosins and/or their respective mRNAs. These include cDNA hybridization experiments in which the cDNA prepared to MHC mRNA may be hybridizing to cellular RNA sequences other than those in MHC mRNAs. For example, different myosins are presumably synthesized from different mRNAs which nevertheless share extensive similarities in RNA sequence. At the same time the different myosins also display large conserved amino acid sequences so that peptide mapping may also fail to provide meaningful data with which to discriminate between skeletal muscle myosin and fibroblast myosin, etc. Therefore, as a result of myosin polymorphism many recent studies utilizing the following criteria for myosin identification may be incomplete and include: (a) studies utilizing the presence of total cell myosin or low salt precipitates of high salt extracts of total cell protein (Benoff and Nadal-Ginard, 1979a); (b) studies utilizing solely the amount of 26S mRNA as a marker for MHC mRNA (Buckingham et al., 1974); (c) studies utilizing cDNA probes to MHC mRNA where extensive heterogeneity of the probe is suggested (Robbins and Heywood, 1978; Dym et al., 1979); (d) studies relying on material migrating on SDS–polyacrylamide gels as 200,000-dalton peptides (Benoff and Nadal-Ginard, 1979a).

Where specific MHC mRNA is present in a cell extract and can be translated in an mRNA-dependent cell-free lysate, the use of specific antibody to myosin is a most reliable, if not a completely quantitative, method for detecting the presence of that mRNA. We have developed a rationale for this approach to measure the relative abundance of MHC mRNA during myogenesis in cell culture, and Perriard et al. (1978) have developed a similar approach for the relative quantitation of mRNA for creatine kinase isozymes also during myogenesis in vitro.

The advantages and assumptions of this approach are as follows. First, utilizing the antibody it is possible to quantitate the total amount of MHC synthesized in a cell-free lysate without complications introduced by synthesis of nonmuscle MHC and by synthesis of other peptides having a MW close to 200,000. Second, a single tissue culture dish will yield sufficient mRNA for an unambiguous translation in a cell-free lysate (Strohman et al., 1977). Third, there is a linear relationship between the amount of RNA added to the lysate and the amount of MHC synthesized (see Fig. 4). Fourth, even when mRNA is present in

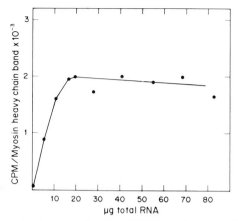

Fig. 4. [³⁵S]Methionine incorporation into MHC as a function of total cellular RNA added to reticulocyte lysate. Conditions for preparation of lysate and for translation of RNA and identification of MHC by immunoprecipitation were as previously reported (Strohman *et al.*, 1977) except that the lysate was preincubated with nuclease by a modification of the procedure of Pelham and Jackson (1976).

the cell in an untranslated form such as in mRNPs, that mRNA is translated by the cell-free lysate (Bag and Sarker, 1975, 1976). Utilizing total cell RNA will therefore give a measure of total MHC mRNA present whether or not it was in a state of active translation during the time of extraction from the cell. The disadvantage of this system is that it does not provide a strict quantitative measure of the number of MHC mRNA transcripts. The reason for the lack of strict quantitation is that the lysates display variable efficiencies in translation of different mRNAs (Lodish, 1976). It is clear, however, that results of translation of a specific mRNA can be quite reproducible within a given experimental series (Strohman *et al.*, 1977; Perriard *et al.*, 1978) and can provide a sound and relative comparison between cultures of the amount of a specific mRNA present.

If increasing amounts of total cellular RNA or poly(A+) RNA are added to reticulocyte lysates under standard conditions (see Fig. 4) and MHC synthesis is measured by precipitation with anti-myosin and analysis of the immunoprecipitate by SDS–polyacrylamide gel electrophoresis, it is seen that a linear relationship exists between 1–15 μg RNA added and synthesis as measured by cpm incorporated into the MHC band of the gel (Fig. 4). Adding equal amounts of RNA within this linear range but from cultures at different stages of myogenic development provides a comparison between stages of the relative amount of MHC mRNA present. Since the linear response is obtained with total cellular RNA, it is preferable to use total rather than poly(A+) RNA since not all of the MHC mRNA will bind to oligo-dT cellulose (Strohman *et al.*, 1977; Benoff and Nadal-Ginard, 1979b). When prefusion myogenic cells are assayed for MHC mRNA content, the translation assay shows that there is a small amount of MHC mRNA present, but at about the time of cell fusion this amount increases at least 30–40 fold (Fig. 5). It is at this time that the rate of myosin synthesis begins to increase in the cell cultures (Strohman *et al.*, 1977). This result is in good agreement with reports using cDNA probes to MHC mRNA which showed that the great majority of un-

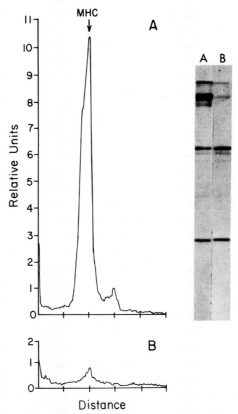

FIG. 5. Relative increase in MHC mRNA in fused myotubes compared with unfused cells of myogenic cell cultures. Procedures as in Fig. 4. (A) Gel fluorographs and scan of translation products of cell-free lysate precipitated by antimyosin. RNA was extracted from myotube cultures at 68 hours of development; (B) same as (A) except cultures were unfused at 38 hours of development. Identical amounts of total cell RNA added in each case.

fused cells did not hybridize with the probe and that at about the time of cell fusion the absolute number of MHC mRNA transcripts increased approximately 40-fold (John *et al.*, 1977). In rat cell cultures Benoff and Nadal-Ginard (1979b) report that the MHC mRNA transcript number increases 200-fold at the time of cell fusion. Paterson and Bishop (1977) have shown a 10–40-fold increase at the time of cell fusion in chick cultures in the high abundance sequences of mRNA which are present as six sequences each in about 15,000 copies per nucleus. This high abundance class includes MHC mRNA. Finally, Devlin and Emerson (1979), also using a translation assay, have reported that the increase in MHC mRNA content is temporally coincident with the increase in myosin synthesis rate in quail cell cultures. In fact, in the latter study there was a parallel between increases in six different myofibrillar peptides with the increase in accumulation of all respective mRNAs. There appears to be excellent agreement, therefore, that terminal differentiation of skeletal muscle involves the activation of gene transcription not only for myosin but for a complex array of functionally related genes which code for the peptides of the myofibril and for muscle-specific related functions. In all of the previously mentioned studies there was no indication that specific myofibrillar mRNAs were synthesized in significant advance of their actual translation. So while there is no question that translational controls play an important role in regulating protein synthesis generally, there is little evidence that these controls play an additional role unique to terminal differentiation of skeletal muscle.

One recent report, however, raises serious questions concerning the use of a translation assay for relative quantitation of specific mRNAs and also provides evidence that significant amounts of MHC mRNA is present in unfused cells of rat cell line cultures in advance of actual translation (Benoff and Nadal-Ginard, 1979a). In this latter paper it has been reported that in rat cell line myogenic cultures dividing myoblasts contain large amounts of MHC mRNA in an untranslated state. This mRNA is reportedly not activated for translation in a cell-free lysate, however, unless the lysate contains high concentrations of potassium. We have reinvestigated this matter of a K^+ ion activation for MHC mRNA activity in the reticulocyte lysate using the radioimmunoassay with antibody to skeletal muscle myosin.

Our results are given in Fig. 6. When approximately equal amounts of total cell RNA from cultures at 22, 42, and 72 hours of development are added to the lysates, it is apparent that (*a*) 22-hour RNA has a higher MHC mRNA activity than RNA from 42-hour cultures, (*b*) by 72 hours there is a marked increase in MHC mRNA activity, and (*c*)

1 2 3 4 5 6 7 8 9 10 11 12 13 14 15 16

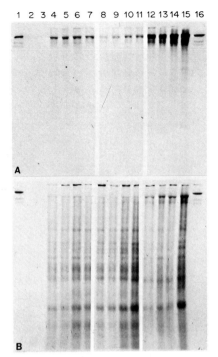

A

B

FIG. 6. Characterization of MHC synthesis in cell-free lysates. Comparison of immunoprecipitation with low salt precipitation as appropriate methods. MHC synthesis is also compared as a function of (a) whether RNA was extracted from fused or unfused cells, and (b) the K^+ ion concentration used in the lysate. Results are presented as fluorographs of SDS–polyacrylamide gels of either immunoprecipitates or low salt precipitates derived from the lysates following protein synthesis in response to added RNA. (A) Immune precipitate: 80 μl of assay + 80 μl 0.08 M sodium pyrophosphate, pH 7.4, 2% Triton X-100, 2% sodium deoxycholate; 4.5 μg column-purified myosin carrier and 30 μl anti-myosin IgG were added. Samples were kept at 4°C for 18 hours, then washed with 0.04 M sodium pyrophosphate, pH 7.4, air-dried, and dissolved in sample buffer. (B) Low salt precipitate: 80 μl of assay + 25 μg column-purified myosin were precipitated by addition of 800 μl cold distilled water. Samples were left on ice for 18 hours, then washed with low salt buffer, dried, and dissolved in sample buffer. (A) Products of total RNA stimulated *in vitro* assays were immune precipitated and were analyzed on polyacrylamide gels. (B) Products of total RNA stimulated *in vitro* assays were low salt precipitated and were analyzed on polyacrylamide gels. (1) ^{3}H-labeled myosin marker; (2) control, no added RNA, 80 mM K^+; (3) control, no added RNA, 168 mM K^+; (4) 14 μg 22 hours, 80 mM K^+; (5) 14 μg 22 hours, 168 mM K^+; (6) 28 μg 22 hours, 80 mM K^+; (7) 28 μg 22 hours, 168 mM K^+; (8) 13 μg 42 hours, 80 mM K^+; (9) 13 μg 42 hours, 168 mM K^+; (10) 26 μg 42 hours, 80 mM K^+; (11) 26 μg 42 hours, 168 mM K^+; (12) 11 μg 72 hours, 80 mM K^+; (13) 11 μg 72 hours, 168 mM K^+; (14) 27 μg 72 hours, 80 mM K^+; (15) 27 μg 72 hours, 168 mM K^+; (16) ^{3}H-labeled myosin marker.

there is no K$^+$ activation of MHC synthesis directed by RNA prepared from prefusion cultures. Furthermore, when RNA from prefusion cultures (22 and 42 hours) is mixed with RNA from postfusion cultures, the MHC mRNA activity is additive, that is, there is no evidence for the presence of inhibitory factors in early RNA preparations which might inhibit later MHC mRNA activity (data not shown). The apparent decrease in MHC mRNA activity from 22 to 42 hours can be explained by the presence of a few myotubes or mature myoblasts in the original cell inoculum. These cells would be postmitotic and would be synthesizing MHC mRNA. However, the amount of total RNA/culture increases more than 2-fold between 22 and 42 hours, and the few myotubes and mature myoblasts present would contribute very little to this new RNA accumulation. Since the total RNA from 42-hour cultures contains less translatable MHC mRNA activity, it is apparent that new RNA accumulated by the majority cell type, the presumptive myoblast, between 22 and 42 hours contributed little or no new MHC mRNA. By 72 hours, following cell fusion, there is a large increase in the MHC mRNA activity associated with a constant amount of total RNA (Fig. 5).

These results agree well with studies previously cited on the temporal correlation between the time of actual myosin synthesis by cells and the appearance of new MHC mRNA. The results do not agree with the recent report that growing myoblasts contain a high amount of MHC mRNA which is not translated within the cell but which may be activated by a high K$^+$ ion concentration in a cell-free lysate (Benoff and Nadal-Ginard, 1979a). Examination of Fig. 5 reveals what could be an explanation of our discordant findings. Benoff and Nadal-Ginard have used a low salt precipitation of the cell-free lysate to measure the newly synthesized myosin. As the figure shows, there is extensive precipitation of nonmyosin peptides in the low salt precipitate, and, in addition, there is extensive loss of newly synthesized MHC compared with material precipitated by the myosin antibody. The autoradiograph of the gel shows there is clearly no enhancement by K$^+$ of the ability of RNA from early prefusion cultures to synthesize MHC as characterized by precipitation by specific antibody. Our conclusion is that the method of low salt precipitation followed by SDS–gel electrophoresis carries along myosin-like peptides which comigrate with muscle-specific MHC, introduces spurious counts, and therefore is not an adequate method for characterizing MHC synthesis in a cell-free lysate.

The general conclusion is that immunoprecipitation of specific polypeptides, either from cellular extracts or from cell-free lysates synthesizing peptides under the direction of exogenous mRNA, offers a working tool for the relative quantitation of specific mRNA content and is a useful adjunct to the more complex and potentially less specific method of cDNA hybridization.

REFERENCES

Adelstein, R. S., Conti, M. A., Johnson, G. S., Pastin, I., and Pollard, T. D. (1972). *Proc. Natl. Acad. Sci. U.S.A.* **69**, 3693–3697.
Astrand, P.-O., and Rodahl, K. (1971). "Text of Work Physiology." McGraw-Hill, New York.
Bag, J., and Sarkar, S. (1975). *Biochemistry* **14**, 3800–3807.
Bag, J., and Sarkar, S. (1976). *J. Biol. Chem.* **251**, 7600–7609.
Bandman, E., Walker, C., and Strohman, R. C. (1978). *Science* **200**, 559–562.
Bayne, E., and Simpson, S. (1975). *Dev. Biol.* **2**, 237–256.
Benoff, S., and Nadal-Girard, B. (1979a). *Biochemistry* **18**, 494–500.
Benoff, S., and Nadal-Girard, B. (1979b). *Proc. Natl. Acad. Sci. U.S.A.* **76**, 1583–1587.
Berl, S., Puszkin, S., and Nicklas, W. J. (1973). *Science* **179**, 441.
Brandon, D. L. (1975). *FEBS Lett.* **58**, 349–352.
Brevet, A., Pinto, E., Stockdale, F., and Peacock, J. (1975). *J. Cell Biol.* **67**, 439–445.
Bruggmann, S., and Jenny, E. (1975). *Biochim. Biophys. Acta* **412**, 39–50.
Buckingham, M. E., Caput, D., Cohen, A., Whalen, R. G., and Gros, F. (1974). *Proc. Natl. Acad. Sci. U.S.A.* **71**, 1466–1470.
Burridge, K., and Bray, D. (1975). *J. Mol. Biol.* **99**, 1–14.
Chi, J. C., Rubinstein, N., Strahs, K., and Holtzer, H. (1975). *J. Cell Biol.* **67**, 523–537.
Coleman, J. R., and Coleman, A. W. (1968). *J. Cell. Physiol.* **72**, Suppl. 1, 19–34.
Dawkins, R. L. (1971). *Proc. Aust. Soc. Med. Res.* **2**, 475.
Devlin, D. B., and Emerson, C. P. (1978). *Cell* **13**, 599–611.
Devlin, D. B., and Emerson, C. P. (1979). *Dev. Biol.* **69**, 202–216.
Dienstmann, S. R. (1974). *J. Cell Biol.* **63**, 83a.
Dym, H. P., and Yaffe, D. (1979). *Dev. Biol.* **68**, 592–599.
Dym, H. P., Kennedy, D. S., and Heywood, S. M. (1979). *Differentiation* **12**, 145–155.
Ebert, J. D. (1953). *Proc. Natl. Acad. Sci. U.S.A.* **39**, 333–344.
Emerson, C. P., and Beckner, S. K. (1975). *J. Mol. Biol.* **93**, 431–448.
Etlinger, J. D., Zak, R., and Fischman, D. A. (1976). *J. Cell Biol.* **68**, 123–141.
Fambrough, D., and Rash, J. E. (1971). *Dev. Biol.* **26**, 55–68.
Fischman, D. A. (1970). *Curr. Top. Dev. Biol.* **5**, 235–280.
Fluck, R. A., and Strohman, R. C. (1973). *Dev. Biol.* **33**, 417–428.
Frank, G., and Weeds, A. G. (1974). *Eur. J. Biochem.* **44**, 317–334.
Fujiwara, J., and Pollard, T. (1976). *J. Cell Biol.* **70**, 181a.
Gauthier, G. F., Lowey, S., and Hobbs, A. W. (1978). *Nature (London)* **274**, 25–29.
Goldberg, A. L., Etlinger, J. D., Goldspink, D. F., and Jableck, C. (1975). *Med. Sci. Sports* **7**, 248–261.
Gwynne, I., Kemp, R. B., Jones, B. M., and Groschel-Stewart, V. (1974). *J. Cell Sci.* **15**, 279–289.
Hauschka, S. D., and Konigsberg, I. E. (1966). *Proc. Natl. Acad. Sci. U.S.A.* **55**, 119.
Holt, J. C., and Lowey, S. (1977). *Biochemistry* **16**, 4398–4402.
Holtzer, H. (1970). *In* "Cell Differentiation" (O. Schjeide and J. de Vellis, eds.), Chapter 17. Van Nostrand-Reinhold, Princeton, New Jersey.

Holtzer, H., Marshall, J., and Finck, H. (1957). *J. Biophys. Biochem. Cytol.* **3**, 705.

Holtzer, H., Sanger, H., Ishikawa, H., and Strahs, K. (1972). *Cold Spring Harbor Symp. Quant. Biol.* **37**, 549–566.

Holtzer, H., Rubinstein, N., Dientsman, S., Chi, J., Biehl, J., and Somlyo, A. (1974). *Biochimie* **56**, 1575–1580.

Holtzer, H., Strahs, K., Biehl, J., Somlyo, A., and Ishikawa, H. (1975). *Science* **188**, 943–946.

Hosick, H., and Strohman, R. C. (1971). *J. Cell. Physiol.* **77**, 145–156.

John, H. A., Patrinou-Georgoulas, M., and Jones, K. W. (1977). *Cell* **12**, 501–508.

Katoh, N., and Kubo, S. (1978). *Biochim. Biophys. Acta* **535**, 401–411.

Konigsberg, I. (1963). *Science* **140**, 1273–1280.

Lodish, H. F. (1976). *Annu. Rev. Biochem.* **45**, 39–72.

Lowey, S., and Holt, J. C. (1972). *Cold Spring Harbor Symp. Quant. Biol.* **37**, 19–28.

Lowey, S., and Steiner, L. (1972). *J. Mol. Biol.* **65**, 111–126.

Lowey, S., Slayter, H. S., Weeds, A. G., and Baker, H. (1969). *J. Mol. Biol.* **42**, 1–29.

Mabuchi, I. (1976). *J. Mol. Biol.* **100**, 569–582.

Masaki, T. (1974). *J. Biochem. (Tokyo)* **76**, 441–449.

Masaki, T., and Yoshizaki, C. (1974). *J. Biochem. (Tokyo)* **76**, 123–131.

Moss, F. P. (1968). *Am. J. Anat.* **122**, 555–564.

Moss, P. (1976). Ph.D. Thesis, University of California, Berkeley.

Moss, P., and Strohman, R. C. (1976). *Dev. Biol.* **48**, 431–437.

Offer, G. (1976). *Proc. R. Soc. London* **192**, 439–449.

Ohnishi, T., Kawamura, H., Takeo, K., and Watanabe, S. (1974). *J. Biochem. (Tokyo)* **56**, 273.

Okazaki, K., and Holtzer, H. (1965). *J. Histochem. Cytochem.* **13**, 727–739.

Okazaki, K., and Holtzer, H. (1966). *Proc. Natl. Acad. Sci. U.S.A.* **56**, 1484–1490.

O'Neill, M. and Stockdale, F. (1972) *J. Cell Biol.* **52**, 52–65.

O'Neill, M. and Strohman, R. C. (1969). *J. Cell. Physiol.* **73**, 61–67.

Ostlund, R., Pastan, I., and Adelstein, R. (1974). *J. Biol. Chem.* **294**, 3903–3908.

Papademitriou, J. M., and Dawkins, R. L. (1973). *Cytobios* **8**, 227–241.

Paterson, B., and Strohman, R. C. (1972). *Dev. Biol.* **29**, 113–138.

Paterson, B. M., and Bishop, J. O. (1977). *Cell* **12**, 751–765.

Pelham, H. R. B., and Jackson, R. J. (1976). *Eur. J. Biochem.* **67**, 247–256.

Pepe, F. A. (1966). *J. Cell Biol.* **28**, 505–526.

Pepe, F. A. (1967a). *J. Mol. Biol.* **27**, 203–225.

Pepe, F. A. (1967b). *J. Mol. Biol.* **27**, 227–236.

Pepe, F. A. (1972). *Cold Spring Harbor Symp. Quant. Biol.* **37**, 97–108.

Perriard, J. C., Perriard, E. R., and Eppenberger, H. M. (1978). *J. Biol. Chem.* **253**, 6529–6535.

Pollard, T., and Weihlung, R. (1974). *Crit. Rev. Biochem.* **2**, 1–65.

Pollard, T., Thomas, S., and Niederman, R. (1974). *Anal. Biochem.* **60**, 258–262.

Przybyla, A., and Strohman, R. C. (1974). *Proc. Natl. Acad. Sci. U.S.A.* **71**, 662–666.

Robbins, J., and Heywood, S. M. (1978). *Eur. J. Biochem.* **82**, 601–608.

Roisen, F., Inczedy-Marcsek, M., Hsu, L., and York, W. (1978). *Science* **199**, 1445–1448.

Rubinstein, N. A., Chi, J., and Holtzer, H. (1976). *Exp. Cell Res.* **97**, 387–393.

Rubinstein, N. A., Pepe, F. A., and Holtzer, H. (1977). *Proc. Natl. Acad. Sci. U.S.A.* **74**, 4524–4527.

Rubinstein, N. A., Mabuchi, K., Pepe, F., Salmons, S., Gergely, J., and Streter, F. (1978). *J. Cell Biol.* **79**, 252–261.

Salmons, S., and Sreter, F. A. (1976). *Nature (London)* **263**, 30–34.

Sanger, J., and Holtzer, H. (1970). *J. Cell Biol.* **47,** 178a.

Schocketman, G., and Perry, R. P. (1972). *J. Mol. Biol.* **63,** 577–590.

Shibata, N., Tatsumi, N., Tanaka, K., Mura, Y., and Senda, N. (1975). *Biochim. Biophys. Acta* **400,** 222–243.

Silberstein, L., and Lowey, S. (1978). *Biophys. J.* **21,** 45a.

Starr, R., and Offer, G. (1973). *J. Mol. Biol.* **81,** 17–31.

Stossel, T. P., and Pollard, T. D. (1973). *J. Biol. Chem.* **248,** 8288–8294.

Strohman, R. C., Moss, P. S., Micou-Eastwood, J., Spector, D., Przybyla, A., and Paterson, B. (1977). *Cell* **10,** 265–273.

Szent-Györgyi, A. G. (1953). *Arch. Biochem. Biophys.* **42,** 305–320.

Trotter, J., and Nameroff, M. (1976). *Dev. Biol.* **57,** 548–555.

Turner, D. C., Maier, V., and Eppenberger, H. M. (1974). *Dev. Biol.* **37,** 63–89.

Turner, D. C., Gmur, R., Siegrist, M., Burckhardt, E., and Eppenberger, H. (1976). *Dev. Biol.* **48,** 258–283.

Vertel, B., and Fischman, D. (1976). *Dev. Biol.* **48,** 438–446.

Walker, C., and Strohman, R. C. (1978). *Exp. Cell Res.* **116,** 341–348.

Walker, C., Bandman, E., and Strohman, R. C. (1979). *Exp. Cell Res.* **123,** 285–291.

Weber, K., and Groeschel-Stewart, V. (1974). *Proc. Natl. Acad. Sci. U.S.A.* **71,** 4561–4564.

Weeds, A. (1978). *Nature (London)* **274,** 417–418.

Weeds, A. G. (1969). *Nature (London)* **223,** 1362–1369.

Weeds, A. G., and Lowey, S. (1971). *J. Mol. Biol.* **61,** 701–725.

Willingham, M., Ostlund, R., and Pastan, I. (1974). *Proc. Natl. Acad. Sci. U.S.A.* **71,** 4144–4147.

Yaffe, D. (1968). *Proc. Natl. Acad. Sci. U.S.A.* **61,** 477–483.

Yaffe, D. (1971). *Exp. Cell Res.* **66,** 33–48.

CHAPTER 14

IMMUNOLOGICAL APPROACHES TO THE STUDY OF MYOGENESIS AND LENS FIBER JUNCTION FORMATION*

Martin Friedlander

THE ROCKEFELLER UNIVERSITY
NEW YORK, NEW YORK

I. Introduction

The potential for using immunological probes in the investigation of development remains as unlimited as the number of antigenic molecules observed during differentiation. Since many such molecules have no known unique enzymatic or compositional properties, identification of such molecules remains elusive. If we are to answer such simple questions as how embryonic cells recognize one another, it is imperative to detail the molecular events that underlie phenotypic specification. Surely it is to the cell surface that we must look if we are to understand the molecular basis of selective cell associations during development. An approach that employed the exquisite sensitivity and specificity of antibody–antigen interactions was undertaken by Weiss (1947) some 30 years ago. By 1972, a refinement of the earlier approaches led to the serological identification of tissue-specific cell surface antigens on various embryonic chick tissues (Goldschneider and Moscona, 1972). Since then, a vast catalog of developmental antigens has been accumulated (see other chapters, this volume, and Volume 13, this series).

We initiated immunological studies on the developing embryonic

* This chapter is dedicated to the late Dr. Beatrice Garber.

321

CURRENT TOPICS IN
DEVELOPMENTAL BIOLOGY, VOL. 14

chick muscle cell surface several years ago in an attempt to identify those molecules or macromolecular arrays that may be muscle tissue- or developmental stage-specific. Our rationale was that such mole- cules, if present, should be displayed on the muscle cell surface and should be capable of eliciting antibody production in animals other than chickens. We have succeeded in identifying such antigens serolog- ically; their role in myogenic cell recognition and subsequent myogenesis remains speculative.

While cell–cell recognition may be mediated primarily via surface displays of certain membrane macromolecules, it has been suggested that the critical event in establishing permanent cell–cell contact may result from an exchange of small molecules between transiently con- nected cells (see Gilula, 1977a). It has been proposed that such "meta- bolic cooperation" occurs via channels between cells in the form of gap junctions (for review, see Pitts, 1977). Such junctions are currently identifiable largely by morphological criteria and there is no effective means for preventing the appearance of intercellular junctions without also affecting nonjunctional cellular activities. The development of a probe specific for the gap junction would permit an analysis of junction biosynthesis, assembly, and turnover. It should also be possible to ob- tain a clearer definition of the developmental significance of such inter- cellular contacts. In an attempt to isolate quantities of junctional polypeptides sufficient to generate specific antibodies we decided to consider systems other than those most widely used by investigators studying gap junctions. For this reason we turned to the lens fiber cell which has been reported to contain extensive amounts of gap junctions (Benedetti *et al.*, 1976). As a result of our studies on the intercellular junctions of the lens, it appears that the junctions present in this tissue are not homologous to gap junctions observed elsewhere (Friedlander *et al.*, 1980; Hertzberg *et al.*, 1980). However, immunochemical and biochemical studies of the lenticular cell membrane have revealed in- teresting information on the major intrinsic membrane protein of the lens. This protein is unusual in its abundance relative to other polypep- tides of the lens membrane and its expression during lens development.

The following discussion of embryonic muscle cell antigens and in- tercellular junctional polypeptides of the lens focuses primarily on our own work. These results have been presented as a summary of reported findings and a brief discussion of work in progress. We recognize that extensive contributions have been made by other laboratories, and we have attempted, whenever possible, to acknowledge such work.

The studies of myogenesis were conducted in the laboratory of Dr. Donald Fischman at the University of Chicago and the work on the lens cell junctions in the laboratory of Dr. N. B. Gilula at The Rockefeller University. Other individuals involved in these projects have been acknowledged where appropriate.

II. Immunological Approaches to the Study of Muscle Development

Myogenesis *in vitro* has been described in the literature [for recent reviews, see Fischman (1972) and Bischoff (1978)] and may be viewed as consisting of three phases of cellular activity: proliferation, fusion, and cytodifferentiation. While there is no obligatory prerequisite for the first two phases for myodifferentiation to proceed, under our culture conditions, the cells undergo a brief (12- to 24-hour) period of mitotic division followed by extensive, and relatively synchronous, cell fusion and, finally, myodifferentiation. We have found that X-irradiation of primary muscle cell suspensions (obtained from the hind limbs of 12-day-old chick embryos by trypsin dissociation) is an effective means of eliminating fibroblasts from late stage (72- to 96-hour) cultures. This procedure and a detailed description of myogenesis in this culture system have been reported previously (Friedlander *et al.*, 1978). The terms "myoblasts" or "prefusion myoblasts" here refer to mononucleated cells found in primary dissociated tissue suspensions or in monolayer for the first 24 hours of culture. "Myotubes" are multinucleated syncitia that arise from the fusion of myoblasts and represent differentiated muscle. Photomicrographs of embryonic chick muscle cultures at different stages of development are shown in Fig. 1.

A comprehensive understanding of the molecular events that occur at the surface of myogenic cells during the course of muscle differentiation will require a far better description of the chemical composition of the plasma membranes of the interacting cells than is currently available. Three general strategies have been used to approach this problem: (a) direct isolation of cell membranes followed by qualitative or quantitative analyses of proteins, lipids, or carbohydrates; (b) radiolabeling of externally exposed macromolecules using reagents that are restricted to the extracellular space, followed by the isolation or extraction of the relevant species; (c) the analysis of specific ligands at the cell surface with high-affinity probes to these macromolecules.

The first approach necessitates the purification of appropriate membranes and is often limited by the amounts of cellular material available. At best, current methods for the purification of plasma membrane from embryonic muscle provide an enrichment of 4- to 5-fold for specific membrane markers (Kent *et al.*, 1974) and are far from achieving the 20- to 40-fold enrichment considered satisfactory in other membrane systems (see Steck, 1974).

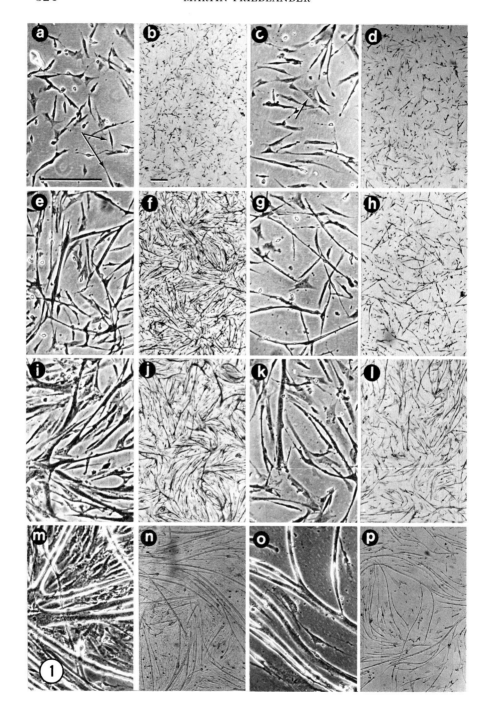

The second approach, which involves external labeling of tyrosine residues in proteins and proteolipids by lactoperoxidase-catalyzed radioiodination, followed by sodium dodecyl sulfate–polyacrylamide gel electrophoresis (SDS–PAGE), has led to the general conclusion that while subtle quantitative changes probably accompany myodifferentiation, there are no detectable qualitative alterations in membrane proteins of myogenic cells (Teng and Ingram, 1974; Kercsmar, 1976; Moss *et al.*, 1978; Cates and Holland, 1978; Pauw and David, 1979). Changes in the amount and distribution of fibronectin (LETS protein) have been demonstrated by iodination (Hynes *et al.*, 1976) and immunocytochemistry (Chen, 1977), but the significance of these changes to myodifferentiation is unclear.

Probes of cell surface ligands offer the most promise at this time, but, to date, have been limited to α-bungarotoxin for the acetylcholine receptor (Fischbach and Cohen, 1973; Sytkowski *et al.*, 1973; Devreotes *et al.*, 1977) and certain endogenous lectins or lectin-binding glycoproteins (Teichberg *et al.*, 1975; Kobiler *et al.*, 1978).

Studies of lipid content of muscle cell membranes reveal that phospholipid composition remains largely unaltered during myogenesis (Kent *et al.*, 1974), although viscosity (Prives and Shinitzky, 1977) and fatty acid composition appear to change significantly (Boland *et al.*, 1977). Carbohydrate analysis has demonstrated a decrease in sialic acid and hexosamines in differentiated muscle cells accompanied by the appearance of glucose–galactose–hydroxylysine units (Winand and Luzatti, 1975). Buckley-Ahrens *et al.* (1977) have noted the presence of glycosaminoglycans on the developing muscle cell surface. From their data they concluded that there are differences in the type or rate of glycosaminoglycan synthesis in myoblasts and myotubes. Another approach to the analysis of carbohydrate and sugar composition has been the application of various lectins to differentiating muscle cell cultures

---

FIG. 1. Phase contrast photomicrographs of developing muscle cultures at 24 (a–d), 39 (e–h), 50 (i–l), and 72 (m–p) hours *in vitro*. Cells were either plated directly following dissociation (a, b, e, f, i, j, m, and n) or first X-irradiated and then plated (c, d, g, h, k, l, o, and p). For each time point, cultures were photographed with 25× (first and third columns) and 10× (second and fourth columns) objective lenses with an inverted microscope. Primary cell suspensions consisted of 85–95% spindle-shaped myoblasts (arrows in a) and a smaller percentage of flattened pleiomorphic fibroblasts (arrow in c). While the use of such morphological critieria to distinguish myogenic from nonmyogenic cells is not absolute, it may be used to estimate relative proportions of cell types within a heterogeneous population (Lipton, 1977). The long calibration bar (a) = 50 μm, the short bar (b) = 30 μm. From Friedlander *et al.* (1978).

and the observation of the effects on myoblast fusion and development (Den *et al.*, 1975; Sandra *et al.*, 1977).

Our approach has been to couple immunological and chemical methods in an attempt to describe the alterations in antigenic specificities that accompany myogenesis (Friedlander, 1976). By using operationally defined, developmental stage specific antisera, we intend to isolate those molecules that may serve to distinguish muscle cells at different stages of development from one another, and from other embryonic and adult cell types. Since our work on antiserum to the prefusion myoblast has already been reported in detail (Friedlander and Fischman, 1977, 1979), it will only be summarized here. More recent data on preliminary immunochemical characterization of the antigens recognized by this antisera will also be described (Marton *et al.*, 1977). Our work with antiserum to well-differentiated myotubes has not been reported in detail elsewhere except in abstract form (Friedlander and Fischman, 1974, 1975) and, hence, will be described in greater detail in this chapter.

A. PREPARATION AND CHARACTERIZATION OF ANTISERA

1. Antiserum to the Prefusion Myoblast (Anti-M-24)

Antiserum to prefusion myoblasts from the embryonic chick hind limb has been prepared and characterized immunologically (Friedlander and Fischman, 1979). Cells from primary cultures of 12-day-old embryonic chick hind limb were enriched for mononucleated myogenic cells (Friedlander *et al.*, 1978) and injected into rabbits, and the resulting antisera were selectively absorbed to obtain serological specificity. Complement-mediated, ^{51}Cr-release cytotoxicity (Wigzell, 1965) and immunohistochemical (immunofluorescence and immunoperoxidase) assays were used to test the antiserum. For cytoxicity experiments, a constant amount of absorbed or unabsorbed antiserum was tested on a standard monolayer. For a detailed discussion of the ^{51}Cr-release assay, see Friedlander and Fischman (1979). Muscle tissue specificity was demonstrated by absorption of Anti-M-24 with freshly homogenized tissues, or acetone powders, of embryonic or adult chick heart, brain, retina, liver, erythrocytes, or skeletal muscle fibroblasts. Such absorption failed to remove all reactivity of Anti-M-24 for myogenic cells both before and after fusion and differentiation (Table I). Cytotoxicity experiments, with Anti-M-24 that had been quantitatively absorbed with various cultured embryonic chick cells, further confirmed the tissue specificity of this antiserum (Fig. 2). In addition, developmental stage specificity could be demonstrated. After absorption with well-

TABLE I[a]

Percentage of Cytotoxicity of Anti-M-24 for Embryonic Chick Cell Monolayers
after Absorption with Various Tissue Homogenates or Acetone Powders[b]

Absorbing tissue		Target cells			
		Myoblasts	Myotubes	Homologous cells used for absorption	Unabsorbed Anti-M-24 on absorbing tissue
Embryonic muscle	A[c]	1 ± 1	3 ± 2		92 ± 6
	H[d]	0	0		
Adult muscle	A	38 ± 2	58 ± 4	—	—
	H	57 ± 6	46 ± 3	—	—
Embryonic liver	A	43 ± 6	52 ± 6	2 ± 1	87 ± 6
	H	60 ± 8	45 ± 9	4 ± 2	
Adult liver	A	70 ± 8	80 ± 9	25 ± 2[e]	—
	H	62 ± 4	57 ± 7	33 ± 8[e]	—
Embryonic heart	A	64 ± 5	42 ± 6	10 ± 4	90 ± 6
Embryonic brain	A	70 ± 9	64 ± 4	2 ± 2	86 ± 8

[a] From Friedlander and Fischman (1979).
[b] See legend for Fig. 2 for details of the cytotoxicity assay.
[c] A, acetone powders.
[d] H, homogenized tissue.
[e] Tested on embryonic liver target cells.

differentiated myotubes, Anti-M-24 no longer reacted with differentiated myofibers, but did react with prefusion myoblasts (Fig. 2). Such absorbed antiserum could be used to label myoblasts selectively in mixed cultures also containing fibroblasts and myotubes.

The myoblast surface antigens detected with Anti-M-24 are components of the muscle cell membrane. Immunofluorescence studies demonstrate that these macromolecules are free to diffuse laterally within the myoblast membrane as evidenced by their capping and patching under appropriate physiological conditions. When intact monolayers of viable myoblasts are used to absorb the antiserum, reactivity of Anti-M-24 for myoblasts is completely removed. In the presence of complement, Anti-M-24 will induce lysis of the muscle cell membrane. In addition, the antigens are not loosely adsorbed culture medium components or an artifact of tissue culture because: (a) absorption of Anti-M-24 with homogenized muscle removed all antibodies to cultured myoblasts; (b) muscle cell surfaces will react with Anti-M-24 in vivo as observed in frozen sections of embryonic chick hind limbs (E. Bayne, unpublished observations); and (c) absorption of the antiserum

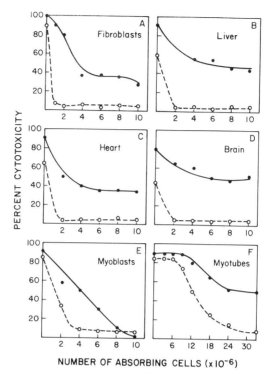

Fig. 2. Quantitative absorption of Anti-M-24 with increasing numbers of (A) embryonic chick fibroblasts, (B) hepatocytes, (C) cardiac myocytes, (D) brain cells, (E) skeletal myoblasts, or (F) skeletal myotubes. For each part except (E), the cytotoxicity, after absorption, of the antiserum for myoblast monolayers is represented by a solid line (●) and for homologous tissue used for absorption by a broken line (○). For (E), the solid line represents the cytotoxicity of Anti-M-24 for 24-hour-old muscle cell monolayers after absorption with muscle cells that had been grown in suspension culture for 4 hours. The broken line represents the same serum absorbed with cells from freshly dissociated hindlimb muscle tissue and then tested on myoblast monolayers. For cytotoxicity assays, cells were preloaded with ^{51}Cr for 12 hours, washed with basal medium, and then incubated with antibody and agar-washed guinea pig complement for 30–60 minutes. Percent cytotoxicity represents the amount of ^{51}Cr released from a microtiter well of cells in the presence of antibody and complement divided by the radioactivity released by detergent solubilization of a comparable cell culture. See Friedlander and Fischman (1979) for further details. From Friedlander and Fischman (1979).

with culture medium did not affect the titer of Anti-M-24 for myoblasts.

We have also obtained data on the protease and neuraminidase sensitivity of myoblast surface antigens (Friedlander and Fischman, 1977). In summary, it was found that trypsin-released muscle cells inhibited, on a per cell basis, the cytotoxicity of Anti-M-24 for 24-

hour-old myoblast monolayers more effectively than did identical cells that had received a 3- to 4-hour suspension culture recovery period from trypsinization. There was no such difference in absorptive capacities observed for any other embryonic chick tissue tested (e.g., brain, retina, liver, heart, and red blood cells) when freshly trypsinized cells were compared to ones that were given a 3- to 4-hour culture period. If freshly trypsinized muscle cells were treated with neuraminidase (30,000 IU/ml packed cells) or high concentrations (30,000 IU/0.1 ml packed cells) of trypsin, there was a selective loss of tissue-specific antigens. When single cells that had been in suspension culture for 3.5 hours were reexposed to low concentrations (10,000 IU/0.1 ml packed cells) of trypsin, more antigenic sites were revealed on their surfaces as detected by an increased absorptive capacity in removing myoblast-binding antibodies from Anti-M-24. This increase in antigen expression was time dependent and inversely related to the length of culture time after trypsinization. Immunofluorescence studies revealed that tissue-specific muscle surface antigens were present both on muscle cells that were freshly dissociated and on those that had been in suspension culture for 3–4 hours. Furthermore, freshly trypsinized myoblasts possessed cell surface components that were highly antigenic; antiserum to such cells reacted extensively with both trypsinized and recovered muscle cells as detected by cytotoxicity assays and immunofluorescence.

From the studies previously reviewed, we have concluded that myoblasts and myotubes possess externally exposed antigens that are undetected on other embryonic and adult chick tissues. In addition, myoblasts exhibit surface determinants that are either masked, absent, or present in very low concentrations on skeletal muscle fibroblasts, embryonic myotubes, or adult myofibers. These antigens are free to diffuse laterally within the myoblast membrane and may be selectively removed by neuraminidase or high concentrations of trypsin. Such macromolecules may be progressively masked, with increasing time of culture after protease dissociation, by molecules that are sensitive to low concentrations of trypsin.

Recently, we have attempted immunochemical isolation and identification of those cell surface antigens that serve to distinguish the prefusion myoblast from other embryonic chick tissue serologically.[1] Single cells from limb muscle of 12-day-old embryonic chicks were radioiodinated by lactoperoxidase in suspension culture (Hubbard and

[1] This work was performed in collaboration with Drs. Linda Marton and Deneys van der Westhuyzen.

Cohn, 1972; Hynes *et al.*, 1976), incubated with antiserum, and subsequently extracted with nonionic detergent. The labeled antigen–antibody complexes were precipitated with formalin-fixed *Staphylococcus aureus,* Type A, Cowan Strain I (Kessler, 1976), which possesses a surface protein that binds strongly and specifically to the Fc region of many mammalian IgG subclasses (Kronvall *et al.*, 1970). This bacterial reagent is an attractive substitute for the second antibody frequently used for indirect immunoprecipitation.

Polypeptide subunits of iodinated proteins in the immune complexes were displayed by SDS–PAGE. Anti-M-24 complexed with a large spectrum of labeled molecules including a major group of

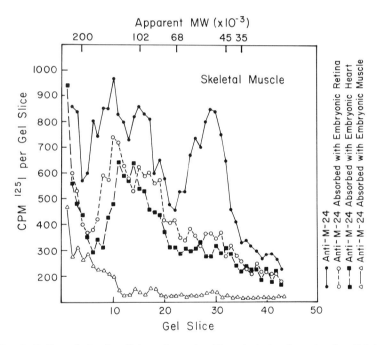

FIG. 3. Sodium dodecyl sulfate–polyacrylamide gel electrophoresis of radiolabeled embryonic chick skeletal myoblast components immunoprecipitated by Anti-M-24 (●—●) or Anti-M-24 absorbed with embryonic retina (○---○), heart (■—■), or muscle (△—△). Suspensions of prefusion myoblasts cultured for 3–4 hours were radiolabeled with ¹²⁵I using lactoperoxidase, incubated with preimmune or immune serum, detergent solubilized, and treated with fixed Staph A; the resultant immunoprecipitates were electrophoresed on SDS–polyacrylamide gels containing 6 *M* urea. Gels were sliced into 2-mm sections and fractions were analyzed for radioactivity. Apparent molecular weights were estimated from parallel gels of protein standards (myosin heavy chain, β-actinin, bovine serum albumin, actin, and tropomyosin).

polypeptides between 35,000 and 70,000 daltons and a number of polypeptides greater than 80,000 daltons (Fig. 3). Very low amounts of radiolabeled material were detected on gels in parallel control experiments using preimmune serum. Absorption of Anti-M-24 with homogenized chick muscle eliminated all reactivity of the serum with myoblast surface molecules (Fig. 3), while absorption with other embryonic chick tissues (heart, liver, or retina) specifically removed reactivity for the low-molecular-weight components (Fig. 3). A similar spectrum of radiolabeled antigens was detected in embryonic chick heart and retina cells with Anti-M-24, but all reactivity was removed by absorption with homologous tissue homogenates (Fig. 4).

To confirm that the iodinated proteins were surface components and not the result of heavy internal labeling of a small percentage of damaged cells, the procedure was carried out using (a) a damaged cell preparation that had been kept on ice for 24 hours before radioiodination and contained 50% nonviable cells as judged by trypan blue exclusion and (b) a cellular homogenate. With both preparations the total incorporation of iodine was increased as were the total counts isolated

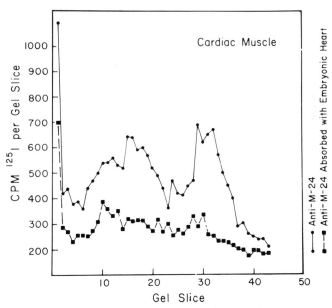

FIG. 4. SDS–PAGE of radiolabeled embryonic chick cardiac myocyte components immunoprecipitated by Anti-M-24 (●—●) or Anti-M-24 absorbed with embryonic heart (■—■). See text and legend for Fig. 3 for further details.

for both Anti-M-24 and preimmune sera. Qualitatively, the electrophoretic patterns of the isolated components changed significantly. The relative proportions of the main fractions were altered and most noticeable was the appearance of a major peak of molecular weight 30,000. It would seem that damage to the cells increased the number of available sites for iodination, increased the accessibility of intracellular antigens, and released substances causing nonspecific aggregation of immunoglobulin. These results support the original presumption that cell surface components were preferentially isolated when intact viable cells were used during the iodination procedure.

To exclude the possibility that precipitated components were horse serum proteins of the culture medium that might have been absorbed to the cell surface, parallel experiments were performed using myoblasts that had never been exposed to horse serum. The electrophoretic patterns of material precipitated from these cells were identical to those from cells cultured by the method previously described in the presence of horse serum for 2.5 hours. It should also be noted that for the absorption experiments previously described, horse serum (10%) was always present and presumably would have absorbed most, if not all, antibodies directed against its components.

The use of Anti-M-24 and indirect Staph A precipitation has permitted the preliminary identification of high-molecular-weight muscle surface proteins which may be those antigens previously identified as muscle specific by immunohistochemical and cytotoxicity techniques. In order to confirm that the muscle surface components detected here are the tissue-specific antigens of the earlier experiments it will be necessary to elute antibody from the high-molecular-weight muscle proteins and show that it has the same immunohistochemical and cytotoxicity properties as Anti-M-24.

2. Antiserum to Myotubes (Anti-M-96X)

Early studies (Friedlander and Fischman, 1974) using an antiserum prepared in rabbits immunized with 144-hour-old cultures of embryonic chick muscle (Anti-M-144) failed to reveal any tissue or developmental stage specificity of that antiserum for well-differentiated myofibers. While absorption of Anti-M-144 with homogenized retina or brain tissue reduced the cytotoxicity of this serum on 144-hour-old muscle cultures by only 20–25% of preabsorption levels, absorption with myotubes, cardiac myocytes, myoblasts, hepatocytes, or red blood cells removed all cytotoxicity. We initially suggested that these data may indicate loss or reduction in quantity of unique skeletal muscle antigenic surface components with progressive differentiation (Friedlander and Fischman, 1974) and the acquisition (or retention) of serologically detectable characteristics shared by other tissues of mesodermal, but not ectodermal, origin (Goldschneider and Moscona, 1972).

While plausible, these findings are a bit surprising in view of the fact that with progressive differentiation, myotubes acquire specific surface characteristics such as synaptic basal lamina antigens (Sanes and Hall, 1979) and acetylcholine receptors (Fambrough and Rash, 1971; Smilowitz and Fischbach, 1978), which may be absent or only poorly detectable in myoblasts and other embryonic tissues. Since myotubes are known to develop a characteristic surface glycocalyx *in vitro* (Shimada *et al.*, 1967; also see Bischoff, 1978, pp. 161–167), we considered that the sarcolemmal structure may serve to mask certain protein-binding sites (antigens) or otherwise interfere with the relative immunogenicity of surface macromolecules characteristic of the mature, or postfusion muscle membrane.

The concept of immunodominance among a vast array of potential immunogens is not without precedent; Staines (1974) has suggested that the bioarchitectural state of surface antigens might influence antigen-processing mechanisms. Thus, we decided to use younger muscle cultures which were relatively free of fusing myoblasts and mononucleated nonmyogenic cells. Rabbits were immunized with 96-hour-old myotube cultures which had been differentially adhered and

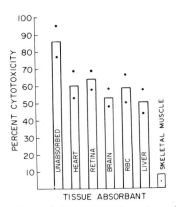

FIG. 5. Anti-M-96X unabsorbed (left most column) or absorbed with selected embryonic tissues (as indicated in each column), and tested in the presence of complement for cytotoxicity on 96-hour muscle cultures. Anti-M-96X was bulk absorbed, diluted one-tenth, and tested on 96-hour muscle cultures. Preimmune serum induced less than 10% of maximum release values and the results indicated for experimental release were identical for both irradiated and nonirradiated cultures. RBC, red blood cells. Points above and below each bar indicate the range of one standard deviation from the mean.

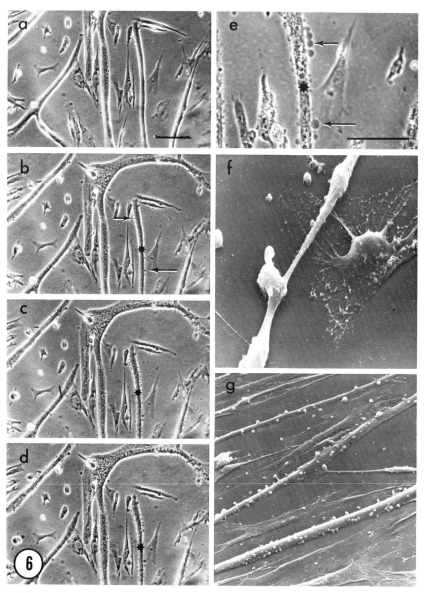

FIG. 6. Phase contrast (a–e) or scanning electron (f and g) micrographs of 96-hour muscle cultures, exposed to Anti-M-96X absorbed with homogenized embryonic heart tissue. In the absence of complement (a) both elongated myotubes and flattened fibroblasts appeared normal. Within 10 minutes of the addition of complement (b), surface blebbing (small arrows) characteristic of antibody complement-mediated cytotoxicity became apparent. Only myotubes (asterisk) were affected, even as long as 30 (c) or 60 (d and g) minutes. By 2 hours, most myotubes had lysed and retracted off the substratum, but several remained attached, exhibiting extensive surface herniations (e and f). Most fibroblasts remained unaffected, but an occasional cell underwent retraction (e and f).

irradiated to enrich for myotubes (Friedlander *et al.*, 1978). The antiserum obtained from these rabbits is referred to as Anti-M-96X.

When 96-hour-old muscle cultures were exposed to Anti-M-96X absorbed with homogenized embryonic heart, retina, brain, liver, or red blood cells, the cytotoxicity of this serum for myotubes was reduced by only 35–50% of preabsorbed levels (Fig. 5). Cytolytic lesions were observed within the first 30 minutes of incubation with antibody and complement only on multinucleated myotubes (Fig. 6a–d, g) and myoblasts, although with time (incubations greater than 60 minutes) fibroblasts also become affected (Fig. 6f). However, this antiserum was no longer cytotoxic for homologous tissue with which it had been absorbed. These observations suggest that Anti-M-96X contained a class(es) of antibodies which, after appropriate absorption, reacted only with cells found in cultures of prefusion myoblasts or differentiated myotubes and not with the other embryonic chick tissues tested.

Quantitative absorption of Anti-M-96X with increasing numbers of pure fibroblasts or heterologous prefusion muscle cultures (which also contained approximately 20% fibroblasts) demonstrated that there was not only tissue specificity, but probably quantitative differences in developmental stage specificity as well. Absorption of Anti-M-96X with 8×10^5 fibroblasts reduced cytotoxicity of this serum to 30% of unabsorbed levels for fibroblast cultures, yet retained 70–75% cytotoxicity for 24-hour-old myoblast or 96-hour-old myotube cultures (Fig. 7). This would suggest that Anti-M-96X specifically detects antigens present at the surface of myogenic cells, but not on the fibroblast cell surface. Operationally defined stage specificity of this serum is also suggested by experiments in which absorption with 35×10^5 cells of myoblast cultures reduced cytotoxicity for myotubes by only 50% whereas this same serum lost all cytotoxic effects for prefusion myoblast or fibroblast monolayers (Fig. 8).

While we have concluded that myoblasts possess antigenic determinants at the cell surface that serve to distinguish these cells from myotubes and other tissues of the chick embryo, it is not clear whether such molecules are unique qualitatively or quantitatively. We have suggested that these "myoblast-specific" antigens may also be present at the surface of myotubes or fibroblasts derived from skeletal muscle, but either in a masked form (Friedlander and Fischman, 1977) or in very low concentrations (Friedlander and Fischman, 1979). Cell sur-

---

Whether these cells were really fibroblasts, or mononucleated myogenic cells that do not conform to general morphological criteria is unclear. Short calibration bar (a–d) = 100 μm; long bar (e–g) = 100 μm.

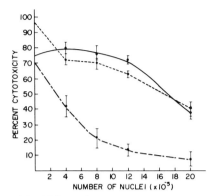

Fɪɢ. 7. Cytotoxicity of Anti-M-96X for 96- or 24-hour-old skeletal muscle or fibroblast monolayers after absorption of the antiserum with increasing numbers of fibroblasts. Skeletal muscle fibroblasts were used to absorb a 1/100 dilution of Anti-M-96X and this serum was then tested on 96-hour-old muscle (————), 24-hour-old muscle (- - - - -), or pure fibroblast (- —- - —) monolayers.

face mosaics that are tissue or developmental stage specific may be displayed through the preferential masking or unmasking of various antigenic sites during progressive differentiation (Bennett *et al.,* 1972; Singer, 1976). Such tissue-specific macromolecular arrangements of common surface molecules may serve to distinguish one cell type from another, and thus form the basis for selective cell association during

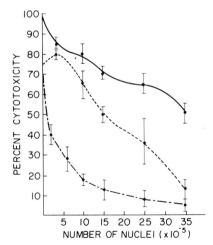

Fɪɢ. 8. Increasing numbers of cells obtained from 24-hour-old skeletal muscle cultures were used to absorb a 1/100 dilution of Anti-M-96X and this serum was then tested on 96-hour-old muscle (————), 24-hour-old muscle (— — — —), or pure fibroblast (- —- - —) monolayers.

development. Certainly, subtle quantitative differences could also serve such a role. The results presented above rest largely on data obtained from cytotoxicity experiments. Absorption procedures and the ^{51}Cr-release assay are subject to complications that have not been discussed in great detail in this chapter. For a more critical discussion of these techniques, the reader is referred to Friedlander and Fischman (1979).

3. The Use of Monoclonal Antibodies

The use of xenogeneic antisera is one approach to the identification of developmental stage or tissue-specific cell surface markers. There are obvious reservations in using such an approach. For example, relatively low amounts of antibodies directed against the molecules of interest may result if the antigen is "dominated" immunologically by other surface components that are either more antigenic or present in greater quantities. It is not clear whether higher titers of myoblast-specific antisera could be obtained if the animals are immunized with a less complex array of cell surface antigens. Work with antisera to embryonic chick myocardial cells has demonstrated that tissue specificity for heart cells in xenogeneic antisera becomes apparent only at high concentrations of such sera (Holoday and Fischman, 1977). One obvious way to circumvent this problem is the use of hybridoma technology in the production of monoclonal antibodies to specific cell surface determinants.

The production of monoclonal antibodies is discussed in great detail elsewhere in this series (Milstein and Lennox, this volume). Large amounts of antibodies specific for relatively weak immunogens within a complex antigenic array of macromolecules may be produced using this method. Providing that the screening method is sufficiently sensitive and specific, antibodies to antigens present in very small amounts may be detected. While there have been no full reports as yet on the application of this method to the study of myogenesis, several preliminary reports have demonstrated the feasibility of such an approach. Coupled with the use of muscle cell lines defective at one developmental stage or another, this may prove to be a very powerful tool in the analysis of those membrane components involved in cell–cell recognition or fusion during myogenesis. Apparently, muscle cells are good immunogens since several laboratories have reported a high incidence (30–40%) of positive clones producing antibodies that bind to the muscle cell surface (Gottlieb and Greve, 1978; Lee and Kaufman, 1979; Grove and Stockdale, 1979; T. Easton and G. Migliolisi, personal communication; E. Bayne and D. M. Fambrough, personal communication). Whether such antibodies will identify specific macromolecules of developmental significance remains to be seen, but at least one group has reported the presence of myoblast-specific antigens that are almost totally absent on myotubes and a developmentally defective, nonfusing subclone of L8 rat myoblasts (Lee and Kaufman, 1979). Myogenic cell-specific monoclonal antibodies that detect developmentally regulated cell surface antigens have also been reported (Grove and Stockdale, 1979).

B. MYOGENESIS IN SUSPENSION CULTURE

The studies of *in vitro* myogenesis reviewed previously utilize monolayer cultures of embryonic tissue. Since myogenesis in such cultures faithfully mimics *in vivo* myogenesis (Shimada *et al.*, 1967), we have assumed that surface molecules important in facilitating cell–cell recognition during myogenesis will be present at the cell surface and available to immunological analysis. Monolayer cultures, however, do differ from the *in vivo* environment in several respects: (*a*) the three-dimensional component of *in vivo* tissue is absent; (*b*) extensive branching of myotubes is observed, probably as a result of the two-dimensional nature of monolayer growth; and (*c*) a collagen sub-stratum is necessary for extensive myoblast fusion and myofibril-logenisis. Rotary suspension culture (Moscona, 1973) permits tissue reconstruction from monodispersed cells and results in a very close approximation to the three-dimensional tissue cytoarchitecture seen *in vivo*. Since we have used cells placed in suspension culture for varying periods of time as tissue absorbants in the experiments previously cited, we were concerned whether myoblasts can differentiate under such culture conditions. In considering the rotary suspension culture system, we felt that several problems in muscle development might be amenable to analysis not readily afforded by the monolayer system. For example, what are the extracellular factors, if any, that may influence the establishment of cellular polarity during myoblast fusion, myotube elongation, and longitudinal orientation of myofibrils? Would his-tiotypic cell sorting be observed during cocultivation of the various cell types obtained from trypsin-dissociated embryonic hindlimb muscle and, if so, would such segregation of the myogenic cell population in-crease the myoblast–myoblast encounters and thus result in more ex-tensive or synchronous cell fusion? Is a preformed collagen substratum in monolayer cultures an absolute requirement for myodifferentiation or can cellular components of the culture provide the necessary secre-tory products? If fusion is observed in suspension cultures, will the re-sultant myotubes be elongated or rounded? While it is not certain that

all these questions may be answered by studying myogenesis in suspension culture instead of monolayers, several interesting conclusions
may be reached based on some preliminary experiments utilizing this
system. In the context of the theme for this volume of "Current Topics
in Developmental Biology," I would like to present data that will illustrate the usefullness of immunological probes in the visualization of
three-dimensional components of muscle cell aggregates. Earlier studies on myogenesis in suspension culture have been reported (Knudson
and Horwitz, 1977; Friedlander, 1978).

Single cell suspensions of freshly trypsinized or suspension-
cultured (for 3–4 hours) myocytes were treated with heat-inactivated
Anti-M-24 or Anti-M-96X, stained with fluorescein-conjugated goat
anti-rabbit serum (GAR-FITC) and observed under fluorescent optics.
For suspension culture, $5–8 \times 10^6$ cells were placed in 3–5 ml of Eagle's
basal medium with glutamine, penicillin–streptomycin, and 10% horse
serum and rotated at 70 rpm in 25-ml Ehrlenmeyer flasks in a
Brunswick gyratory shaker bath heated to 37°C. After fluorescent
antibody staining, single cells exhibited patching and capping of surface antigens when treated under appropriate conditions (see Friedlander and Fischman, 1977, 1979 for more extensive discussion). If
cells were fixed prior to antibody treatment, uniform surface fluorescence was observed. More interestingly, when multicellular aggregates
were fixed with hot (50°C for 10 minutes) paraformaldehyde (2.0% in
phosphate-buffered saline) and then treated with antisera and GAR-
FITC, individual cells would be visualized within the aggregates under
fluorescence optics. Within 3–4 hours of culture, multicellular aggregates were observed, and by 12 hours contained many round single
cells that stained evenly along their entire surface (Fig. 9a–c). By 24
hours, elongate structures resembling myotubes were observed parallel to one another within the aggregates (Fig. 9d–g). These structures
often extended the entire width of an aggregate. Thus, by using appropriate fixation conditions and immunofluorescence, it is possible to observe three-dimensional intercellular arrangements within such
aggregates.

Ultrastructural observations revealed that the elongate structures
seen by immunofluorescence were multinucleated syncitia characteristic of developing skeletal muscle (Fig. 10). Extensive myofibril-
logenesis was apparent by 36 hours and closely resembled that seen *in
vivo;* hexagonal arrays of thick and thin filaments were distributed
throughout the sarcoplasm concomitant with the appearance of sarcoplasmic reticulum and t-tubules. Ribosomes were frequently observed
along single filaments and the outer membranes of closely apposed

340   MARTIN FRIEDLANDER

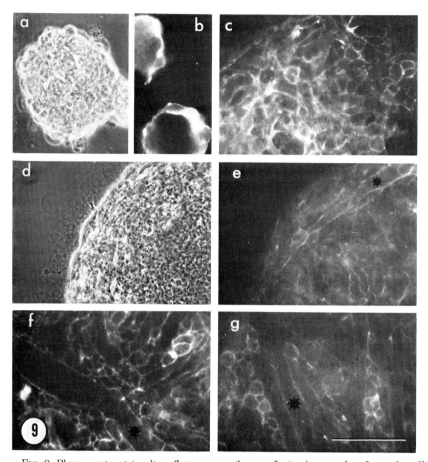

Fig. 9. Phase contrast (a, d) or fluorescence (b, c, e, f, g) micrographs of muscle cell aggregates. Primary chick hindlimb muscle cells were placed in rotary suspension culture for varying periods of time, and then incubated in Anti-M-24 absorbed with embryonic chick brain or Anti-M-96X absorbed with embryonic chick heart, followed by GAR-FITC. Unfixed 12-hour-old aggregates (a, b) exhibited uniform fluorescence around their perimeter after antibody treatment (b). However, if aggregates were first fixed with warm (56°C) paraformaldehyde for 10–30 minutes, and then stained with antibody and GAR-FITC, individual cells within the aggregates could be visualized. Using such a procedure, it was possible to determine rapidly that at 12 hours the aggregates consisted primarily of single rounded cells (c). By 24 hours elongated structures resembling myotubes (asterisk) became apparent (e). The identical aggregate viewed by phase contrast optics exhibited no cellular substructure (d). By 36 hours (f) and 48 hours (g) extensive myogenesis was evident and the relative number of small, rounded cells had dramatically decreased. Calibration bar = 10μm.

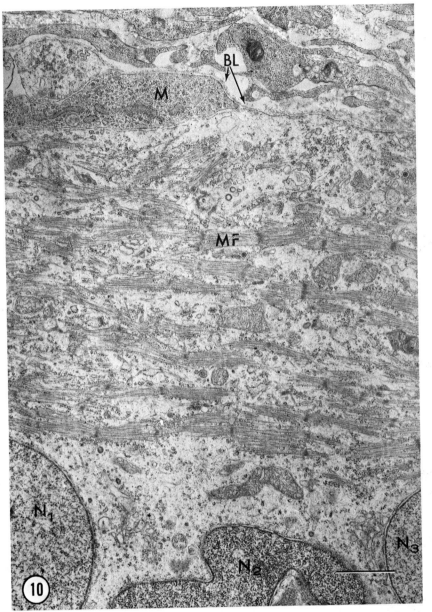

FIG. 10. Thin-section image of a 36-hour-old muscle cell aggregate demonstrating the appearance of myofibrils (MF) within a multinucleated myotube. Examination of this field under low power revealed the presence of at least six nuclei and a longitudinal orientation (vs a "myoball"-like structure) of the myotube. Note the presence of a myoblast-like cell (M) under the basal lamina (BL) of the myotube. N, nucleus. Calibration bar = 0.1 μm.

nuclear envelopes were often fused. A characteristic basal lamina appeared on the surface of myotubes and an occasional mononucleated cell would be observed beneath this glycocalyx (Fig. 10). Mononucleated fibroblast-like cells containing heterochromatic nuclei, extensive rough endoplasmic reticulum, and associated extracellular collagen-like fibrils were found on the periphery of the aggregates. Suspension culture may be the system of choice for studying the effects of myoblast-specific antibodies on myogenesis. A common problem in applying bivalent antibodies to cells in monolayer cultures is that the cells retract and lift off the substratum when the antiserum is added (Wylie et al., 1979). In suspension cultures, the cells are rounded to begin with and not attached to a flat substratum. Thus, the biological effects of antibodies on developing tissues in culture may be assessed more directly. Such approaches have been explored in the study of cell–cell interactions in retinal cell aggregates (Hausman and Moscona, 1979).

The study of myogenesis in suspension culture warrants further study. Myogenesis in such a system is precocious, relative to that seen in monolayer, and it may be concluded that myofibril assembly and the longitudinal orientation of sarcomeres are inherent properties of the myogenic developmental program that do not require an oriented substratum or embryo extract to be expressed.

III. Immunological Approaches to the Study of Intercellular Communication

The molecular basis for cell–cell recognition may rest solely on cell surface displays of specific molecules or macromolecular mosaics (Moscona, 1974; Edelman, 1976). Another possible mechanism may be one that establishes intercellular communication by direct, nonspecific cell–cell contacts which permit the transfer of low-molecular-weight substances between cells. It has been suggested that such a passage of molecules or ions through low-resistance channels in the cell membrane can occur via gap junctions, resulting in electrotonic coupling and/or metabolic cooperation between adjacent cells (Cox et al., 1970; Pitts, 1971; Johnson and Sheridan, 1971; Revel et al., 1971). While the data thus far accumulated are not unequivocal, there is a high index of association between the incidence of gap junctions, electrical coupling, and the transfer of low-molecular-weight dyes between cells that form selective associations with one another (Gilula et al., 1972; Azarnia et al., 1972). The potential role for gap junctions in the modulation of cell interactions during development (see Sheridan, 1976) has been reported in studies of amphibian neurulation (Decker and Friend, 1974), *in vivo* and *in vitro* myogenesis (Blackshaw and Warner, 1976; Rash and Fambrough, 1973; Kalderon *et al.*, 1977), preovulatory follicular development (Gilula *et al.*, 1978), and early mouse embryogenesis (Ginzberg and Gilula, 1979; Lo and Gilula, 1979). While it is easy to understand why such low-resistance pathways should exist between electrically excitable tissues such as nerve (Furshpan and Potter, 1959) or myocardium (Dewey and Barr, 1962), the presence of such a structure, with its associated physiological properties, in nonexcitable tissues is intriguing and may represent a mechanism for cell–cell transfer of information (see Furshpan and Potter, 1968; Gilula, 1977a,b; Lawrence *et al.*, 1978; Pitts, 1977; Loewenstein, 1979).

Recently, considerable effort has been directed toward the isolation of gap junctions with the rationale that a better understanding of junction structure and biochemistry would provide the basis for understanding membrane components involved in informational transfer. The identification and isolation of such macromolecules would also be interesting in the context of examining cell membrane protein synthesis and turnover: do junctions form *de novo* via direct membrane insertion of newly synthesized proteins, or is there a pool of preformed subunits in the membrane that aggregate under appropriate conditions to form the junctional complex? This question will have to be answered before we can understand the role of gap junctions in modulating intercellular communication. Since junctions, at present, are identifiable only on morphological criteria, it will be necessary to develop probes that specifically identify gap junction subunits. This approach is not simple; gap junctions have no known associated enzymatic activity and do not specifically bind to any lectins or other commonly used probes. For this, an antibody specific for the gap junction would be an invaluable tool in the investigation of gap junction biogenesis and physiology. Clearly, such a probe could also be useful in analyzing the biological properties associated with the presence or absence of gap junctions in developing (and other) systems.

A. GAP JUNCTION ISOLATION AND CHARACTERIZATION

The isolation and characterization of gap junctions has proven difficult due to the extremely hydrophobic nature and protease sensitivity of the component polypeptides. In spite of this, a vast literature has accumulated, replete with controversy (Benedetti and Emmelot, 1968; Goodenough and Stoeckenius, 1972; Evans and Gurd, 1972; Duguid and Revel, 1975; Goodenough, 1976; Culvenor and Evans, 1977; Ehrhard and Chauveau, 1977; Hertzberg and Gilula, 1979; Henderson *et al.*, 1979; Finbow *et al.*, 1980).

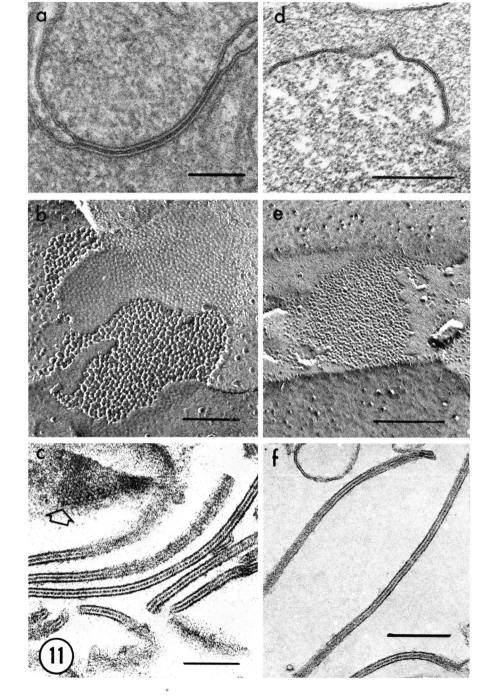

The most recent data on gap junctions isolated from mouse, rat, and bovine liver indicate that the major subunit is a nonglycosylated polypeptide of 25,000–27,000 MW. These polypeptide subunits are arranged into a polygonal lattice which exhibits a high degree of stability to exogenously induced alterations in the protein components (Hertzberg and Gilula, 1979; Henderson et al., 1979). In negatively stained electron microscopic images, the junctions appear as septalaminar structures. En face profiles reveal plaques of gap junctions containing particles of 8.5 nm diameter with 9.0 nm center-to-center spacing. A central circular electron-dense 1.5- to 2.0-nm region is observed in the junctional subunits (Fig. 11).

Despite these advances, there are several disadvantages to working with the liver system as a source of gap junctions: (a) extremely low yields (30- to 150-μg junctions from 500-g wet weight livers) are the norm; (b) hepatocytes contain many endogenous proteases that may result in uncontrolled proteolysis; (c) gap junctions represent a relatively small proportion of the total membrane components and, during the isolation procedures, are closely associated with contaminating material such as collagen and other components of the extracellular matrix. Our early efforts to prepare antibodies to rat liver gap junctions resulted in antisera of ambiguous specificity. It is not clear whether this was due to the relatively poor immunogenicity of so ubiquitous a membrane component or to the low amounts of antigen available for use in immunization. For these and other reasons we turned to another tissue as a potential source for gap junction antigens.

B. INTERCELLULAR JUNCTIONS OF THE LENS

Over 20 years ago electron microscopic studies of the vertebrate lens demonstrated the presence of extensive junctional regions at the surface of lens epithelial cells (Wanko and Gavin, 1958). These junctions appeared pentalaminar and, as such, were classified as tight junc-

FIG. 11. Electron micrographs of liver (a–c) and lens (d–f) gap junctions. Thin sections of mouse liver (a) or calf lens (d) reveal septalaminar or pentalaminar profiles, respectively. In freeze-fracture images, mouse liver gap junction plaques (b) form a closely packed lattice of uniform particles while those observed in calf lenses (e) are loosely packed arrays of variably sized particles. Enriched gap junction fractions may be isolated from rat liver (c) or calf lens (f) and visualized in thin sections following fixation and treatment with tannic acid. In (c), note the periodic striations in cross-sections while in oblique sections a polygonal lattice of particles with centrally located electron dense dots is visible (arrow). Parts (a) and (b) are reprinted, with permission of the publisher, from Gilula (1976). Part (c) is reprinted, with permission of the publisher, from Hertzberg and Gilula (1979). The calibration bars = 0.1 μm.

tions. Since that time, and with the advent of higher resolution electron microscopy, better fixation and staining procedures, and freeze-fracture technology, many of these structures appear to resemble gap junctions more closely (Leeson, 1971; Bloemendal *et al.*, 1972; Nonaka *et al.*, 1976; Goodenough *et al.*, 1978). By morphological and biochemical criteria, they appear to be slightly different from gap junctions described in other tissues (Fig. 11). For example, the packing of subunit particles is less ordered, there is heterogeneity in particle size, and the appearance in thin sections is a pentalaminar instead of the usual septalaminar structure (see Goodenough *et al.*, 1978). The solubility properties also differ from those of liver gap junctions (Dunia *et al.*, 1974). Such differences may reflect the unusual physiological state of the lens (Rae, 1979) or a genuine biochemical structural dissimilarity between the junctions of the lens and those seen elsewhere. The junctions cover a significant area of the lens cell surface, as measured in freeze-fracture images, and may be separated from the nonjunctional regions of the membrane by urea and detergent treatment. For recent reviews of lens junction structure see Goodenough (1979) and Maisel *et al.* (1980).

The lens is a relatively "clean" system to work with for those investigators interested in obtaining large amounts of cell membranes and associated junctions; the cytoplasm is largely devoid of organelles and the predominant proteins are the crystallins, conveniently soluble in low-ionic strength buffers (see Bloemendal, 1977). A highly enriched membrane fraction may be isolated following simple tissue homogenization, salt extraction of the crystallins, urea extraction of peripheral membrane proteins, and sucrose density gradient centrifugation. When these membranes are solubilized in sodium dodecyl sulfate, a relatively simple gel profile is obtained in which nearly half of the Coomassie stained protein is in a single band of 25,000–26,000 apparent molecular weight (Fig. 12). Other major bands are one membrane protein of 34,000 MW and several residual crystallins. There is an extensive literature on the immunochemistry (Alcala and Maisel, 1978; Broekhuyse *et al.*, 1979) and biochemistry of lens cell crystallins and membrane proteins (Alcala *et al.*, 1975, 1977; Broekhuyse and Kuhlmann, 1978; Goodenough, 1979; Horwitz and Wong, 1980). A recent monograph summarizes the more interesting biological and biochemical features of this system (Bloemendal, 1980).

For the purposes of this chapter, I will focus only on work from our own laboratory that emphasizes the relationship between the 25,000- to 26,000-MW component (MP26) and the membrane fraction enriched for lens cell junctions. This discussion will focus on the immunochemistry of the MP26 polypeptide and the use of two-dimensional im-

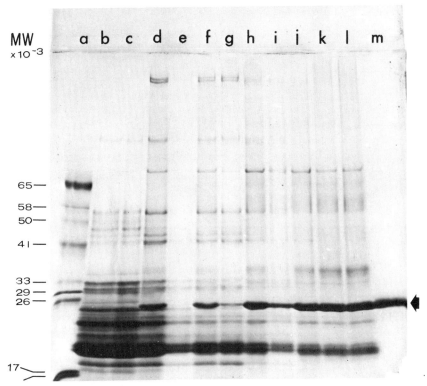

FIG. 12. SDS–PAGE analysis of fractions obtained during the isolation of calf lens membranes. Samples were prepared for electrophoresis by heating at 100°C for 1–2 minutes in 50 mM Na$_2$CO$_3$, 50 mM dithiothreitol, and 2.0% SDS. After solubilization, samples were alkylated with iodoacetamide and 50–100 μl volumes were loaded onto 1.2-mm-thick 7.5–15% gradient gels prepared by the method of Laemmli and Favre (1973). (a) Molecular weight standard proteins: bovine serum albumin (68,000); catalase (58,000); rabbit IgG heavy chain (50,000); ovalbumin (44,000); uricase (33,000); carbonic anhydrase (29,000); chymotrypsinogen (26,000); myoglobin (17,000). (b) Whole lens homogenate (85 μg protein). (c) 1.0 mM Na$_2$CO$_3$, 5.0 mM EDTA supernatant fraction (75 μg protein). (d) Same buffer as (c), pellet (60 μg protein). (e) 5.0 mM Tris–HCl, 1.0 mM EDTA, 1.0 mM CaCl supernatant fraction (40 μg protein). (f) Same buffer as (e), pellet (50 μg protein). (g) 4 M urea, supernatant fraction (40 μg protein). (h) 4 M urea, pellet (40 μg protein). (i) 7 M urea, supernatant fraction (35 μg protein). (j) 7 M urea, pellet (35 μg protein). (k) Membrane fraction obtained from sucrose gradient centrifugation (35 μg protein). (l) Same as (k). (m) MP26 after electroelution and reelectrophoresis (15 μg protein). For all fractions, supernatants were discarded and pellets were carried through to the next step of the membrane isolation procedure.

munoelectrophoresis to examine its cross-reactivity with other lens proteins. It should again be emphasized that the junctional structures of the lens may differ from those described for gap junctions of other tissues. Whether these junctions, in fact, provide the structural basis for the electrical coupling observed between lens fibers (Rae, 1979) remains to be confirmed. We felt, however, that there were enough similarities to typical gap junctions that the development of antibodies to lens junctional polypeptides may provide immunological probes that are also reactive with gap junctions in other tissues. At the very least, MP26 is the major developmentally regulated integral membrane protein of the lens and, as such, may provide information concerning the general phenomena of membrane protein synthesis, assembly, and turnover.

C. Immunochemistry of the Major Intrinsic Membrane Protein (MP26)[2] of the Lens

Antisera have been prepared against a urea-washed membrane fraction of calf lens (Anti-mb) and purified, SDS-denatured major intrinsic protein of the lens membrane (Anti-26K). The purpose of this discussion is to (a) demonstrate the specificity of Anti-26K for MP26 as assessed by immunodiffusion (ID) and two-dimensional rocket immunoelectrophoresis (2D-IEP); (b) discuss the relationship between MP26, other membrane proteins, and junctions of the lens; and (c) emphasize the usefulness of preparative gel electrophoresis and antimembrane protein antisera in the examination of cell–cell interactions.

The isolation of lens cell membranes and associated junctional regions is discussed in detail by Goodenough (1979) and will not be reviewed here. It should, however, be emphasized that it is possible to obtain very large yields of relatively pure junction-enriched membrane regions that, when examined by SDS–PAGE, consist predominantly of one polypeptide with only a few other associated proteins (Fig. 12). In fact, it is possible to obtain 30–40 mg of total membrane protein from just 50 calf lens (70–80 g, wet weight). Since over half of the lens membrane protein appears as a single band on SDS gels of 25,500 apparent molecular weight, 15 mg of MP26 polypeptide may be obtained from a single preparation. Membranes were solubilized in SDS and bicarbonate, reduced and alkylated, and electrophoresed on preparative (2 mm × 22 cm × 33 cm) 10% acrylamide gels. For antigen isolation,

[2] Using methods described by Weber and Osborn (1969), I have calculated the apparent molecular weight of this polypeptide to be 25,500. This differs from previously reported values of 26,000–27,000 (Alcala et al., 1975; Broekhuyse and Kuhlmann, 1978). For the sake of consistency with the literature, I will refer to the major intrinsic protein of the lens membrane as MP26.

2-cm-wide strips were removed from each preparative gel with a serrated pizza cutter, stained with Coomassie Blue, destained, and realigned with the original gel to permit removal of single bands that contained as much as 3–4 mg of a single polypeptide. This was accomplished with a high degree of accuracy by careful realignment of the stained edge and unstained gel over a piece of gridded graph paper and a light box. A straight pizza cutter permitted accurate strip slicing. I consistently obtained much greater yields of purified polypeptide by electroelution (see Lazarides, 1976, for description of electroelution) of unfixed gel strips compared with strips that had been fixed by staining. Electroelution for 24–36 hours provided quantities of relatively pure antigen sufficient for immunization of animals (Fig. 12).

Response to MP26 was positive in the rabbits immunized and each of four mice and four rats. The immunization schedule consisted of a primary injection of 0.5–1.0 mg antigen in complete Freund's adjuvant administered via intraperitoneal, intramuscular, and subcutaneous routes, followed 1 month later by two to four weekly boosts of 0.5 mg antigen with or without adjuvant. When electroeluted antigen was used, there was very little response observed until after the second boost. The titer, as assessed by immunodiffusion against electroeluted MP26, rose to a maximum 2 weeks after the final boost and fell off rapidly after that time (Fig. 13a). Far better results were obtained if MP26 was immunized in the form of crushed gel strips. These were prepared simply by removing the selected stained gel strip, equilibrating with physiological saline, and dispersing the gel in a Dounce homogenizer with a small amount of saline and adjuvant. After immunization with such crushed gel strips, the antiserum titer began to rise 3–5 weeks after the second boost and remained high as long as 156 days after this injection (Fig. 13b). The antiserum reacted strongly with a single component in solubilized whole membranes (Fig. 13c) as well as with the electroeluted MP26. Serum obtained from early bleedings (7–14 days postboosting) of rabbits immunized with whole membranes reacted with SDS-solubilized MP26 (Fig. 13d) and a single prominent antigen in solubilized whole membranes (Fig. 13e). When 2D-immunoelectrophoresis (2D-IEP) (Chua and Blomberg, 1979) was used to determine which of the membrane components was reactive with Anti-26K serum, we observed a rocket at the position of MP26 (Fig. 14a). Since we had also detected slight reactivity of Anti-26K with electroeluted MP34 (Fig. 13g), we used 2D-IEP to examine the nature of this reactivity. It appears that the reactive component in electroeluted MP34 is a minor contaminant of apparent molecular weight 25,500 (Fig. 14b). I have observed that with progressive storage of electroeluted MP34, a small amount of protein at the position of

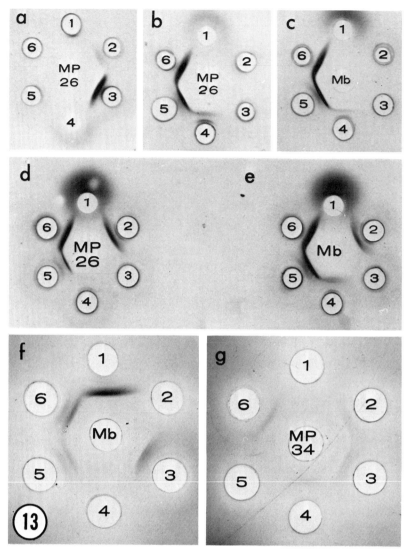

FIG. 13. Immunodiffusion of electroeluted MP26 (a, b, d), solubilized calf lens membranes (c, e, f), or electroeluted MP34 (g) with various antisera. Electroeluted polypeptides and membranes were isolated as described in the text. For immunodiffusion, MP26, MP34, or membranes were solubilized by boiling in 2.0% SDS and dithiothreitol. After cooling to room temperature, an equal volume of 20% Lubrol PX was added to each sample. Diffusion was carried out in 1.1% agarose in Tris–acetate buffer (Converse and Papermaster, 1975) containing 1.5% Lubrol PX for 48 hours at room temperature. Plates were washed extensively in saline and then water prior to staining with Coomassie Brilliant Blue. The plates were destained in a mixture of 40% methanol and 7% acetic acid and then air dried. Antigens were placed in the central wells: (a, b, d) 25 μl of MP26 (0.6 mg/ml); (c, e, f) 25 μl of solubilized calf lens membranes (1.2 mg/ml); and (g) 25 μl of MP34 (1.0 mg/ml). In (a) preimmune serum was placed into well (1) and the remaining wells received antiserum to electroeluted MP26 obtained 7 (2), 14 (3), 21 (4), 28 (5), or 35 days (6) after the third injection of antigen. In (b), preimmune serum was placed into well

MP26 will gradually appear. It is uncertain as to whether this represents a proteolytic fragment of MP34 that is generated with time, or whether a small amount of native MP26 originally associated with MP34 becomes dissociated upon storage. It is clear, however, that conclusions concerning the immunological cross-reactivity of two antigens based upon ID studies that utilize presumably pure preparations of single antigens must be viewed with caution.

If lens from calf, bovine, mouse, or rat eyes are treated with Anti-26K or Anti-mb followed by GAR-FITC, intense membrane fluorescence is observed uniformly along the cell membrane of lenticular fiber cells (Fig. 15). The capsule and cuboidal epithelial cell layer that surrounds the lens fibers, as well as any extraocular tissues tested thus far, are negative with regard to fluorescence after treatment with either antiserum (Friedlander et al., 1980). These antisera also react with frozen sections of lens from chick eyes. Again, fluorescence is restricted to fiber regions.

In summary, our results concerning the immunochemical characterization of MP26 indicate that: (a) specific antisera may be raised in rabbits following immunization with crushed acrylamide gel strips containing MP26 or with purified, electroeluted MP26 itself; (b) this antisera reacts with SDS-denatured MP26 as well as with native membrane protein as evidenced by ID, 2D-IEP, and immunofluorescence on frozen sections of lens tissue; (c) the reactive component in a mixture of lens membrane polypeptides is MP26; (d) MP26 is not antigenically related to MP34 or the crystallins; (e) the antigen appears to be lens fiber cell specific, but is present in lens membranes obtained from several different species. The last two points are supported by biochemical analyses using limited peptide mapping techniques. Such studies demonstrate little homology between MP26 and

---

(1) and the remaining wells received antiserum to MP26 in crushed acrylamide gels (Anti-26K) obtained 7 (2), 14 (3), 21 (4), 28 (5), or 156 days (6) after the third immunization. Each peripheral well in (c) was loaded identically to those in (b). For this immunodiffusion plate, the central well contained solubilized lens membranes. In (d) and (e) the peripheral wells were loaded with: (1) preimmune serum; (2) Anti-26K; (3) serum from a nonresponding rabbit injected with electroeluted MP26; (4) serum from a nonresponding rabbit injected with lens membranes; (5) and (6) sera from two different rabbits injected with lens membranes. In (f), two responding rabbits were hyperimmunized with lens membranes and then bled, resulting in polyspecific antisera which were placed in peripheral wells (5) and (6). The remaining peripheral wells in (f) contained: (1) Anti-26K; (2) preimmune serum from rabbit producing Anti-26K; (3) antiserum to electroeluted MP26; (4) preimmune serum from rabbit immunized with lens membranes. In (g) the peripheral wells contained: (1) preimmune serum; (2) antimembrane serum (rabbit #14-67); (3) antimembrane serum (rabbit #14-68); (4) Anti-26K; (5) serum from nonresponding rabbit immunized with electroeluted MP26; (6) antiserum to electroeluted MP26.

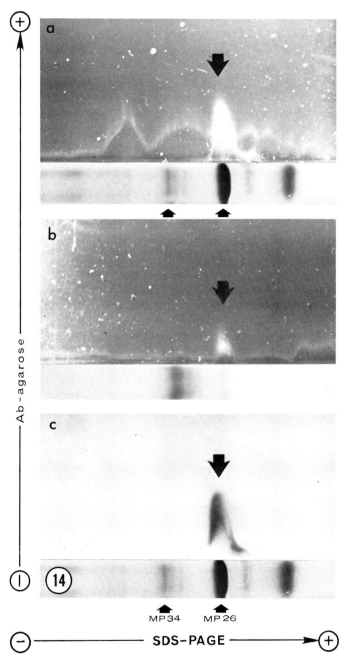

FIG. 14. Two-dimensional rocket immunoelectrophoresis of lens membrane polypeptides with Anti-26K serum. Samples were prepared and electrophoresis carried out as described by Chua and Blomberg (1979). The first dimensional strips contained 35 μg of solubilized lens membranes (a and c) or 15 μg of electroeluted MP34 (b). The antibody

other lens membrane proteins or the crystallins (L. J. Takemoto, personal communication; Hertzberg *et al.,* 1979) or with the major gap junctional polypeptides of rat, bovine, or mouse liver (E. L. Hertzberg, personal communication). Preliminary results suggest that Anti-26K does not strongly react with the 27K or 47K liver gap junction polypeptides (M. Friedlander, unpublished observations). This is consistent with biochemical and morphological data that suggest the lens "gap junctions" may, in fact, differ substantially from gap junctions observed in other tissues. These observations might lead to the following questions. Is MP26 uniquely associated with the lens junction? Is the lens junction truly a gap junction as defined for other tissues (McNutt and Weinstein, 1973)? While the answers to these questions await further investigation, it is already clear that MP26 is an integral membrane protein worthy of interest beyond that generated as a putative gap junctional polypeptide.

From a developmental perspective, MP26 becomes even more interesting. It is the major intrinsic protein of the lens fiber cell membrane, yet is undetectable in the epithelium. While much attention has focused on developmental aspects of the lens crystallins (see Bloemendal, 1976) and those cytoplasmic structural elements responsible for lens fiber elongation (Piatagorsky *et al.,* 1976), the lens membrane proteins have remained relatively unexplored until only recently. Considering the paucity of subcellular metabolic and synthetic organelles in mature lens fibers, it seems remarkable that such large amounts of MP26 can be accumulated and maintained for periods of time up to the lifespan of the individual. Surely, some protein turnover must occur.

The biogenesis of lens MP26 can be studied by translating mRNA obtained from the tissue in an *in vitro* protein synthesizing system. In collaboration with David Anderson at The Rockefeller University, we have isolated total cellular RNA from calf lens by direct tissue extraction using the SDS/phenol/chloroform/isoamyl alcohol method (Aviv and Leder, 1972). When a wheat germ cell-free protein synthesizing system (Roberts and Paterson, 1973) is programmed with this RNA, a pattern of ^{35}S-labeled translation products is obtained which is indistinguishable on SDS gels from the proteins observed in a total lens homogenate. Immunoprecipitation of these *in vitro* synthesized proteins, after SDS denaturation, with Anti-MP26 sera yields a polypep-

gels contained 0.3–0.4 mg of immunoglobulin cm^{-2}. In (a) and (b), the antibody gels were photographed immediately after electrophoresis. The only precipitin line is one at the position of MP26 (large arrow). In (c), the gels were washed and stained prior to photographing. Note the absence of detergent artifact lines as seen in (a) and (b). SDS–PAGE, sodium dodecyl sulfate polyacrylamide gel electrophoresis; Ab-agarose, antibody-agarose.

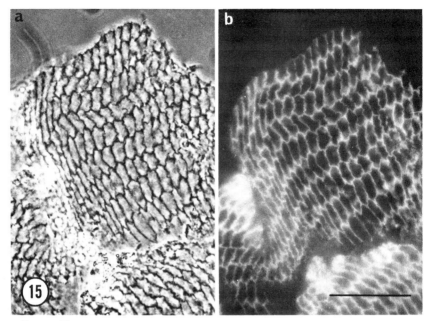

FIG. 15. Phase contrast (a) and fluorescence (b) photomicrographs of frozen sections of calf lens treated with Anti-26K serum and GAR-FITC. See text for details. The lens fibers have been cut in cross-section and appear as polygonal structures with uniform membrane fluorescence. Calibration bar = 50 μm.

tide with an electrophoretic mobility that is indistinguishable from that of native MP26 on 10–15% gradient Laemmli slab gels. When the *in vitro* translation system is supplemented with dog pancreatic rough microsomes, the *in vitro* MP26 is observed to cosediment with these membranes through sucrose gradients at pH 10, a condition which removes most peripheral membrane proteins. This membrane association is not observed if the membranes are added to the translation system after MP26 has been synthesized. This suggests that *in vitro*, MP26 is inserted into membranes by a cotranslational mechanism similar to that described for the assembly of viral transmembrane proteins (Katz *et al.*, 1977). While these experiments are still preliminary, such an approach may provide valuable information about the synthesis, assembly, and membrane insertion of the major intrinsic protein of the lens cell membrane, a structure that is composed largely of intercellular junctions.

The observation that MP26 is uniformly distributed throughout the membrane (Alcala *et al.*, 1975, 1977; Broekhuyse *et al.*, 1979) in junctional as well as extrajunctional sites may not be consistent with current speculation on junction assembly. This raises the interesting possibility that, at least for the lens, a general class of intramembranous protein particles may exist that are capable of modulation and assembly into intercellular junctions. The challenge remains to identify those conditions that may account for the assembly of these proteins into a biologically active junctional structure. The role of such a structure in maintaining the normal electrical and metabolic activities of the avascular lens remains speculative at this time. Surely, the use of antibodies will be invaluable in such studies of membrane protein biosynthesis and the ultrastructural localization of the assembled gene products.

IV. Concluding Remarks

While seemingly disparate, lens fiber cell differentiation and myogenesis represent two examples of developing systems amenable to analysis of questions with broad developmental significance. In each system, there is a proliferating pool of progenitor cells that undergo dramatic morphological alterations along with the elaboration of specific gene products which account for a significant percentage of total cell protein. Prior to terminal differentiation, the lens cells and myoblasts withdraw from the cell cycle. Each set of cells requires a highly specialized cell membrane to accommodate specific cellular associations prior to differentiation (muscle) or to maintain stable intercellular contacts which may provide the structural basis for metabolic cooperation in an avascular tissue (lens). By the production of antisera to specific membrane components of each cell type, we hope to gain a better understanding of those molecules involved in the phenomena of intercellular communication. Only when specific molecular probes are available for monitoring the presence, absence, or organizational state of such cell surface macromolecules or macromolecular structures will it be possible to determine what role, if any, they may play in development. The precise relationship between the intercellular junctions observed in the lens and gap junctions is uncertain at this time, but the notion that lens junctions may represent a specialized structure facilitating intercellular communication or metabolic cooperation is an intriguing one and warrants further investigation.

ACKNOWLEDGMENTS

I would like to acknowledge the support and constructive criticism offered by many colleagues at the University of Chicago and The Rockefeller University. In particular, Dr. Donald Fischman in Chicago and Drs. Norton B. Gilula and Nam-Hai Chua in New York have been most generous. Portions of this work were carried out in collaboration with Drs. Linda Marton, Deneys van der Westhuyzen, Eric Beyer, and Ellen Bayne in Chicago and Drs. David Anderson and Elliot Hertzberg in New York. I am especially grateful for the extensive contribution of Dr. Sheila Fallon to the completion of this project. Mrs. Madeleine Naylor was exceptionally patient and supportive in her typing of the manuscript. Kathryn Wall and Asneth Kloesman provided excellent assistance in the preparation of the illustrations. Drs. Thomas Easton, Norton B. Gilula, Eliot Hertzberg, Ted Lawrence, and Aron Moscona provided many helpful comments in the preparation of this chapter. At various times, the research of M. F. was supported by fellowships from the Muscular Dystrophy Association of America, the Rockefeller Foundation, and the National Institutes of Health (SF 32 GM06418). The support of the Esther Dymant Memorial Fund is also gratefully acknowledged.

REFERENCES

Alcala, J., and Maisel, H. (1978). *Exp. Eye Res.* **26**, 219–221.

Alcala, J., Lieska, N., and Maisel, H. (1975). *Exp. Eye Res.* **21**, 584–595.

Alcala, J., Maisel, H., and Lieska, N. (1977). *Exp. Eye Res.* **109**, 63–69.

Aviv, H., and Leder, P. (1972). *Proc. Natl. Acad. Sci. USA* **69**, 1408–1412.

Azarnia, R., Michalke, W., and Loewenstein, W. R. (1972). *J. Memb. Biol.* **10**, 247–261.

Benedetti, E. L., and Emmelot, P. (1968). *J. Cell Biol.* **38**, 15–24.

Benedetti, E. L., Dunia, I., Bentzel, C. J., Vermorken, A. J. M., Kibbelaar, M., Bloemendal, H. (1976). *Biochim. Biophys. Acta* **457**, 353–384.

Bennett, D., Boyse, E. A., and Old, L. J. (1972). *In* "Cell Interactions" (L. G. Silvestri, Ed.), pp. 247–263. North-Holland, Amsterdam.

Bischoff, R. (1978). *In* "Membrane Fusion" (G. Poste and G. L. Nicolson, Eds.), pp. 127–179. Elsevier/North-Holland, Amsterdam.

Blackshaw, S. E., and Warner, A. E. (1976). *J. Physiol. (London)* **255**, 209–230.

Bloemendal, H. (1977). *Science* **197**, 127–138.

Bloemendal, H. (Ed.). (1980). "Molecular Biology of the Eye." Wiley, New York.

Bloemendal, H., Zweers, A., Vermorgen, F., Dunia, I., and Benedett, E. L. (1972). *Cell Differen.* **1**, 91–106.

Boland, R., Chyn, T., Roufa, D., Reyes, E., and Martonosi, A. (1977). *Biochim. Biophys. Acta* **289**, 349–359.

Broekhuyse, R. M., and Kuhlmann, E. D. (1978). *Exp. Eye Res.* **26**, 305–320.

Broekhuyse, R. M., Kuhlmann, E. D., and Winkens, H. J. (1979). *Exp. Eye Res.* **29**, 303–313.

Buckley-Ahrens, P., Solursh, M., and Meier, S. (1977). *J. Exp. Zool.* **202**, 375–388.

Cates, G. A., and Holland, P. C. (1978). *Biochem. J.* **174**, 873–881.

Chen, L. B. (1977). *Cell* **10**, 393–400.

Chua, N.-H., and Blomberg, F. (1979). *J. Biol. Chem.* **254**, 215–223.

Converse, C. A., and Papermaster, D. S. (1975). *Science* **189**, 469–472.

Cox, R. P., Krauss, M. R., Balis, M. E., and Dancis, J. (1970). *Proc. Natl. Acad. Sci. USA* **67**, 1573–1577.

Culvenor, J. G., and Evans, W. H. (1977). *Biochem. J.* **168**, 475–481.

Decker, R. S., and Friend, D. S. (1974). *J. Cell Biol.* **62**, 32–47.

Den, H., Malinzak, D. A., Keating, H. J., and Rosenberg, A. (1975). *J. Cell Biol.* **67**, 826–834.

Devreotes, P. N., Gardber, J. M., and Fambrough, D. M. (1977). *Cell* **10**, 365–373.

Dewey, M. M., and Barr, L. (1962). *Science* **137**, 670–672.

Duguid, J. R., and Revel, J. P. (1975). *Cold Spring Harbor Symp. Quant. Biol.* **40**, 45–47.

Dunia, I., Ghosh, C. S., Benedetti, E. L., Zweers, A., and Bloemendal, H. (1974). *FEBS Lett.* **45**, 139–144.

Edelman, G. M. (1976). *Science* **192**, 218–226.

Ehrhard, J.-C., and Chauveau, J. (1977). *FEBS Lett.* **78**, 295–299.

Evans, W. H., and Gurd, J. W. (1972). *Biochem. J.* **128**, 691–700.

Fambrough, D. M., and Rash, J. E. (1971). *Dev. Biol.* **26**, 55–68.

Finbow, M., Yancey, S. B., Johnson, R., and Revel, J. P. (1980). *Proc. Natl. Acad. Sci. USA* **77**, 970–974.

Fischbach, G. D., and Cohen, S. A. (1973). *Dev. Biol.* **31**, 147–162.

Fischman, D. A. (1972). *In* "The Structure and Function of Muscle" (G. Bourne, Ed.), pp. 75–148. Academic Press, New York.

Friedlander, M. (1976). An immunological analysis of developing embryonic muscle cell surfaces. Ph.D. Thesis, Univ. Chicago, Chicago, Ill.
Friedlander, M. (1978). *J. Cell Biol.* **79**, 326a (abst.).
Friedlander, M., and Fischman, D. A. (1974). *J. Cell Biol.* **63**, 105a (abst.).
Friedlander, M., and Fischman, D. A. (1975). *J. Cell Biol.* **67**, 124a (abst.).
Friedlander, M., and Fischman, D. A. (1977). *J. Supramolec. Structure* **7**, 323–338.
Friedlander, M., and Fischman, D. A. (1979). *J. Cell Biol.* **81**, 193–214.
Friedlander, M., and Beyer, E., and Fischman, D. A. (1978). *Dev. Biol.* **66**, 457–469.
Friedlander, M., Morales, E., and Gilula, N. B. (1980). Submitted for publication.
Furshpan, E. J., and Potter, D. D. (1959). *J. Physiol. (London)* **143**, 289–325.
Furshpan, E. J., and Potter, D. D. (1968). *In* "Current Topics in Developmental Biology" (A. A. Moscona and A. Monroy, Eds.), Vol. 3, pp. 95–127, Academic Press, New York.
Gilula, N. B. (1976). *In* "Cellular Membranes and Tumor Cell Behavior," pp. 219–237. Williams & Wilkins, Baltimore.
Gilula, N. B. (1977a). *In* "Cell Interactions in Differentiation" (M. Karkinen-Jaaskelainen, L. Saxen, and L. Weiss, Eds.), pp. 325–338. Academic Press, New York.
Gilula, N. B. (1977b). *In* "International Cell Biology" (B. R. Brinkley and K. R. Porter, Eds.), pp. 61–69. Rockefeller Univ. Press, New York.
Gilula, N. B., Reeves, O. R., and Steinbach, A. (1972). *Nature (London)* **235**, 262–265.
Gilula, N. B., Epstein, M. L., and Beers, W. H. (1978). *J. Cell Biol.* **78**, 58–75.
Ginzberg, R., and Gilula, N. B. (1979). *Dev. Biol.* **68**, 110–129.
Goldschneider, I., and Moscona, A. A. (1972). *J. Cell Biol.* **53**, 435–449.
Goodenough, D. A. (1976). *J. Cell Biol.* **68**, 220–231.
Goodenough, D. A. (1979). Submitted for publication.
Goodenough, D. A., and Stoeckenius, W. (1972). *J. Cell Biol.* **54**, 646–656.
Goodenough, D. A., Paul, D. L., and Culbert, K. E. (1978). *In* "Birth Defects: Original Article Series," Vol. XIV, No. 2, pp. 83–92.
Gottlieb, D., and Greve, J. (1978). *Current Topics Microbiol. Immunol.* **81**, 40–44.
Grove, B. K., and Stockdale, F. E. (1979). *J. Cell Biol.* **83**, 28a (abst.).
Hausman, R., and Moscona, A. A. (1979). *Exp. Cell Res.* **119**, 191–204.
Henderson, D., Hansjora, E., and Weber, K. (1979). *J. Mol. Biol.* **132**, 193–218.
Hertzberg, E. L., and Gilula, N. B. (1979). *J. Biol. Chem.* **254**, 2138–2147.
Hertzberg, E. L., Friedlander, M., Anderson, D., and Gilula, N. B. (1980). Submitted for publication.
Holoday, M. Z., and Fischman, D. A. (1977). *J. Cell Biol.* **75**, 72a (abst.).
Horwitz, J., and Wong, M. M. (1980). *Biochim. Biophys. Acta* **62**, 134–143.
Hubbard, A., and Cohn, Z. A. (1972). *J. Cell Biol.* **55**, 390–405.
Hynes, R. O., Martin, G. S., Shearer, M., Critchley, D. R., and Epstein, C. J. (1976). *Dev. Biol.* **48**, 35–46.
Johnson, R. G., and Sheridan, J. D. (1971). *Science* **174**, 717–719.
Kalderon, N., Epstein, M. L., and Gilula, N. B. (1977). *J. Cell Biol.* **75**, 788–806.
Katz, F. N., Rothman, J. E., Lingappa, V. R., Blobel, G., and Lodish, H. (1977). *Proc. Natl. Acad. Sci. USA* **74**, 3278–3282.
Kent, C., Schimmel, S. D., and Vagelos, P. R. (1974). *Biochim. Biophys. Acta* **360**, 312–321.
Kercsmar, C. (1976). *Anat. Rec.* **184**, 445 (abst.).
Kessler, S. W. (1976). *J. Immunol.* **117**, 1482–1490.
Knudson, K. A., and Horwitz, A. F. (1977). *Dev. Biol.* **58**, 328–338.
Kobiler, D., Beyer, E., and Barondes, S. H. (1978). *Dev. Biol.* **64**, 265–272.
Kronvall, G., Seal, U. S., Finstad, J., and Williams, R. C. (1970). *J. Immunol.* **104**, 140–149.
Laemmli, U. K., and Favre, M. (1973). *J. Molec. Biol.* **80**, 575–589.

Lazarides, E. (1976). *J. Supramol. Struct.* **5**, 531–563.

Lawrence, T. S., Beers, W. H., and Gilula, N. B. (1978). *Nature (London)* **272**, 501–506.

Lee, H. U., and Kaufman, S. F. (1979). *J. Cell Biol.* **83**, 386a (abst.).

Leeson, T. S. (1971). *Exp. Eye Res.* **11**, 78–82.

Lipton, B. H. (1977). *Dev. Biol.* **60**, 26–47.

Lo, C., and Gilula, N. B. (1979). *Cell* **18**, 411–422.

Loewenstein, W. R. (1979). *Biochim. Biophys. Acta* **56**, 1–65.

McNutt, N. S., and Weinstein, R. S. (1973). *Progr. Biophys. Molec. Biol.* **53**, 435–449.

Maisel, H., Bradley, R., Alcala, J. A., Harding, C. V., and Kuszak, J. (1980). *In* "Molecular Biology of the Eye" (H. Bloemendal, Ed.). Wiley, New York (in press).

Marton, L., van der Westhuysen, D. R., and Friedlander, M. (1977). *J. Cell Biol.* **75**, 319a.

Moscona, A. A. (1973). *In* "Cell Biology in Medicine" (E. E. Bittar, Ed.), pp. 571–593. Wiley, New York.

Moscona, A. A. (1974). *In* "The Cell Surface in Development" (A. A. Moscona, Ed.), pp. 67–99. Wiley, New York.

Moss, M., Norris, J. S., Peck, E. J., and Schwartz, R. J. (1978). *Exp. Cell Res.* **113**, 445–450.

Nonaka, T., Nishiura, M., and Ohkuma, M. (1976). *J. Electron Microsc. (Tokyo)* **25**, 35–36.

Pauw, P. G., and David, J. D. (1979). *Dev. Biol.* **70**, 27–38.

Piatagorsky, J., Rothschild, S. S., and Milstone, L. M. (1973). *Dev. Biol.* **34**, 334–335.

Pitts, J. D. (1971). *In* "Ciba Foundation Symposium on Growth Control in Cell Cultures."

Pitts, J. D. (1977). *In* "International Cell Biology" (B. R. Brinkley and K. R. Porter, Eds.), pp. 43–49. Rockefeller Univ. Press, New York.

Prives, J., and Shinitzky, M. (1977). *Nature (London)* **268**, 761–763.

Rae, J. L. (1979). *In* "Current Topics in Eye Research" (J. A. Zadunaisky and H. Davson, Eds.), pp. 37–90. Academic Press, New York.

Rash, J. E., and Fambrough, D. (1973). *Dev. Biol.* **30**, 166–186.

Revel, J. P., Yee, A. G., and Hudspeth, A. J. (1971). *Proc. Natl. Acad. Sci. USA* **68**, 2924–2928.

Roberts, B. E., and Paterson, B. M. (1973). *Proc. Natl. Acad. Sci. USA* **70**, 2330–2334.

Sandra, A., Leon, M. A., and Przybylski, R. J. (1977). *J. Cell Sci.* **28**, 251–272.

Sanes, J. R., and Hall, Z. W. (1979). *J. Cell Biol.* **83**, 357–370.

Sheridan, J. D. (1976). *In* "Cell Surface in Animal Embryogenesis and Development" (G. Poste and G. L. Nicolson, Eds.), pp. 409–448. North-Holland, Amsterdam.

Shimada, Y., Fischman, D. A., and Moscona, A. A. (1967). *J. Cell Biol.* **35**, 445–453.

Singer, S. J. (1976). *In* "Surface Membrane Receptors" (R. A. Bradshaw, W. A. Frazier, R. C. Merrell, D. I. Gottlieb, and R. A. Hogue-Angeletti, Eds.), pp. 1–24. Plenum, New York.

Smilowitz, H., and Fischbach, G. D. (1978). *Dev. Biol.* **66**, 539–549.

Staines, N. A. (1974). *Transplantation* **17**, 470–476.

Steck, T. L. (1974). *J. Cell Biol.* **62**, 1–19.

Sytkowski, A. J., Vogel, Z., and Nirenberg, M. W. (1973). *Proc. Natl. Acad. Sci. USA* **70**, 270–274.

Teichberg, V. I., Silman, I., Beitsch, D. D., and Resheff, G. (1975). *Proc. Natl. Acad. Sci. USA* **72**, 1383–1387.

Teng, N., and Ingram, V. M. (1974). *J. Cell Biol.* **63**, 345a(abst.).

Wanko, T., and Gavin, M. A. (1958). *Arch. Ophthalmol.* **60**, 868–879.

Weber, K., and Osborn, M. (1969). *J. Biol. Chem.* **244**, 4406–4412.

Weiss, P. (1947). *Yale J. Biol. Med.* **19**, 235–278.

Wigzell, H. (1965). *Transplantation* **3**, 423–431.

Winand, R., and Luzatti, D. (1975). *Biochim. Biophys. Acta* **57**, 764–771.

Wylie, D. E., Damsky, C. H., and Buck, C. A. (1979). *J. Cell Biol.* **80**, 385–402.

CHAPTER 15

IMMUNOLOGY AND DEVELOPMENTAL BIOLOGY: SUMMARY AND CONCLUDING REMARKS[1]

Elizabeth D. Hay

DEPARTMENT OF ANATOMY
HARVARD MEDICAL SCHOOL
BOSTON, MASSACHUSETTS

Immunology, as Boyse points out in the Conspectus of Volume 13 in this series, is today both master and servant to developmental biology. Whether or not the rather specialized pattern of differentiation of the immune system will prove a meaningful model for generalizations about morphogenesis is a challenging question, which will be discussed at the end of this chapter. What is not controversial is the increasingly important role immunology is playing as servant. Some of the more imaginative technologies that have sprung from the remarkable ability of the lymphocyte to produce antibodies include immunohistochemistry, radioimmunoassay, the fluorescent-activated cell sorter, and the monoclonal antibody technique with its considerable potential for antigen purification using antibody-affinity methods. These techniques are discussed in Volumes 13 and 14, along with a number of other applications of immunology to developmental biology. For all of these, we are truly indebted to our providers, the lymphocytes, whose abilities to recognize and respond to foreign antigens seem almost unlimited. In the following summary of the contents of these volumes, the research will be classified as it bears on the developing immune

[1] The original work described in this chapter was supported by N.I.H. grants HD-00143 and CA-17007.

CURRENT TOPICS IN
DEVELOPMENTAL BIOLOGY, VOL. 14

system, somatic cell genetics, and localization of intracellular and extracellular proteins.

I. The Immune System

The classification of the rather similar appearing lymphocytes into T cells and B cells, their precursors and sublines, is one of the outstanding achievements of modern immunological and cell-marking techniques. Presumably derived from a pluripotent stem cell that has yet to be identified morphologically, T cells are characterized by the antigens Thy-1, TL, G_{1X}, Ly-1,2,3,5, and B cells by PC-1, Ly-4,6,7 (Goldschneider, Vol. 14). The precursor cells lack surface immunoglobulin and receptors for Fc, all of which occur on B cells, but like most cells, they possess major and minor histocompatibility antigens. Ia antigens, which distinguish B cells from most T cells, have been characterized biochemically (Winchester, Vol. 14). They are absent from plasma cells and most other differentiated cell types, but Ia molecules occur on monocytes, melanoma cells, leukemic granulocytes, myeloblasts, and pronormoblasts (Winchester, Vol. 14). Certain antigens, then, are present on immature, but not mature cells and others are present on both mature and immature lymphocytes. Considerable effort has been made to correlate the presence or absence of surface antigens with different stages of lymphocyte (Goldschneider, Vol. 14) and myelocyte (Winchester, Vol. 14) development. The expectation is that some molecules, like Ia, while intimately involved with specific immune functions, also function as "differentiation" antigens that control aspects of hemopoietic proliferation (Winchester, Vol. 14). Milstein and Lennox (Vol. 14) review in some detail the numerous monoclonal antibodies that have now been produced against lymphocyte, tumor and other cell surface antigens.

II. Somatic Cell Genetics

The genetics of the immune system has been investigated extensively (D'Eustachio and Ruddle, Vol. 14). Patterns of inheritance in the human suggest that the genes coding for immunoglobulin fall into three unlinked clusters. Production of some of the surface antigens of mouse T cells has been mapped to specific chromosomes. Somatic cell genetics provides a new and very promising approach to the genetic analysis of the immune system and this approach is described in some detail by D'Eustachio and Ruddle (Vol. 14). Cell hybrids between stimulated T cells and T cell lymphomas have already been produced. Analysis of such clones could lead to functional and biochemical data on the T cell factors they produce and to an understanding of the relative roles of structural and regulatory genes in the production of such factors. Our knowledge of the relation between the genetic markers and the molecular basis of immune function is still meager. Cell hybrids have also been used to explore the complex controls governing expression and turnover of the TL antigens of thymocytes and leukemia cells (Liang and Cohen, Vol. 13).

An interesting application of somatic cell genetics and immunology is seen in the work described by Jones and Puck (Vol. 13). Stable cell hybrids have been developed between Chinese hamster ovary cells and human cells which retain one or a few human chromosomes. The human antigens expressed on the cell surface are those whose genetic loci are carried on the contained human chromosomes. This system can be exploited to detect human genetic insults that result from multigene deletions.

III. Intracellular Proteins

Immunological methods have been used successfully to localize intracellular proteins and to unravel aspects of their function. An interesting application to cytogenetics is discussed by Silver and Elgin (Vol. 13). Immunofluorescent studies of nonhistone chromosomal proteins reveal staining patterns that are correlated with gene activity; the results suggest that a change in chromatin structure is associated with gene activity during puffing in polytene chromosomes. These authors point out quite clearly the technical problems to be encountered in immunocytology, as do Fujiwara and Pollard in Volume 14.

The intracellular contractile proteins of muscle cells and dividing cells have been extensively studied by immunohistochemistry and related methods (Strohman et al., Vol. 14; Fujiwara and Pollard, Vol. 14). Such approaches obviously have considerable potential for identifying intracellular as well as extracellular molecules that are significant in development. As we shall see, the extracellular molecules that have received the greatest share of attention are the so-called cell surface antigens.

IV. Embryonic Cell Surface: Invertebrates

The principal thrust of the immunological studies that have been done on invertebrates has been in the area of cell–cell adhesion. Gerisch (Vol. 14) has used immunological methods to study cell aggregation in slime molds. Intact immunoglobulins agglutinate living cells and induce antigen redistribution, whereas monovalent Fab fragments do not exhibit this nonspecific effect. Fab against a membrane fraction of growth phase *Dictyostelium* cells specifically inhibits their adhesion.

In aggregating cells, this same Fab inhibits side-by-side, but not end-to-end, adhesion. A Fab that blocks end-to-end adhesion (contact site A) can be extracted from aggregation-competent cells. Efforts have been made to map these contact sites with ferritin-conjugated antibodies and the sites have been quantitated by measuring binding of radioactive antibodies. Contact site A binds concanavalin A, as do a number of other *Dictyostelium* glycoproteins (see also Burridge and Jordan, Vol. 14).

Specific Fab fragments have also been used to inhibit adhesion of sea urchin cells selectively. Using antibodies against two sea urchin species, McClay (Vol. 13) showed that only the maternal genotype can be detected prior to gastrulation. After gastrulation begins, maternal–paternal hybrid cells adhere to cells of both the maternal and the paternal genotype. Another example of an antigen with a putative function in cell adhesion is a protein called "bindin" which aggregates unfertilized sea urchin eggs and is liberated onto the cell surface from the sperm acrosome (Moy and Vacquier, Vol. 13). The possible role of substances like bindin and of the egg coat in sperm–egg recognition and binding is discussed by Monroy and Rosati (Vol. 13), who also review the question of egg polarity and segregation of cell lines in sea urchin development.

V. Embryonic Cell Surface: Vertebrates

These two volumes are dominated by the stated and unstated expectation that differentiating cells of vertebrate embryos will be found to possess specific cell surface antigens at different stages of development and that catalogs of these antigens will lead to a better understanding of morphogenesis. Thus, muscle cells may express muscle-specific antigens (Friedlander, Vol. 14), sperm cells, sperm-specific antigens (Millette, Vol. 13), and nerve cells, nerve-specific antigens (Akeson, Vol. 13; Fields, Vol. 13; Schachner, Vol. 13). There is, however, often a considerable overlap of surface antigens among the tissues that have been examined, even when antibodies are prepared by the monoclonal technique.

Sperm cells, for example, express "nervous system" antigens, NS-3, NS-4, CbL, together with PCC4, F9, H-Y, LLY, and Ia antigens (Millette, Vol. 13). It does not seem likely to this author that these proteins have been put there because the sperm is "pluripotent" or derepressed (Monroy and Rosati, Vol. 13). Rather, these molecules probably perform on the sperm cell surface, a function that is common to several other cell types. Interestingly, sperm precursors in different stages of development can be dispersed by collagenase and trypsin and separated by sedimentation velocity at unit gravity (Millette, Vol. 13). With this technique, antibody prepared against mouse type B spermatogonia can be shown to react with surface antigens that are later sequestered to the residual body; other specializations occur during spermatogenesis. One would like to know the role of these "cell surface" proteins in the physiology of the cell.

Characterization of cell surface antigens in the early mammalian embryo has been the subject of fairly intense study. Several histocompatibility and testicular teratoma antigens are distributed in variable (and controversial) fashion in different stages of the early mouse embryo (Monroy and Rosati, Vol. 13; Jacob, Vol. 13; Solter and Knowles, Vol. 13; Wiley, Vol. 13; Ostrand-Rosenberg, Vol. 14). The F9 teratocarcinoma antigen is present on the surface of the fertilized egg through cleavage to the blastocyst stage, when it is present in both mouse trophoblast and inner cell mass (Monroy and Rosati, Vol. 13; Jacob, Vol. 13; Ostrand-Rosenberg, Vol. 14). PCC4, and embryonal carcinoma cell antigen, can be detected in the inner cell mass but not in trophoblast. Human ABH blood group antigens occur on many embryonic epithelia as well as on erythrocytes (Szulman, Vol. 14). Mouse "antiplacenta" and "antiblastocyst" sera have been prepared (Wiley, Vol. 13). Many of these embryonic "surface" antigens have been discovered by injecting cells and bits of embryos into hosts from whom antisera are obtained. In addition to blood-borne antibodies, however, cell mediated immune responses have been studied by sensitizing lymphocytes to mouse blastocyst cell lines *in vitro* (Ostrand-Rosenberg, Vol. 14).

Turning to the nervous system, we can get an indication of the nature of the approach by inspecting the names of some of the antigens: myelin basic protein, synaptosomal antigen, glycolipid antigen, glial fibrillary acidic antigen, S-100 antigen, differentiated and undifferentiated N-18 neuroblastoma antigens (Akeson, Vol. 13), MBA1, MBA2, NS1-7, N1,2,3, Ran-1 (for Schwann cells, Fields Vol. 13), galactocerebroside, and "corpus callosum" antigen (Schachner, Vol. 13). NS-4 to NS-7 antigens are found in adult and embryonic brain and cross-react with kidney and sperm (Akeson, Vol. 13; Schachner, Vol. 13). The embryonal carcinoma cell line F9 also expresses NS-4 and NS-5 antigens. Astrocytes and a number of neurons express the "lymphocyte" antigen Thy-1 (Fields, Vol. 13). Antisera against nervous system antigen NS-4 and mouse cerebellum cross-react with preimplantation mouse embryos, including trophoblast and inner cell mass (Solter and Knowles, Vol. 13). NS-5, NS-6, and NS-7 may also be present in preimplantation mouse embryos (Solter and Knowles, Vol. 13; Schachner, Vol. 13). These data are rationalized by some authors as indicating

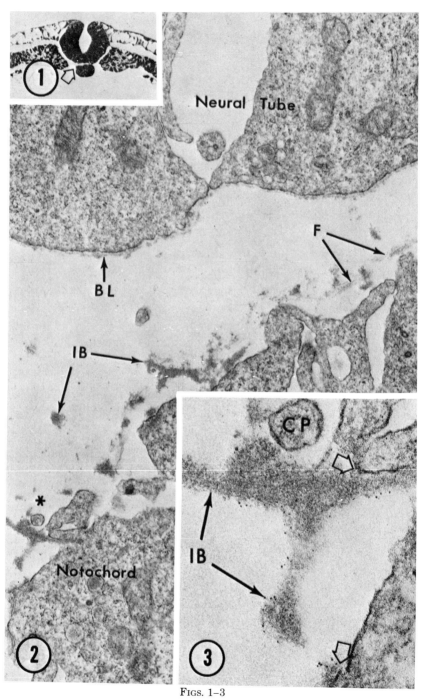

FIGS. 1-3

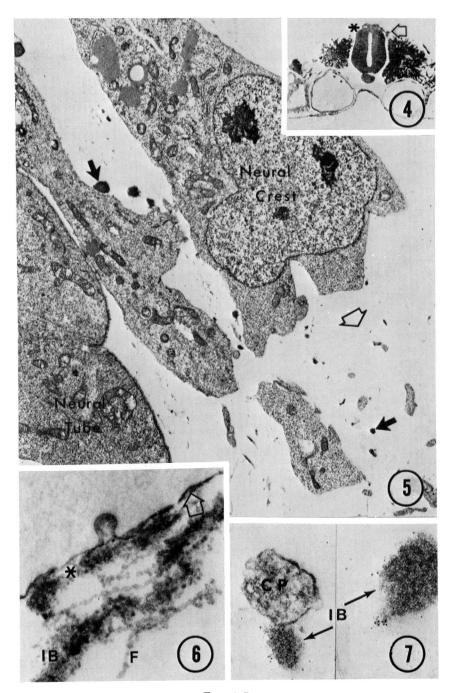

Figs. 4–7

that "totipotent" embryonic cells express all antigens, but the fact is that the distribution is rather difficult to understand as the results stand now.

The difficulty of interpretation along these lines is further illustrated by experiments using such antibodies to disrupt morphogenesis. An antiserum to human chorionic gonadotrophin reacting against mouse trophoblast and inner cell mass arrests development of mouse morula, but its reaction with the preimplantation mouse embryo is removed by absorption with *adult* mouse tissues (Wiley, Vol. 13). Injection of antibodies into embryos has been used to interrupt neural morphogenesis, with the result that a variety of head abnormalities are produced which are difficult to understand (Akeson, Vol. 13). Here again, interpretation of the experiments would be considerably enhanced if the function of the antigen(s) being detected were known.

Along these lines, Jacob (Vol. 13) considers in some detail the possible function of the surface antigen F9. The inhibitory effect of anti-F9

FIG. 1–3. Distribution of fibronectin in the 2-day-old embryonic chick trunk is revealed by ferritin-labeled antibodies using the indirect technique. Figure 1 is a light micrograph for orientation; the arrow indicates the region of the embryo depicted in Fig. 2. Note in Fig. 1 that the endoderm was removed to allow penetration of antibody into the ventral region of the aldehyde-fixed embryo. Figure 3 is a magnified view of the area below the asterisk in Fig. 2. The notochord is surrounded by fine fibrils (F, Fig. 2) and dense extracellular clumps called interstitial bodies (IB, Figs. 2 and 3). These bodies are composed of amorphous-appearing material that labels with antifibronectin (black dots in Fig. 3 are ferritin particles). The interstitial material is closely applied to the cell surface (open arrows, Fig. 3). The basal lamina (BL, Fig. 2) of the neural tube and the fine fibrils (F, Fig. 2) are also labeled by antifibronectin (not shown). It is likely that these structures also contain collagen and glycosaminoglycan. Since fibronectin extends throughout the extracellular matrix, it is misleading to think of it as just a cell surface protein. CP, Cell process from notochord. Figure 1, ×105; Fig. 2, ×19,500; Fig. 3, ×100,000. From Mayer *et al.* (1980).

FIGS. 4–7. At a level anterior to Fig. 1, the relation of fibronectin to migrating neural crest (arrow, Fig. 4) can be seen. The ectoderm was removed to allow penetration of antibody into the dorsal region of the embryo (top, Fig. 4). The neural crest cells are migrating in the direction indicated by the open arrow in Fig. 5. They are surrounded by fine fibrils (not shown) and interstitial bodies (solid arrows, Fig. 5) that label with ferritin, indicating the presence of fibronectin (IB, Fig. 7). The crest cells contact interstitial bodies by cell processes (CP, Fig. 7) and also along their lateral surfaces (Fig. 5). The dorsal surface of the neural tube (asterisk, Fig. 4) is shown in Fig. 6; this embryo was treated with rabbit antifibronectin that was linked to peroxidase-antiperoxidase (PAP) by antirabbit IgG. With this method, penetration is better than with ferritin-labeled antibodies. The whole substance of the interstitial body (IB, Fig. 6) stains with PAP. Also stained are the fine fibrils (F, Fig. 6), basal lamina-like material (asterisk, Fig. 6) and the cell surface (arrow, Fig. 6). Figure 4, ×113; Fig. 5, ×5500; Fig. 6, ×60,000; Fig. 7, ×67,000. From Mayer *et al.* (1980).

Fab fragments on compaction of the mouse egg is similar to that of removing calcium from the medium and thus he reasons that anti-F9 may interfere with junction formation. If so, anti-F9 Fab should inhibit junction formation in other developing systems. There is, in fact, some evidence that intercellular communication among PCC3 cells is affected by anti-F9 (Jacob, Vol. 13). This interesting idea could be pursued to advantage with sophisticated morphological methods. One of the current deficiencies in the state of the art of this general field is the lack of meaningful ultrastructural correlates. The cell "surface" is rarely defined, except in the broadest generalities, and the fact that vertebrate cells are organized into tissues containing extracellular matrix that merges with the cell surface is rarely considered. As a case in point, let us look at the "cell surface" protein, fibronectin.

VI. Fibronectin and the Extracellular Matrix

Fibronectin (LETS protein) cannot be detected on the surface of blastomeres in the cleaving mouse embryo, but appears at the blastocyst stage in the inner cell mass. In cultures of the inner cell mass, the ectoderm rather than the endoderm seems to express LETS (Wiley, Vol. 13). LETS antigen occurs on "accessory" cells in the nervous system (Fields, Vol. 13; Schachner, Vol. 13), has a wide distribution in the embryo and on fibroblasts *in vitro* (Hedman *et al.*, 1978; Kurkinen *et al.*, 1979; Thesleff *et al.*, 1979; Wartiovaara *et al.*, 1979), and may be one of the active components of the anti-L cell sera described by Wiley. It is absent on certain transformed cells, hence the name "large external transformation sensitive" (LETS) protein (Hynes, 1976).

The name "fibronectin" is now most often used to identify this large external surface protein, one of the reasons being that recent light and electron microscope studies, using immunohistochemistry, have shown it to be fibrous in nature and distributed throughout the extracellular matrix in a meshwork *in vitro* (Hedman *et al.*, 1978). *In vivo*, it is associated with embryonic extracellular fibrils and interstitial bodies (Mayer *et al.*, 1980; Figs. 1–7) and certain basement membranes (Linder *et al.*, 1975). Where fibronectin strands touch the surfaces of cells in culture, actin cables seem to attach to the plasmalemma (Hynes and Destree, 1978; Singer, 1979). What is emerging as a result of the morphological studies is the idea that fibronectin is a structural component of the embryonic extracellular matrix, which like collagens and proteoglycans is distributed in different amounts in various tissues and plays a role in the development as well as the function of the organ in question.

The localization of fibronectin to the extracellular matrix raises a point about the structure of the vertebrate body which deserves some emphasis. In contrast to lymphocytes and other hemopoietic cells, the cells of most vertebrate tissues reside inside (e.g., fibroblasts) or on top of (e.g., epithelia) extracellular matrices that contain proteoglycans, collagens, and other glycoproteins (such as fibronectin). While any or all of these components can be closely related to cell surfaces, they are not peripheral membrane proteins by Nicolson's (Vol. 13) definition, because they occur throughout the extracellular matrix, not just next to the cell membrane. It is possible that what is being described as a "cell surface" protein appearing for the first time in the mammalian inner cell mass may turn out to be connective tissue protein making its initial entrance on the scene. Moreover, one must keep in mind the continuum of the extracellular matrix and the attachment of cells to matrix components when preparing antibodies to cell "surfaces." The method of isolation of cells and tissues and thus the amount of extracellular matrix left around cells could vary considerably from one laboratory to another, grossly affecting the polyspecificity of antibodies derived by injecting cells into animals.

It has been possible to make antibodies against highly purified collagens of several types and to localize these in extracellular matrices and within the cells that produce matrix proteins for secretion (von der Mark, Vol. 14). In spite of the fact that collagen is a weak immunogen, it can be used to raise monoclonal antibodies (Linsenmayer et al., 1979). Immunohistochemistry at the electron microscope level has been used to localize proteoglycans, and immunological techniques promise to help clarify the biosynthesis of proteoglycans (Dorfman et al., Vol. 14). Fibronectin, collagens, and proteoglycans have been implicated in embryonic tissue interactions and as substrata for cell migration and adhesion (Hynes, 1976; Yamada and Olden, 1978; Hay, 1978). Immunohistochemical methods can contribute measurably to our understanding of the relation of the matrix proteins to each other and to the cells they surround.

VII. The Lymphocyte as a Model for Ontogeny

Hemopoietic tissues have long served as models for differentiation, but, before the advent of modern immunology and immunogenetics, the granulocytic and erythrocytic components of the system received the main share of attention. Producing a clearly recognizable, terminal cell type, the myeloid and erythroid precursors pass through such a regular progression from mitotic to postmitotic cells that developmental biologists viewing hemopoietic tissue as master, formulated a quantal mitosis theory of differentiation (Holtzer and Abbott, 1968). The generality of this theory has been strongly challenged, however (Konigsberg and Buckley, 1974). Mature cells, especially those comprising stable rather than renewing populations, often retain the ability to divide (Hay, 1974) and thus their differentiation does not seem to entail quantal (terminal) mitosis. The lymphocyte exhibits perhaps the most specialized proliferative pattern of all, the objective being to perpetuate particular antigen-activated clones (Nossal, 1977).

There are a number of other differences between the hemopoietic and stable tissues that should cause us to beware of generalizing from one to the other. The lymphocyte cell surface is not designed to interact with extracellular matrix in any stable manner; the cells are mobile and readily extracted from tissues. Nor does the lymphocyte interact in a permanent way with adjacent cells via specialized intercellular junctions, such as desmosomes. The lymphocyte cell surface is geared to detect, with the aid of other hemopoietic cells, specific foreign antigens and to respond to them. One could argue that such a cell surface is far too specialized to serve as a general model for the development of the cell types that are in residence among the body matrices.

The "extraordinary large number and diversity of foreign substances capable of eliciting an immune response" (Cohen and Liang, Vol. 13) has given rise to the idea that "each of the hundreds of different cell types found in adult organisms is precisely defined by its biochemical and morphological characteristics and is quite different from any other cell type in the same organism" (Solter and Knowles, Vol. 13). On the contrary, cells comprising tissues of the body may have much more in common with each other than this idea implies. Embryologists have long recognized and tried to exclude from definitions of differentiation, these "in-common" functions of cells, but more and more often the molecules cells possess turn out to be directly related to their physiology and not to any inherent desire on their part to be recognized by us as "differentiated." Thus, for example, many cells possess actin, myosins, and components of the contractile system once attributed to "differentiated" muscle cells and certain epithelial cells produce collagens once believed to be specific for cartilage. The plasmalemmal proteins of cells with similar physiology can be expected to overlap as well. Before attributing morphogenetic significance to so-called "jumping" antigens and "differentiation" antigens, we should be aware of the possible *in situ* functions of the proteins we use in our immunological studies. We need, as well, to keep in mind the structure and organization of embryonic tissues in our attempts to isolate specific antigens and in our efforts to evolve meaningful models of ontogenic principles.

REFERENCES

Hay, E. D. (1974). *In* "Concepts of Development" (J. W. Lash and J. R. Whittaker, eds.), pp. 404–428. Sinauer, Stamford.

Hay, E. D. (1978). *Growth* **42**, 399–423.

Hedman, K., Vaheri, A., and Wartiovaara, J. (1978). *J. Cell Biol.* **76**, 748–760.

Holtzer, H., and Abbott, J. (1968). *In* "The Stability of the Differentiated State" (H. Ursprung, ed.), pp. 1–16. Springer-Verlag, Berlin.

Hynes, R. O. (1976). *Biochim. Biophys. Acta* **458**, 73–107.

Hynes, R. O., and Destree, A. T. (1978). *Cell* **15**, 875–886.

Konigsberg, I. R., and Buckley, P. A. (1974). *In* "Concepts of Development" (J. W. Lash and J. R. Whittaker, eds.), pp. 179–196. Sinauer, Stamford.

Kurkinen, M., Alitalo, K., Vaheri, A., Sterman, S., and Saxen, L. (1979). *Dev. Biol.* **69**, 589–600.

Linder, E., Vaheri, A., Rusolahti, E., and Wartiovaara, J. (1975). *J. Exp. Med.* **142**, 41–49.

Linsenmayer, T., Hendrix, M. J. C., and Little, C. (1979). *Proc. Natl. Acad. Sci. U.S.A.*, in press.

Mayer, B. W., Hay, E. D., and Hynes, R. O. (1980). *Dev. Biol.*, in press.

Nossal, G. J. W. (1977). *In* "International Cell Biology 1976–1977" (B. R. Brinkley and K. R. Porter, eds.), pp. 103–111. Rockefeller Univ. Press, New York.

Singer, I. I. (1979). *Cell* **16**, 675–685.

Thesleff, I., Stenman, S., Vaheri, A., and Timpl, R. (1979). *Dev. Biol.* **70**, 116–126.

Wartiovaara, J., Leivo, I., and Vaheri, A. (1979). *Dev. Biol.* **69**, 247–257.

Yamada, K. M., and Olden, K. (1978). *Nature (London)* **275**, 179–184.

SUBJECT INDEX

A

ABH blood group antigens, 127–144
  distribution, 130–135
  function of, 135–138
α-Actinin, 276
Adhesion, cellular
  analysis of, with Fab, 247–257
  changes in slime mold development, 246
  quantitation of, in slime mold, 252–254
Affinity chromatography, 280
Amino sugars of ABH blood group substances, 129
Amoebae, 245
Antigenicity, retention of after denaturation of protein, 229
Antigens, cell surface
  ABH 127–144
  antigen receptor, 23
  changes with development
    of lens, 353
    of muscle, 326
    of slime mold, 246
  Dictyostelium discoideum contact sites, 247
  discoidin, 262
  embryonic, general classes of, 148
  embryo-specific, 150–154
  fibronectin, 239, 364
  G_{IX} 41, 63
  H-2, 148–150
  hemopoietic stem cells 37
  HLA, *see* HLA antigens
  H-Y, 154
  Ia, 115–125, 150
  I-J, 63
  "jumping," 26
  Lewis, 129

Ly (Lyt), 47, 51, 63
  lymphocyte-associated, 14, 37
  macrophage-specific, 16
  mouse-specific B cell, 40
  myoblasts, 326–332
  myotubes, 332–337
  neural
    brain associated stem cells, 41
    Thy-I, 41
    transmitter-like P substance, 25
  "null" cell, 40
  rat cortical thymocyte, 39
  rat low electrophoretic mobility
    thymocyte antigen, 39
  Thy-1, 41–43
  T lymphocyte stem cell antigen (SC-1), 41
  trophoblast cell, 150
  T/t gene product, 42
  tumor-specific, 10–12
  viral, associated with G_{IX}, 41
Antisera, effects on kidney tubule formation, 138
Antisera to
  ABH blood groups, 127–144
  collagen, 203–205
  contractile proteins, 272, 305
  core protein, 189
  D. discoideum contact sites, 249
  differentiation antigens
    immune system, 13–23
    muscle and neural tumors, 25
    preimplantation embryo, 24, 148
  fibronectin, 239, 364
  hemopoietic stem cells, 37
  histocompatibility antigens, 38, 99, 148
  Ia antigens, 121
  mouse specific B lymphocyte antigen, 40

371

CONTENTS OF PREVIOUS VOLUMES